Contents

Preface

The GCSE Science for CCEA series comprises of three books: GCSE Biology for CCEA, GCSE Chemistry for CCEA, and GCSE Physics for CCEA, which together cover all aspects of the material needed for students following the CCEA GCSE specifications in:

- Science: Double Award (Modular)
- Science: Double Award (Non-Modular)
- Science: Biology
- Science: Chemistry
- Science: Physics

GCSE Biology for CCEA covers all the material relating to the biology component of the CCEA Science Double Award (Modular and Non-modular), together with the additional material required for the CCEA Science: Biology specification.

Rose McIlwaine and James Napier are both biology teachers and examiners with CCEA.

Identifying Specification and Tier

The material required for each specification and tier is clearly identified using the following colour code:

Material required for foundation tier students following either the Science Double Award (Modular and Non-Modular) or the Science: Biology specifications is identified by a green line running down the left-hand side of the text.

Material required for higher tier students following either the Science Double Award (Modular and Non-Modular) or the Science: Biology specifications is identified by text with a green tinted background.

Material required for foundation tier students following the Science: Biology specification is identified by an orange line running down the left-hand side of the text.

Material required for higher tier students following the Science: Biology specification is identified by text with an orange tinted background.

Scientific Investigation

During your course you will be required to carry out a number of scientific investigations. You will need to provide a written report which focuses on the following three skills:

1 Planning – Here you will need to write about what you intend to do. You will need to think clearly about what you are planning to investigate and what apparatus you will need. You will also need to use your scientific knowledge and understanding to plan a procedure, identifying key factors that will need to be either varied, controlled or considered. In addition you will need to make a prediction about what you think your investigation will demonstrate and to justify your prediction. Finally you will need to outline a strategy for dealing with your results.

2 Obtaining evidence – Here you will need to demonstrate that you can collect and record evidence in an accurate and systematic way. Your teacher will want to be sure that you are working safely and that you have checked and repeated your work where necessary. To gain the highest possible marks you will need to demonstrate that you can carry out the work skilfully, and can obtain and record an appropriate range of reliable evidence.

3 Interpreting and evaluating – In this skill area you need to use diagrams, charts or graphs as the basis for explaining the evidence that you have collected. You will be expected to use numerical methods, such as averaging, where necessary. Your teacher will want to be sure that you can draw a valid conclusion, which is consistent with your evidence, and that draws on your knowledge and understanding. In addition you will need to explain the extent to which your conclusion supports the prediction you made in your plan. Finally you will need to consider the reliability of your evidence and whether your procedure could have been improved. Is there enough evidence to support your conclusion? Are there any strange results, and if so can you explain how they arose?

BIOLOGY for CCEA

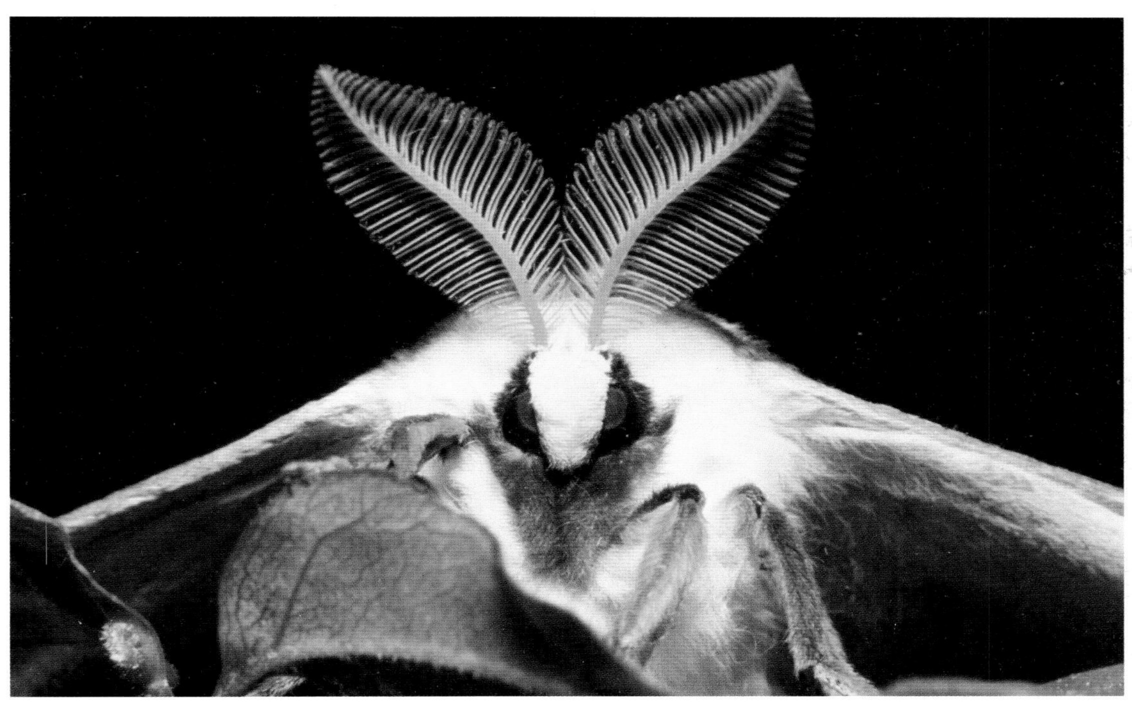

Rose McIlwaine
James Napier

Hodder Murray
A MEMBER OF THE HODDER HEADLINE GROUP

Acknowledgements

The publishers would like to thank the following individuals, institutions and companies for permission to reproduce photographs in this book. Every effort has been made to trace ownership of copyright. The publishers would be happy to make arrangements with any copyright holder whom it has not been possible to contact:

Action Plus (2 top); AKG Photo (202 top); Bruce Coleman/Bob Glover (223 top right)/Chris Gomersall (114 right, 202 bottom, 221 top)/Gerald Cubitt (220 right)/HPH Photography (224 left)/Johnny Johnson (224 right)/Jules Cowan (114 left)/Kevin Cullimore (221 bottom)/Kim Taylor (199 both)/Marie Read (220 left)/Rod Williams (223 bottom)/Sir Jeremy Grayson (114 middle)/Stephen Kraseman (1); Corbis (30 left, 222 left)/Chinich Gryniewicz (136 top)/Ed Young (94)/Hulton-Deutsch Collection (74 top right)/James Leynse (136 right)/Janos Jurka (223 top left)/Jennie Woodcock (153)/Jonathan Blair (222 right)/Lester Lefkowitz (134)/Nathan Benn (30 middle)/Ricki Rosen (110)/Roger Tidman (140 right)/Sally Morgan (140 left); Hodder & Stoughton (32, 188); Holt/Bob Gibbons (212 right)/Duncan Smith (217)/Nigel Cattlin (25, 85, 93 both, 204 right, 212 left, 213 left, 219, 220 top)/Uwe Walz (213 right); Life File/Gary Rolfe (116 left); Popperphoto (204 left); R D Battersby (72); Science Photo Library (74 top middle, 103)/A Barrington-Brown (181 left)/Adam Hart-Davis (98 both)/Alexander Tsiaris (74 bottom)/Andrew McClenaghan (30 right)/Andrew Syred (79, 215)/Andy Harmer (116 right)/Biophoto Associates (31 right)/David Sharfe (2 bottom)/Dr Tim Evans (181 right)/James Stevenson (153)/John Durham (73)/Manfred Kage (161)/Martin Bond (193)/National Cancer Institute (55)/National Library of Medicine (165, 197))/St Mary's Hospital Medical School (31 left, 74 top left,)/Saturn Stills (108).

Orders: please contact Bookpoint Ltd, 130 Milton Park, Abingdon, Oxon OX14 4SB.
Telephone: (44) 01235 827720. Fax: (44) 01235 400454. Lines are open from 9.00–5.00, Monday to Saturday, with a 24 hour message answering service.

You can also order through our website www.hodderheadline.co.uk

British Library Cataloguing in Publication Data
A catalogue record for this title is available from the British Library

ISBN 978 0 340 85825 7

First Published 2003
Impression number 10 9 8 7 6
Year 2009 2008 2007

Cover photo from Science Photo Library

Typeset by Tech-Set Limited, Gateshead, Tyne and Wear

Printed in Italy for Hodder Education, a member of the Hodder Headline Group, an Hachette Livre Uk company, 338 Euston Road, London NW1 3BH

Chapter 1

Living Organisms and Life Processes

Learning objectives

By the end of this chapter you should know that all living organisms:

- Feed or produce food
- Respire
- Move
- Excrete waste products
- Respond to stimuli
- Grow
- Reproduce

Life processes – the characteristics of living organisms

It is usually easy to tell if an object is living or non-living. It is more difficult to work out the characteristics that all living organisms have. Living organisms carry out all seven of the **life processes** described in the following sections.

Feeding

All living organisms need food to produce energy. Animals eat plants or other animals. Plants are unique in that they can make their own food. They do this in a process called photosynthesis.

Respiration

All living organisms respire to release energy. The process of **respiration** involves the controlled combustion of food, a process that usually requires oxygen. **Gas exchange** between the organism and the environment is part of the respiration process and its purpose is to provide the body's cells with the oxygen that it uses to release energy from food. Many of the animals we are familiar with use lungs for breathing in the process of gas exchange. We can tell an animal is living if it is breathing, but it is important to remember that plants and small animals respire even though they do not breathe to obtain the oxygen they need.

Figure 1 This dead wildebeest provides food for many different types of animals

Movement

An important characteristic of living organisms is the ability to move. Most types of animals move to catch food or to avoid becoming the food of a larger animal. They also move to find shelter, to find a mate, or for a large number of other reasons. Can you think of any more reasons?

Some animals, for example many shellfish, only move part of their body. Plants move when they grow and they also move in response to some environmental factors. The most obvious is the growth of a plant stem in the direction of a light source.

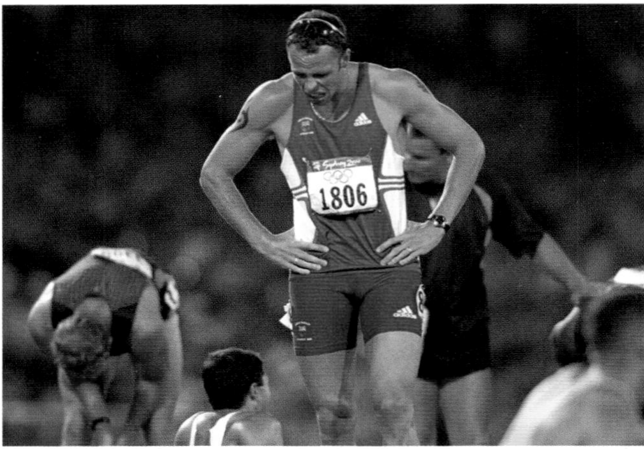

Figure 2 This athlete shows the effects of moving very quickly

Excretion

All organisms produce waste substances as a result of the chemical reactions that take place in the cells. **Excretion** is the removal of these waste products. Plants produce carbon dioxide as a by-product of respiration. The carbon dioxide simply passes out of the leaves and into the atmosphere. Plants also store some waste products in their leaves. These waste products are removed when the leaves fall off.

Animals also produce carbon dioxide as a waste product during respiration but they produce a range of other excretory products as well. Urine and sweat contain a number of excretory products.

Sensitivity

Living organisms are **sensitive** to the environment in which they live. Plants are sensitive to light and other things such as gravity. Animals are sensitive to many environmental conditions. Large animals are especially sensitive to their environment due to the presence of complex sense organs.

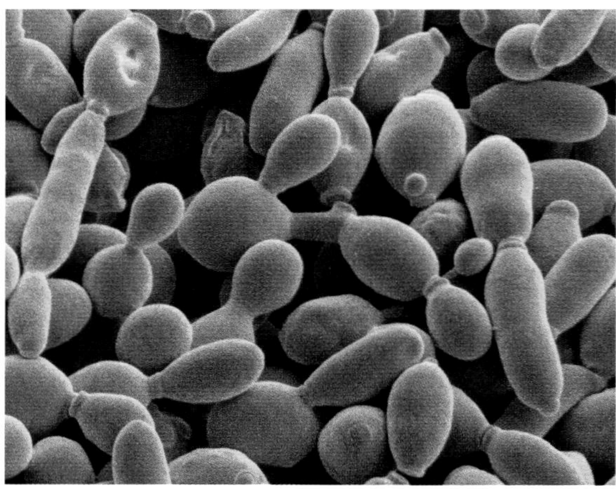

Figure 3 These yeast cells are budding to reproduce

Growth

Living organisms grow. Growth is a permanent increase in body size. In most plants and animals the rate of growth is not the same throughout the lifetime of the organism. In humans we have usually stopped growing by the time we reach twenty.

Reproduction

All living organisms have a life span. This means they will only live for a certain period of time. Organisms need to reproduce to produce new individuals, otherwise all life would cease.

Questions

1 What is the link between feeding and respiration?
2 Explain the following sentence: 'An organism may still be living even if it is not visibly breathing'.

Each of the life processes mentioned above will be discussed in much more detail in later chapters of this book.

Websites

http://web.ukonline.co.uk/webwise/spinneret/life/7chars.htm
More examples of these life processes.

Chapter 2

The Cell

Learning objectives

By the end of this chapter you should:

- Be able to state that all living organisms are made of cells
- Be able to draw and identify the structures found in animal and plant cells and state their functions
- Be able to state the differences between a general animal cell and plant cell
- Be able to draw, identify and explain how palisade, root hair, ciliated epithelial cells and sperm cells are specialised for their function
- Be able to give examples of tissues and organs and state what the difference is between them
- Be able to state the main organs in a plant
- Be able to state the parts of the main organ systems in animals and the functions of these systems
- Be able to explain how to make a slide of onion epidermis
- Be able to state how to focus a microscope slide using low power and high power

Life processes

All living organisms have certain characteristics in common. To live they need to feed (nutrition), they need to respire to produce energy, they need to move, they need to grow and respond to stimuli in their environment, and they need to reproduce if their species is to survive. Some organisms carry out all these functions within one cell, for example bacteria, but most organisms are composed of many cells which enable them to carry out all these functions. In such multicellular organisms, such as animals and many plants, there are a variety of cells that look different because they are specially designed to carry out a particular function.

Cells

Animal cells

Figure 1 shows a typical animal cell with its three structures.

The different structures have different functions.

The **nucleus** is the control centre of the cell and contains the genetic information of the cell (see Chapter 22).

The **cytoplasm** is a jelly like substance surrounding the nucleus. This is where the chemical reactions of the cell take place.

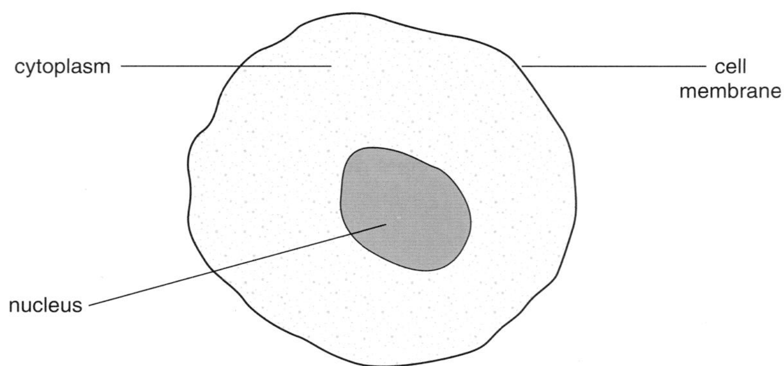

Figure 1 An animal cell

The **cell membrane** (plasma membrane) surrounds the cytoplasm and encloses it. It provides a barrier that allows some substances into and out of the cell. This helps control what enters and leaves the cell. The fact that only some substances can pass across this membrane means that it is described as **partially permeable** or **selectively permeable**.

Plant cells

Figure 2 shows a typical plant cell. It has all the structures present in an animal cell but it has two additional structures.

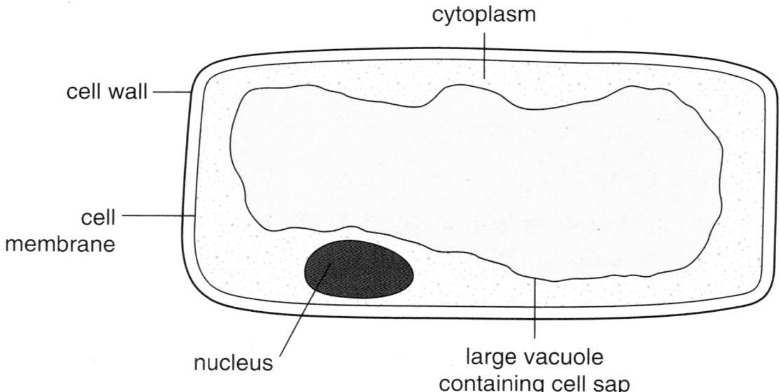

Figure 2 A plant cell

These extra structures are the vacuole and the cell wall. The **vacuole** is a fluid filled space surrounded by a membrane. It contains a fluid called cell sap, which is made up of water, minerals and dissolved food materials. Its main function is to help keep the shape of the plant cell, since it pushes out on the cytoplasm, cell membrane and cell wall. In this way the plant cell is kept rigid and when plant cells push on each other they give the plant support.

The **cell wall** lies outside the cytoplasm. It is made of a chemical called **cellulose** that is only found in plants. This layer provides a rigid structure, which gives the plant cell a particular shape, and this helps the plant support itself.

One other difference between a plant cell and an animal cell is that in a plant cell the nucleus tends to be pushed to one side in the cytoplasm, because of the large vacuole in the centre of the plant cell.

Using a microscope

To look at cells you need to use a microscope to magnify them. Figure 3 shows the main parts of a light microscope.

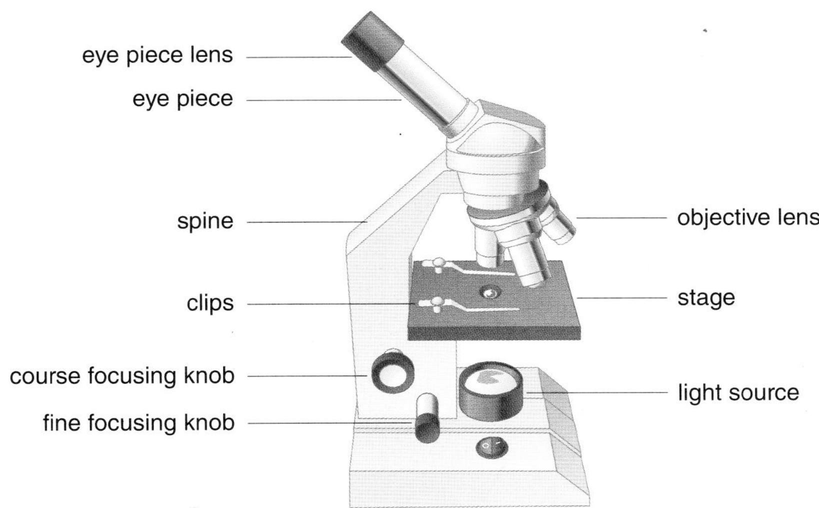

Figure 3 A light microscope

Practical activity

How to focus a slide to view at low power

When focusing a slide to view it on the microscope:

- Make sure the microscope is plugged in and switched on.
- Place the slide on the stage of the microscope and secure it with the clips.
- With the low power lens in place use the coarse adjustment knob and turn it very slowly until you start to see something when you look down the eyepiece.
- Then turn the fine adjustment knob slowly until you see a clear image.

It sometimes takes a while to get used to this process – if you have difficulties ask your teacher to assist you.

How to focus a slide at high power

- First focus the slide using the low power lens as described above.
- Centre the image in the field of view.
- Then very carefully move a higher power lens into place making sure that it does not make contact with the slide. (If it looks as if it will contact the slide DO NOT CONTINUE as you may break the high power objective lens which is very expensive to replace.)
- Using only the fine focus knob turn it very slowly to obtain a clear image.

Sometimes it is not possible to obtain a clear image of some slides with the high power lens. If this is the case change the lens and focus using the medium or low power objective lenses.

magnification of an object = magnification of eye piece lens × magnification of objective lens

Practical activity

Looking at onion cells

1. Get a clean microscope slide.
2. Take a small piece of onion.
3. Using a pair of forceps, lift up the thin layer on the outside of the onion. Try starting at the corner and peeling off as much of this layer as you can.
4. Place the layer of onion onto the microscope slide and wearing eye protection place a couple of drops of iodine on top of the layer of onion.
5. Carefully lower a coverslip over the layer of onion using a mounted needle.
6. View your slide by placing it on the stage of the microscope at low power.
7. When you have focused the slide at low power, draw a couple of the onion cells.
8. Switch to a higher lens and look again at the cells.

The reason for using the mounted needle and slowly lowering the cover slip is to prevent the formation of air bubbles. If you get air bubbles on your slide, you will see thick black circles on your slide when you examine it under the microscope.

The iodine is used as a stain because the onion cells are quite clear, without iodine it can be difficult to see them. If you have time you could repeat this process just using a few drops of water instead of the iodine.

Your cells should look like those in Figure 5. You will see lots of them packed close together.

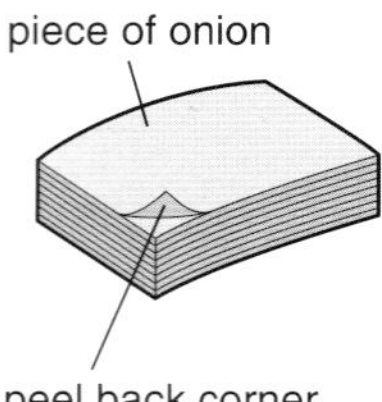

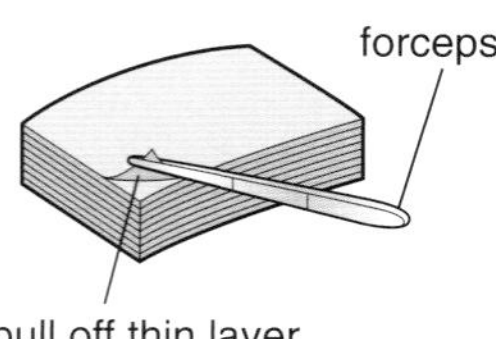

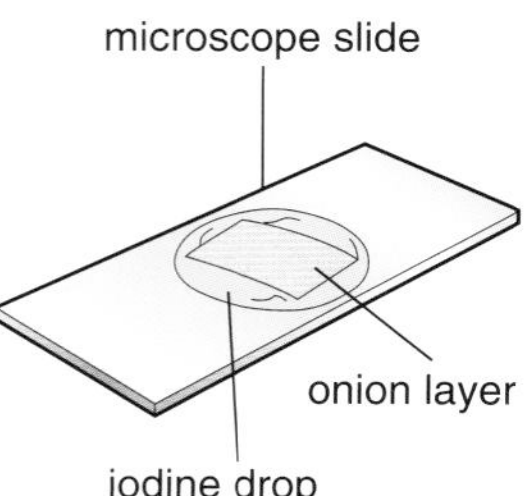

Figure 4

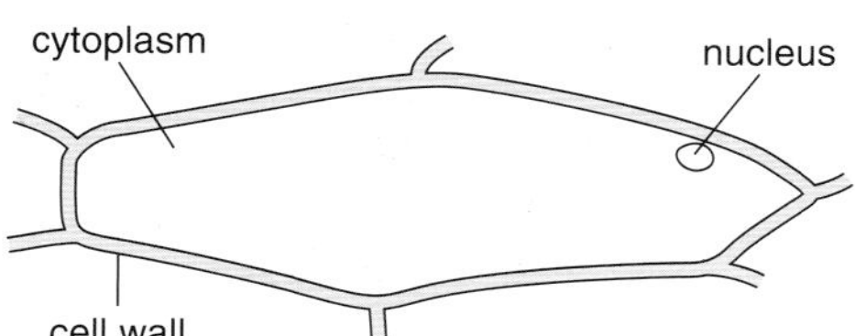

Figure 5

Specialised cells

Many animal and plant cells do not look like the general diagrams of cells because they are adapted to carry out a particular function – we say they are specialised. Examples in plants include palisade cells and root hair cells. In animals they include ciliated epithelial cells and sperm cells.

Later in the course you will meet other examples, including xylem and phloem cells in plants, and blood and nerve cells in animals.

Palisade plant cells

Palisade cells are found in the leaves of plants. They have within them a lot of **chloroplasts** which contain the pigment **chlorophyll**, to trap the light from the sun for photosynthesis. These cells are long and thin, so that many of them can be packed into a layer in the leaf, and they have a large surface area to obtain the light.

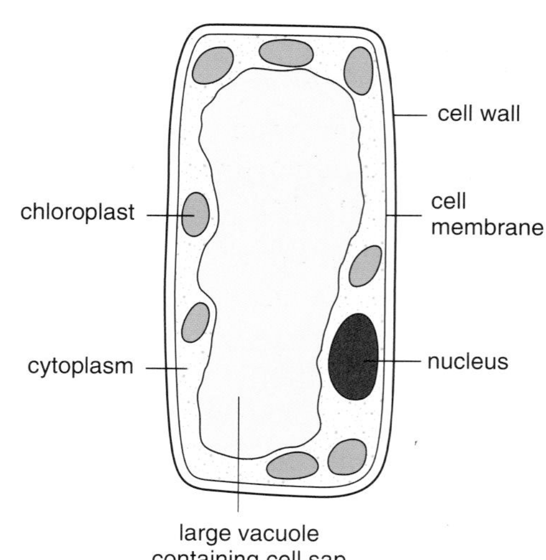

Figure 6 Palisade cell

Root hair cells

These cells have an extension called the root hair, which gives them extra surface area for the absorption of water and minerals from the soil. Notice also that since they are found in the plant beneath the soil they do not contain any chloroplasts.

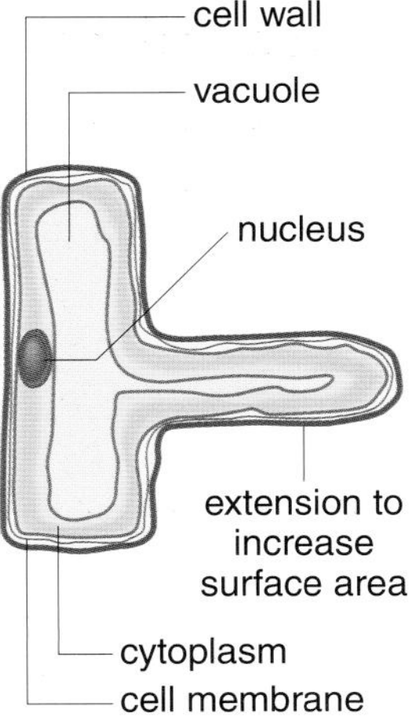

Figure 7 Root hair cells

Ciliated epithelial cells

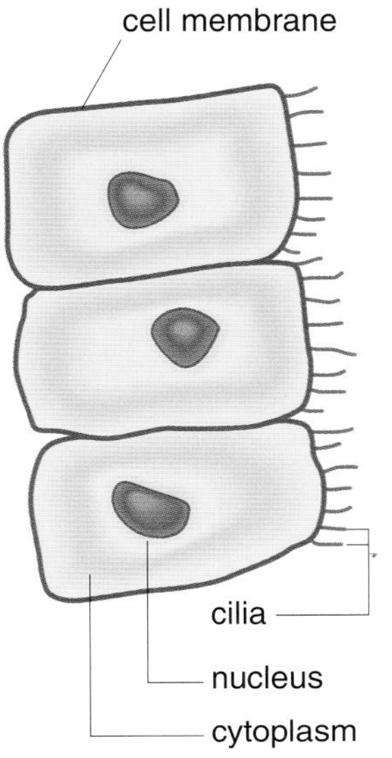

Figure 8 Ciliated epithelial cells

These cells are found lining the passageways of the respiratory system, for example in the bronchi. The **cilia** on their surface help to trap dust and microbes. The cilia move in co-ordination with each other and pass these trapped substances along with mucus back up the respiratory system into the back of the throat, from where they are swallowed and pass into the digestive system to be destroyed. This process helps to protect the lungs.

Sperm cell

The sperm cell is a different shape from other cells to enable it to swim to the egg cell (ovum).

It has a nucleus which contains only half the genetic information that most other cells contain, for example in humans the sperm nucleus contains 23 chromosomes whereas most human cells contain 46 chromosomes.

It has structures that carry out respiration to give the sperm energy. The sperm cell has a tail to help it swim to the egg cell (ovum) in the oviducts.

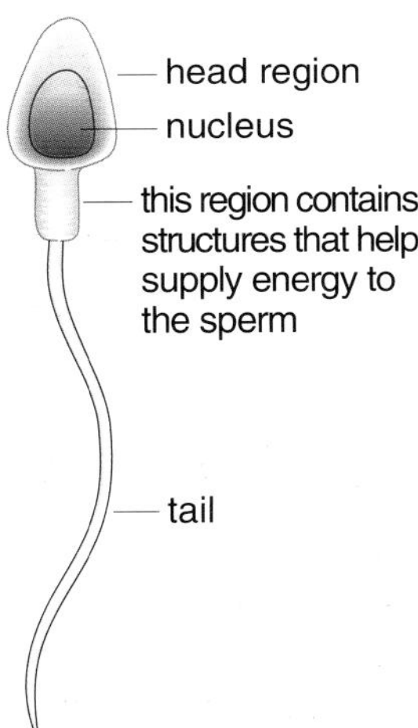

Figure 9 Sperm cells

Tissues and organs

Tissues

When similar cells are grouped together they form a **tissue**, for example epithelial cells will form epithelial tissue, which covers surfaces inside or outside the body. In plants palisade cells will form palisade tissue within the leaf.

Organs

An **organ** is a structure made up of several types of tissues that work together to carry out a particular function. In animals the heart is an organ that contains blood tissue and muscle tissue.

In plants there are three main organs.

1. The root – which contains several tissues that allow the root to anchor the plant and absorb water and minerals from the soil. The root contains root hair tissue, epidermal tissue, and xylem and phloem tissue which transport materials through the plant.
2. The stem – which gives support to the plant, holds the leaves in place and transports substances up and down the plant. The stem contains epidermal, xylem and phloem tissue.
3. The leaf – which provides a large surface area to trap light and carry out photosynthesis to feed the plant. The leaf contains epidermal, palisade, xylem and phloem tissue.

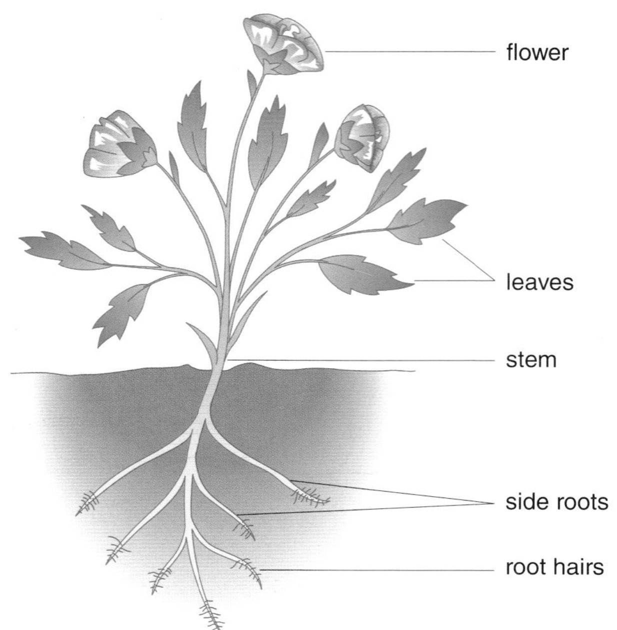

Figure 10 Plant organs

Organ systems

In animals several organs that operate together to carry out a particular function are called an **organ system**.

You will meet these in detail as you go through the course. The table below provides a summary of most of the organs systems found in animals, the main organs involved and their functions.

Organ system	Function	Main organs
Digestive system	break down and absorb molecules from food	mouth, stomach, small and large intestines
Respiratory system	gas exchange – taking in oxygen and getting rid of carbon dioxide	trachea, bronchi and lungs
Skeletal system	support, movement and protection	ribs and backbone
Circulatory system	transport materials and heat around the body, protection against disease	heart and blood vessels (arteries, veins and capillaries)
Excretory system	removal of toxic waste from the kidneys	liver, kidneys and bladder
Reproductive system	production of gametes and fertilisation	testes and ovaries
Nervous system	respond to stimuli and co-ordination of response	brain and spinal cord

Questions

1 Draw a table like the one below. Complete the table to show what structures are found in the different types of cells.

Structures found in animal cells	Structures found in plant cells

2 Draw labelled diagrams of two specialised cells and give two reasons for each to explain how they are specialised.

Websites

http://www.cellsalive.com/toc.htm
Information about cells, cell division and microscopy.

http://library.thinkquest.org/3564/lessons.html
Information about cells, parts of cells and blood cells.

http://www.biology.arizona.edu/
Information about cell biology, membranes and the applications of cell biology.

http://personal.tmlp.com/jimr57/tour/cell/cell_nucleus2.htm
Information about parts of the cell.

Exam questions

1 a) The diagram shows the nucleus and membrane of a plant cell.

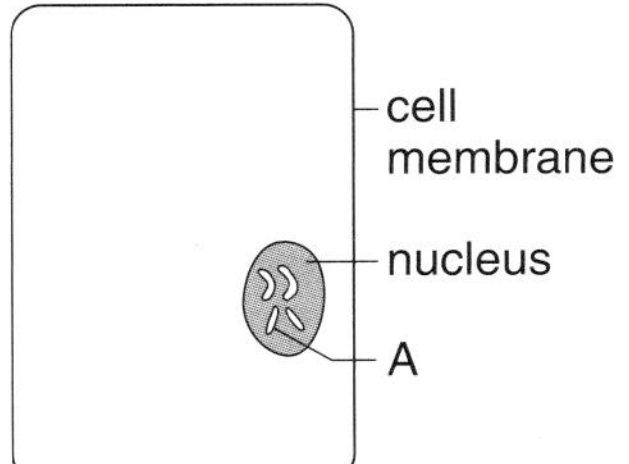

(i) Name structure A.

(1 mark)

(ii) Copy the diagram above and draw and label the cell wall and a large vacuole.

(2 marks)

2 The diagram shows a plant.

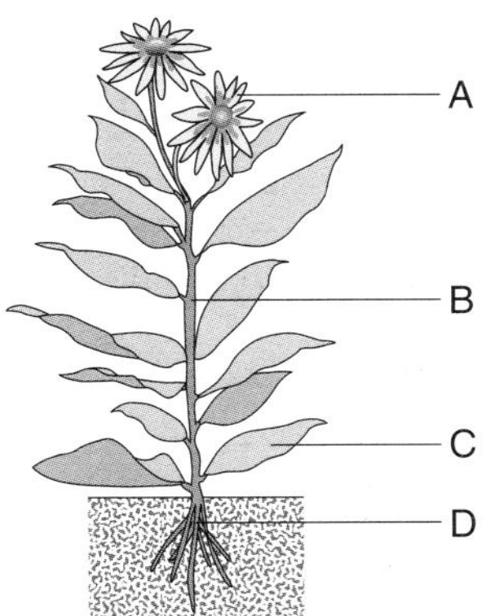

a) Give **one** function of organs A, B and C.

(3 marks)

b) Name organs C and D.

(2 marks)

3 The diagram shows two cells.

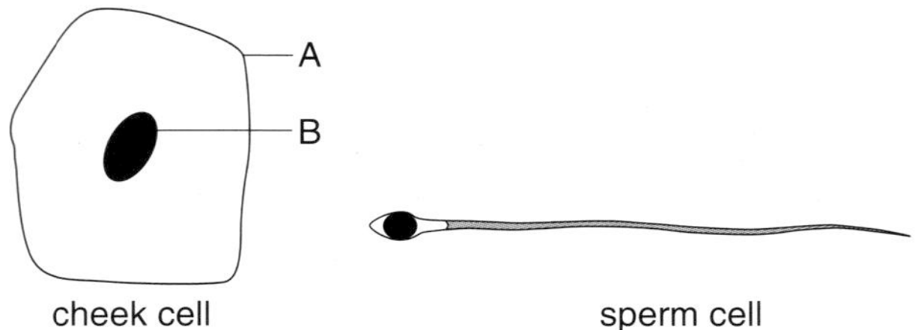

a) Name parts A and B. *(2 marks)*

b) How is the structure of the sperm cell adapted to its function? *(2 marks)*

4 The diagram shows a microscope.

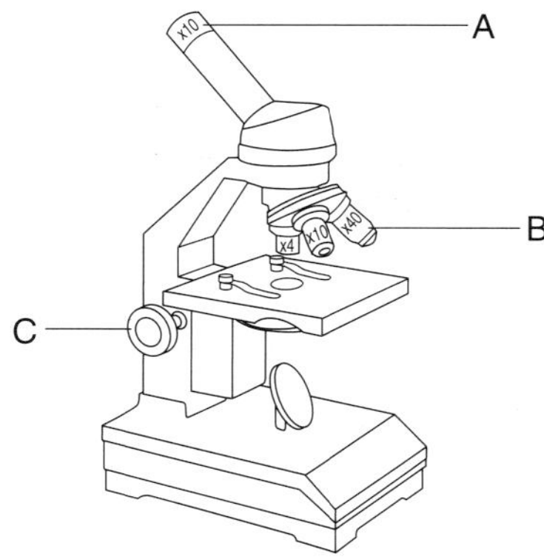

a) Calculate the magnification being used. Show your working. *(2 marks)*

b) Name the parts A and B. *(2 marks)*

c) Give the function of C. *(1 mark)*

d) Give **two** reasons why a specimen must be viewed under low power before changing to a higher magnification. *(2 marks)*

5 a) Copy and complete the table showing the functions of some cell structures.

Cell structure	Function
1	Contains chromosomes
2 Permanent vacuole	
3	Traps light for photosynthesis

(3 marks)

b) Give two structures found only in plant cells. *(1 mark)*

c) Suggest why plant cells are harder to digest than animal cells. *(1 mark)*

6 a) Ellen looked at a prepared slide of human cheek cells under a microscope. The eyepiece lens magnification was ×10 and the objective lens magnification was ×25.

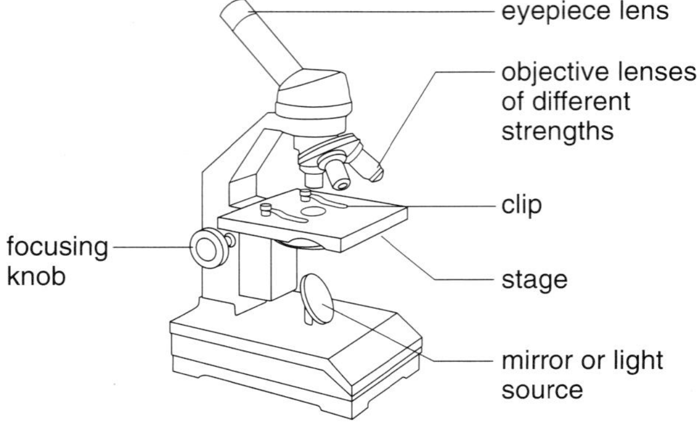

(i) Calculate the total magnification that Ellen used. *(1 mark)*

(ii) The image that Ellen saw was blurred. Suggest how she could have obtained a clearer image. *(1 mark)*

The diagram shows a cheek cell.

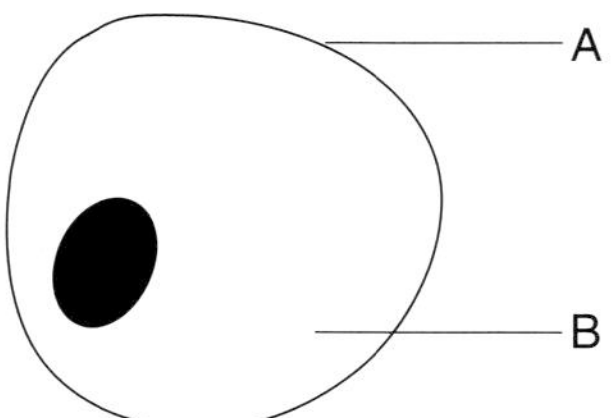

(iii) Name parts A and B. *(2 marks)*

Next, Ellen looked at a prepared slide of leaf cells.

(iv) Name **one** structure that she saw in the leaf cells that was **not** present in the cheek cells. *(1 mark)*

b) A sperm cell is a specialised animal cell.

(i) To which body system do sperm cells belong? (1 mark)

(ii)
- Give the function of a sperm cell.
- Give one way in which it is adapted for this function.

(2 marks)

Chapter 3

The Movement of Substances Into and Out of Cells

Learning objectives

By the end of this chapter you should know:

- The process of diffusion
- Osmosis as a special type of diffusion
- The importance of concentration gradients in both diffusion and osmosis
- Active uptake as an energy requiring process that moves substances against the concentration gradient

In a living cell it is important that essential materials can enter and also that waste products can leave. For this to occur these substances must be able to pass through the plasma (cell) membrane. In both animal and plant cells it is the plasma membrane that controls what passes in or out. In effect this membrane is selectively or **partially permeable**. This means that the membrane will allow some substances through, but will prevent the movement of others. Plant cells are also surrounded by a cell wall. The cell wall is totally permeable and has no role in controlling the transport of substances.

There are several factors that affect the movement of substances across plasma membranes. Two of the most important are:

- **The size of the particles.** The plasma membrane has small pores in its structure. Not surprisingly, very small particles will find it easier to pass through the membrane than larger particles. For example, oxygen and water can pass through relatively easily, but larger molecules such as sucrose find it much more difficult, or impossible to cross the membrane.
- **The concentration gradient.** This refers to the balance of a particular substance on either side of a membrane. Normally a substance will move from where it is in a high concentration to where it is in low concentration, i.e. down the concentration gradient. This is important in both diffusion and osmosis, two processes that are important in the movement of substances into and out of cells.

The processes of **diffusion, osmosis** and **active uptake** are the principal methods by which substances enter and leave cells.

Diffusion

Diffusion is very important in the movement of gases. Gases move about at random and will move from where they are in high concentration to where they are in a lower concentration. This is called diffusion. For example the smell of perfume will rapidly spread throughout a room from a single source. If the perfume is sprayed in one corner of a room it will be in a high concentration in that place. The perfume molecules spread from there to the other parts of the room where the concentration is lower. Eventually the perfume will be evenly spread throughout the room and there will be no concentration gradient between the different parts of the room.

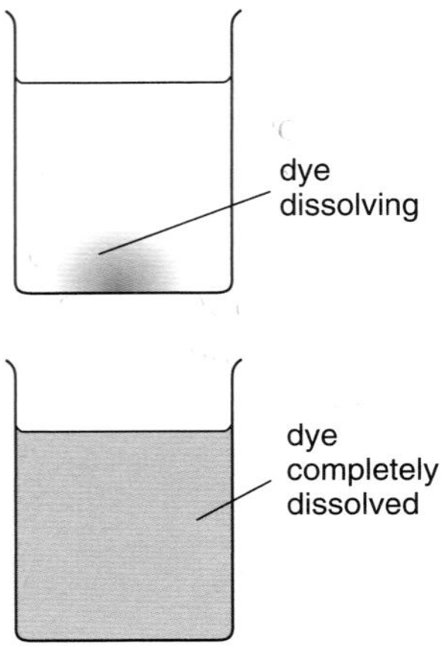

dye dissolving

dye completely dissolved

Figure 1 Dye will eventually spread evenly through the water

Questions

1 Using a similar example can you explain why smoke is visible when it comes out of a chimney but usually becomes invisible very quickly?

Diffusion can also occur in liquids, for example watch a drop of dye or ink spread through water. Diffusion in liquids is usually slower than in gases as gas particles move much faster than liquid particles.

Diffusion is particularly important in the passage of gases through cell membranes. Examples include the diffusion of oxygen from the air spaces in the lungs into the blood stream and the movement of gases into and out of leaves during photosynthesis.

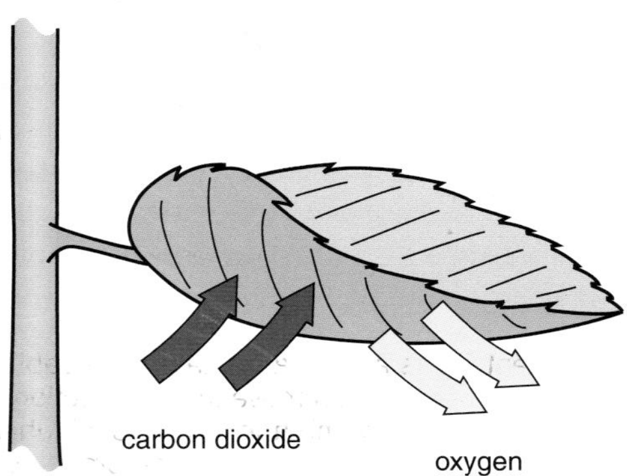

Figure 2 Diffusion is important in the movement of gases into and out of leaves

As diffusion is so important, many plant and animal cells and body parts are adapted to allow diffusion to occur at a rapid rate. Important adaptations include large surface areas and thin barriers across which the gas or liquid has to diffuse. Figure 3 shows how the surface area of the cells surrounding the gut is increased by the presence of very thin extensions called microvilli. The increased surface area that these microvilli provide is important in the absorption of soluble food products.

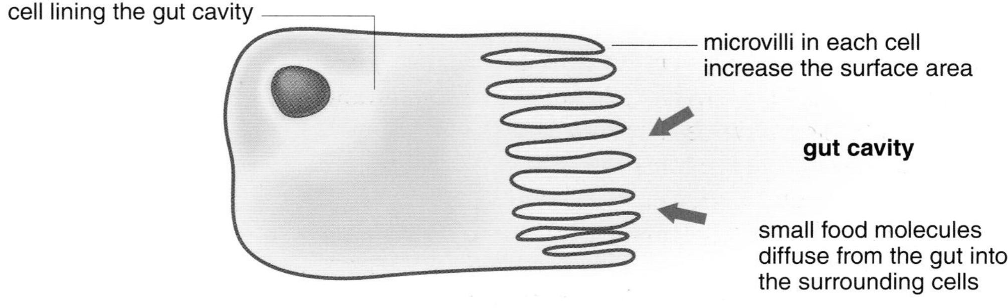

Figure 3 Increasing diffusion rates

Osmosis

Osmosis is a special type of diffusion involving the movement of water molecules through a partially permeable membrane.

If pure water and a strong sugar solution are separated by a partially permeable membrane, such as dialysis or visking tubing, then osmosis will occur. The water will move from where it is in a higher concentration (pure water) to where it is in lower concentration (sugar solution). Another way of describing this is that the water moves from the weaker to the stronger solution.

Osmosis can be defined as the movement of water from an area of greater concentration of water to an area of lower concentration of water through a partially permeable membrane.

The movement of water will stop when the concentration of water on either side of the membrane becomes equal.

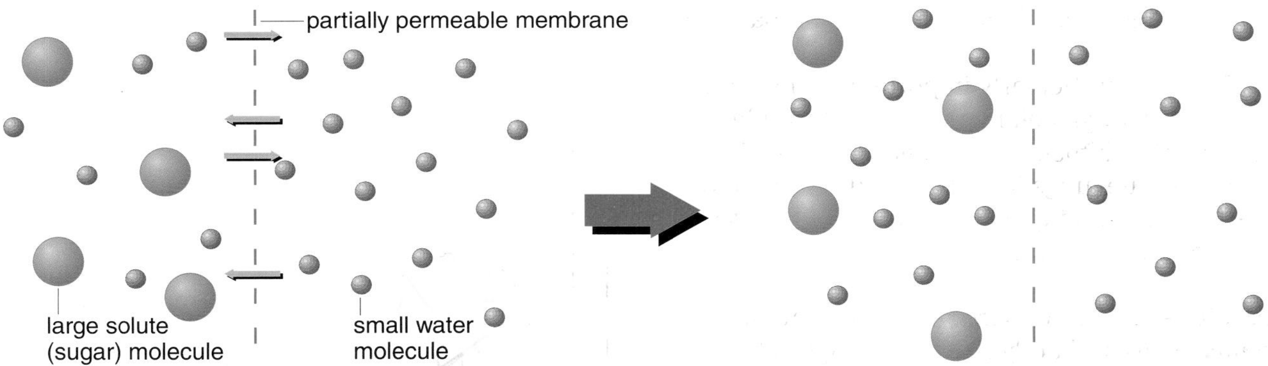

A concentration gradient exists across a partially permeable membrane. The water molecules can move in any direction through the partially permeable membrane. There is a higher concentration of water on the right side of the membrane so there will be a net movement of water to the left.

The water molecules have moved through the partially permeable membrane until there is the same concentration on each side.

Figure 4 Osmosis

The cell membrane is an example of a partially permeable membrane. In living organisms water can enter and leave cells by osmosis.

Osmosis in animal cells

If a red blood cell is placed in pure water (or a very weak sugar solution) water will enter the cell by osmosis. This will occur because a concentration gradient exists – there is a greater concentration of water surrounding the cell than in the cell itself. The water moves down the concentration gradient into the cell. In this example so much water would enter the red blood cell by osmosis that it would swell up and burst. Clearly this does not happen in the body or we would have no blood cells left! The reason our cells do not burst is because the concentration of the blood is carefully controlled to ensure that large volumes of water do not enter or leave the blood cells by osmosis.

Questions

2 What would happen if red blood cells were placed in a strong sugar solution?

Osmosis in plant cells

Water also moves into and out of plant cells depending on the concentration of the solutions surrounding the cells. When water moves into a plant cell the vacuole increases in size pushing the cell membrane against the cell wall. In a plant cell the cell wall prevents too much water entering and the cell bursting as would happen in animal cells. The force of the membrane pushing against the cell wall makes the cell firm or turgid. **Turgor** gives the cell support and in non-woody plants is essential in keeping the plant upright. The importance of turgor in providing support can be seen when there is a shortage of water. When plant cells do not receive enough water they cannot remain turgid and wilting occurs. Cells that are not turgid are described as being **flaccid**.

If a plant cell loses too much water by osmosis a condition called **plasmolysis** occurs. During plasmolysis so much water leaves the cell that the cell contents shrink pulling the cell membrane away from the cell wall. Although loss of turgor and wilting is a common occurrence in many plants, plasmolysis is much less likely to occur in healthy plants. This is just as well as plasmolysed cells are unlikely to survive!

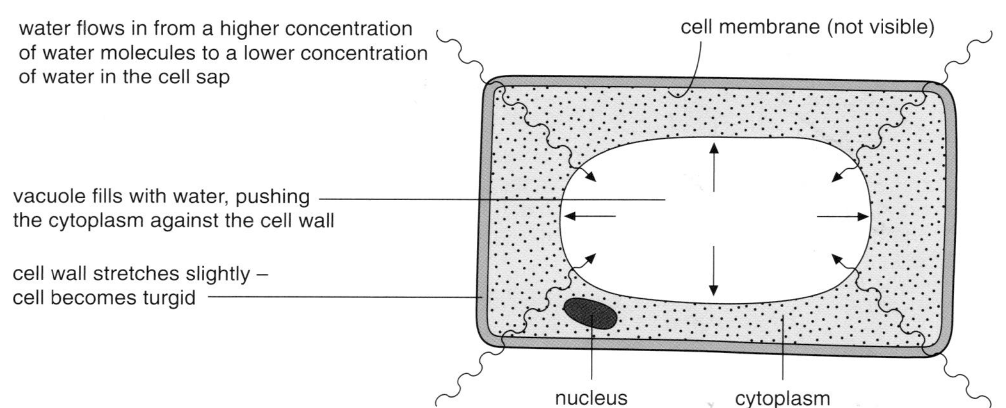
water flows in from a higher concentration of water molecules to a lower concentration of water in the cell sap
cell membrane (not visible)
vacuole fills with water, pushing the cytoplasm against the cell wall
cell wall stretches slightly – cell becomes turgid
nucleus
cytoplasm

Figure 5a This cell is surrounded by pure water

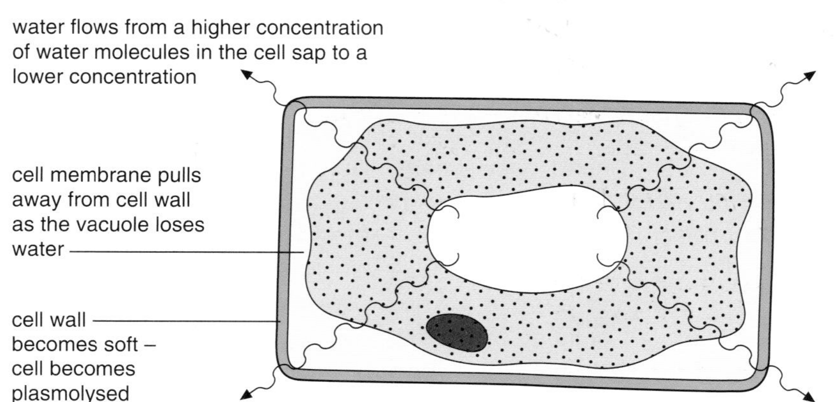
water flows from a higher concentration of water molecules in the cell sap to a lower concentration
cell membrane pulls away from cell wall as the vacuole loses water
cell wall becomes soft – cell becomes plasmolysed

Figure 5b This cell is surrounded by a solution with a lower concentration of water molecules

Active uptake

Plants require a range of mineral ions for normal development. Ions such as nitrates and magnesium ions are absorbed from the soil and used by the plant. This absorption takes place in the epidermal cells that form the outermost layer of plant roots. In most soils there are more of these ions in the root epidermal cells than in the surrounding soil. Therefore for more ions to enter the plant root it is necessary to absorb them against the concentration gradient.

This means the ions move from where they are in a lower concentration to where they are in a higher concentration.

Active uptake (active transport) requires energy to move the ions against the gradient. The energy is released during the process of respiration. For active uptake in roots to occur at a rapid rate it is important that the soil is well aerated (rich in oxygen).

Epidermal cells are specialised for active uptake. Figure 6 shows that these cells are extended to form root hairs. Epidermal cells with root hairs are called root hair cells. These root hairs increase the surface area over which the active uptake can take place.

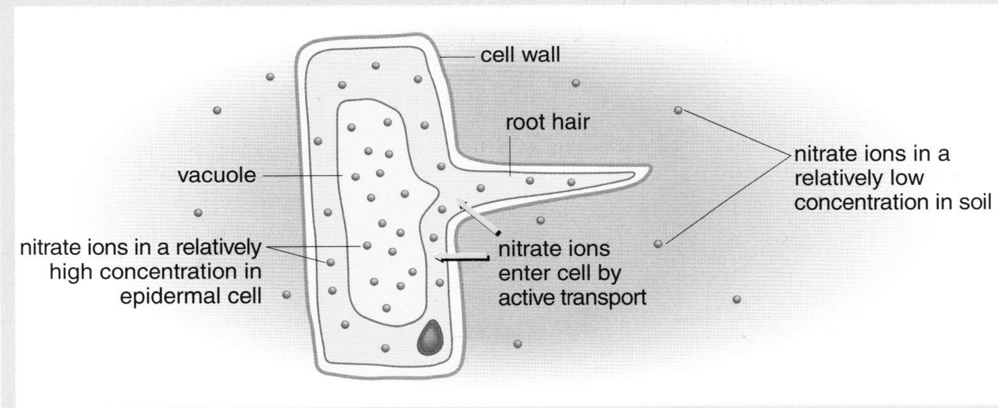

Figure 6 Active uptake of nitrates in an epidermal cell

Websites

http://www.revise.it/reviseit/content/GCSE/Biology
Good examples of diffusion, osmosis and active transport.

http://web.ukonline.co.uk/webwise/spinneret/life/osmosis.htm
Good explanations of key terms and good diagrams of osmosis.

http://www.purchon.com/biology/osmosis.htm
Another site with good explanations of the important points.

http://www.microscopy-uk.org.uk/mag/art97/maysnp2.html
This site has pictures of turgid and plasmolysed cells.

Exam questions

1 A pupil examined the effect of placing onion epidermal cells in pure water (A) and in a strong sugar solution (B).

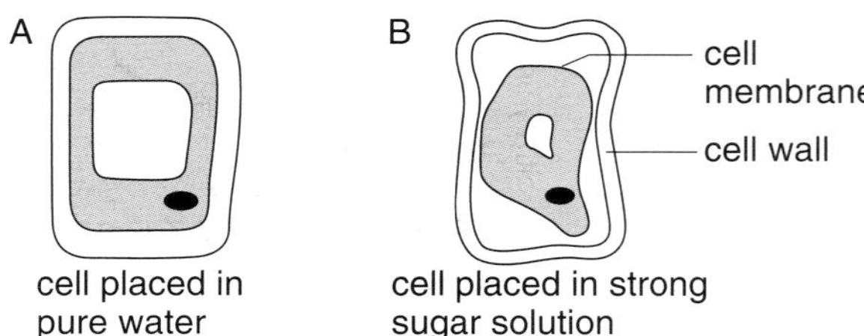

a) Describe and explain what has happened to the cell in B.

(4 marks)

b) If a red blood cell is placed in pure water, it will eventually burst. Suggest why this does not happen to the cell in diagram A.

(1 mark)

2 Diagrams A and B represent two root hair cells. A is from a root in very dry soil and B is from the same root after water has been added to the soil.

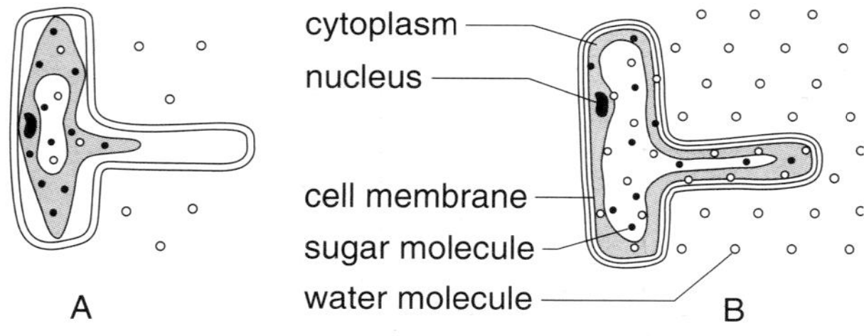

a) Give two ways cell B differs in structure from cell A.

(2 marks)

b) What has entered cell B?

(1 mark)

c) Name the process which has occurred in cell B.

(1 mark)

d) What cell structure limits this process?

(1 mark)

3 a) Name **one** use of water in plants.

(1 mark)

b) The experiment shown was used to investigate water movement through a potato.

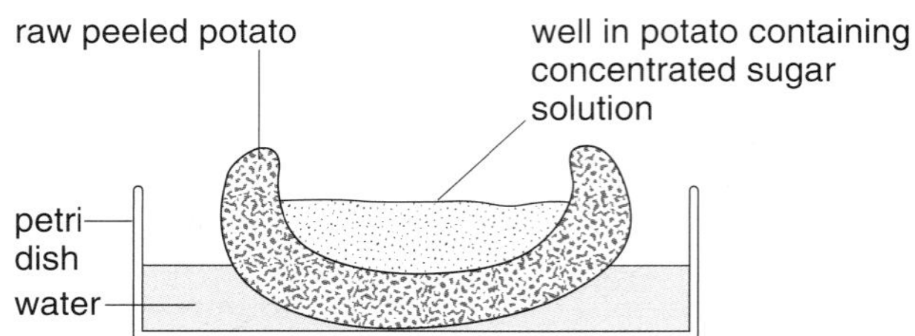

After two hours it was noted that the level of water in the petri dish had fallen while the level in the well of the potato had risen. Explain this observation.

(3 marks)

4 Potato cylinders were cut to 50 mm long and placed in different liquids. After one hour, the cylinders were measured again by placing them on graph paper.

Liquid	Cylinder placed on graph paper
Water	10 mm
5% sucrose	
10% sucrose	

a) Measure the length of the three cylinders and record each length in a table like the one below. Calculate the change in length for each cylinder, using + for an increase and − for a decrease.

Liquid	Length of cylinder (mm)	Change in length (mm) + or −
Water		
5% sucrose		
10% sucrose		

(2 marks)

b) Explain the change in length for the cylinder placed in water.

(2 marks)

5 Slices of fresh potato were weighed and placed in different concentrations of sugar solution.

They were reweighed 24 hours later and the percentage change in mass calculated.

The results are shown in the graph.

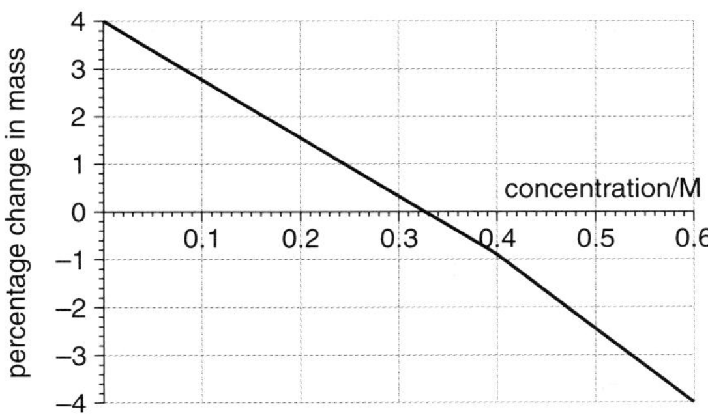

a) Which concentration of sugar solution caused no percentage change in the mass of potato?

(1 mark)

b) Suggest why the percentage change in mass was used rather than the actual change in mass.

(1 mark)

c) Explain how osmosis brought about the increase in mass of the potato in the 0.1 M sugar solution.

(2 marks)

d) Explain how active transport differs from osmosis.

(2 marks)

6 The graph below shows the uptake of mineral ions by barley seedlings when air was bubbled through a solution containing minerals essential for plant growth and also the uptake of mineral ions when no air was bubbled through.

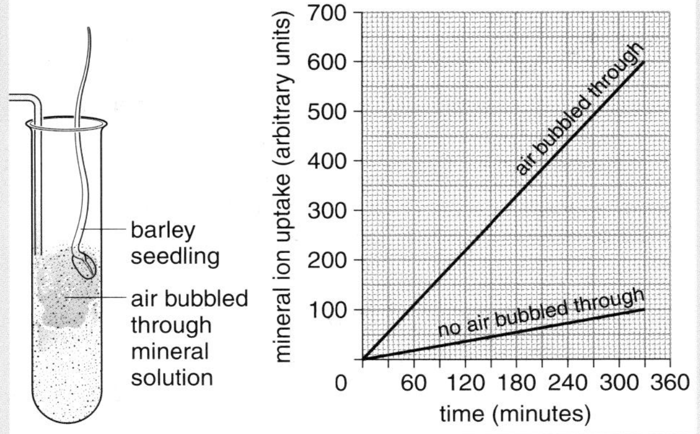

Describe and explain the difference in mineral ion uptake shown in the two graphs.

(4 marks)

7 The graph shows the concentration of mineral ions in a plant's roots and in the soil water surrounding the plant.

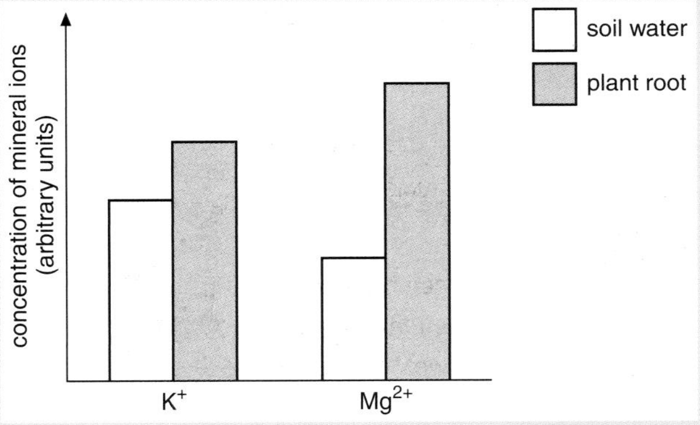

Explain how plants are able to build up higher concentration of ions in their roots than in the surrounding soil water.

(3 marks)

Chapter 4

Plant Nutrition

Learning objectives

By the end of this chapter you should know:

- The raw materials and products of photosynthesis
- Investigations which show that light, carbon dioxide and chlorophyll are needed for photosynthesis
- Factors affecting the rate of photosynthesis
- The balance between photosynthesis and respiration
- Minerals and plant nutrition
- The economic implications of enhancing environmental factors in crop production
- The structure of a leaf and its adaptations for photosynthesis
- The chloroplast as the site of photosynthesis

All living organisms require energy to survive. Energy comes from food. A very important difference between plants and animals is in the source of their food. Animals must feed on material that is, or was, plant or animal. Plants are able to use light energy to make their own food.

Plants do this by converting the raw materials of carbon dioxide and water to glucose (sugar). The glucose is usually converted immediately into starch. This process is called **photosynthesis** and it takes place in the green parts of plants, particularly in the leaves. The green pigment **chlorophyll** is an important part of photosynthesis as it traps the light energy from the sun that is needed to drive the process. Oxygen is produced as a waste product. Photosynthesis can be summarised by the equation:

$$\textbf{carbon dioxide + water} \xrightarrow[\textit{by chlorophyll}]{\textit{Light energy trapped}} \textbf{glucose + oxygen}$$

In photosynthesis light energy from the sun is converted into chemical energy (food). Photosynthesis is important for animals, as well as plants, as it provides a source of food and also releases oxygen back into the atmosphere.

Leaves (and other parts of the plant) that are carrying out photosynthesis in bright light will take carbon dioxide into the leaves and oxygen will move out. Not surprisingly, the brighter the light the faster the process will take place.

Photosynthesis experiments

It is possible to carry out investigations to show that photosynthesis is taking place or that particular raw materials are needed for the process.

The starch test

This test can be used to show that starch is produced in green leaves during photosynthesis. The starch test consists of a series of steps, these are:

- Removing a leaf from a plant that has been placed in bright light.
- The leaf is placed in boiling water for at least 30 seconds. This will kill the leaf and ensure that no further reactions can take place.
- The leaf is then placed in boiling ethanol (Figure 1a). This will remove the chlorophyll from the leaf. This procedure must take place using a water bath as ethanol is flammable and must not be exposed to a direct flame.
- The leaf should then be dipped in boiling water again. This will make the leaf soft again as the ethanol makes the leaf very brittle.
- The leaf is then spread out on a white tile and iodine is added to the leaf (Figure 1b).
- If starch is present the iodine will turn the starch blue-black. If there is no starch present the leaf will remain a yellow-red colour (the colour of the iodine).

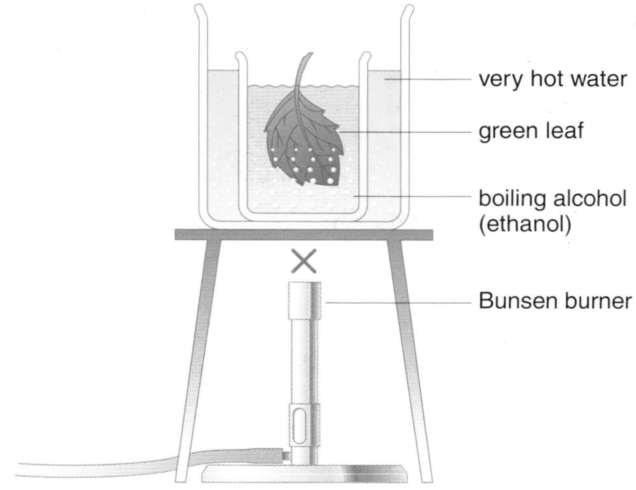

Figure 1a

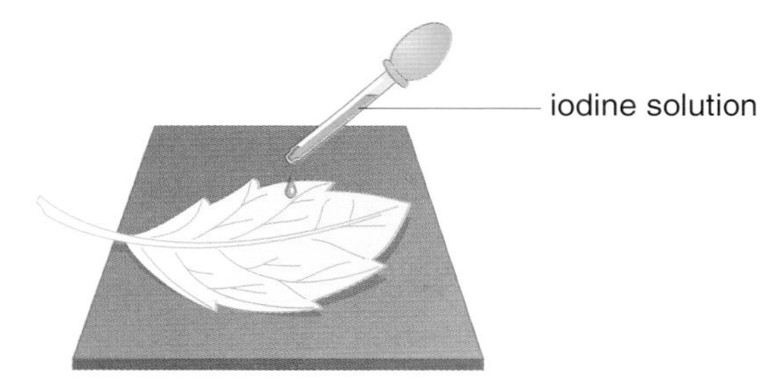

Figure 1b

Investigations that show that light, carbon dioxide and chlorophyll are necessary for photosynthesis

To carry out these experiments it is necessary to destarch the leaves of the plant first. Leaves can be **destarched** by leaving the plant in the dark for at least two days. This will ensure that any starch already in the leaves will be removed and stored elsewhere in the plant, or used by the plant during this period. The importance of this is that if the starch test at the end of the investigation is positive, it shows that the starch must have been produced during the period of the investigation.

Light

A leaf is partially covered with black paper or light-proof foil as shown in Figure 2. After a period of time the leaf is tested for starch as described above.

Questions

1 If light is essential for photosynthesis what result would you expect?

Carbon dioxide

To show that carbon dioxide is an essential raw material for photosynthesis it is necessary to compare a leaf that is deprived of carbon dioxide with a leaf that has a good supply of carbon dioxide. This can be achieved by preparing two leaves as shown in Figure 2. Sodium hydroxide or potassium hydroxide will remove carbon dioxide from the air surrounding the experimental leaf. The control leaf will only have water (or a chemical that increases carbon dioxide levels) in its flask and therefore there will be carbon dioxide present.

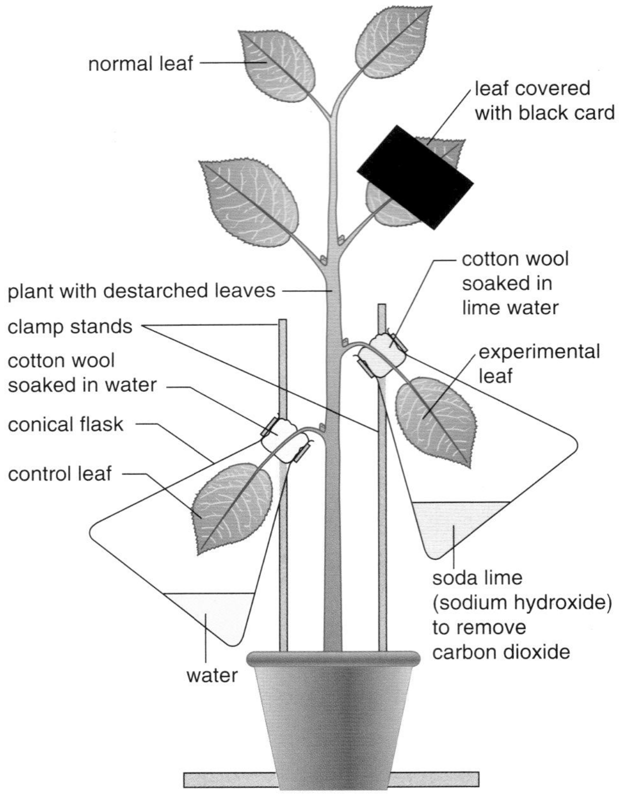

Figure 2

Questions

2 If carbon dioxide is an essential raw material for photosynthesis what results would you expect?

Chlorophyll

Some plants have leaves that are part green and part white. These leaves are described as being **variegated**. If a variegated leaf is tested for starch it will be apparent that starch is only produced in the green parts of the leaves. This shows that chlorophyll, the substance that gives leaves their green colour, is necessary for photosynthesis.

Measuring the rate of photosynthesis in different conditions

Using apparatus similar to that shown in Figure 3 it is possible to demonstrate that oxygen is produced in photosynthesis. The rate of photosynthesis will affect the rate at which the bubbles of oxygen will be given off and this can be used to compare photosynthesis rates in different conditions. For example, by moving the position of the lamp it is possible to investigate the effect of light intensity on photosynthesis.

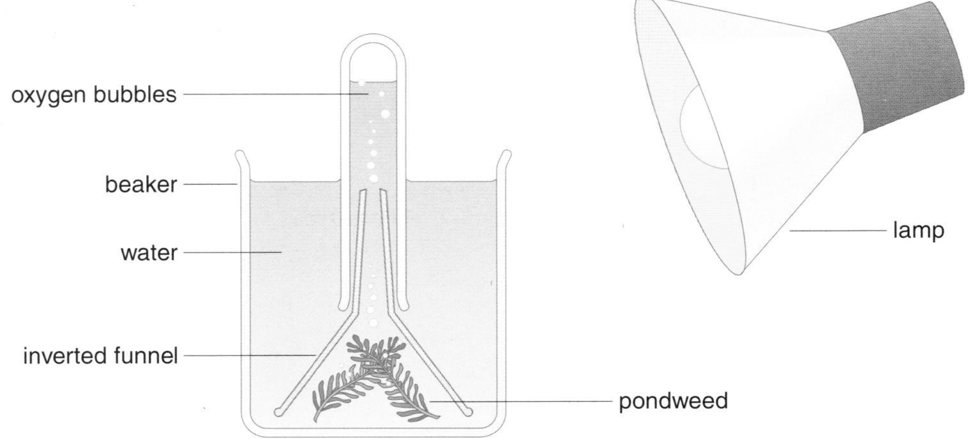

Figure 3 Measuring the rate of photosynthesis

The rate of photosynthesis can be more accurately calculated by measuring the volume of oxygen produced.

Questions

3 Why is it more accurate to measure the volume of oxygen collected?

Alternatively, an oxygen electrode connected to a data logger can be used to measure changes in oxygen levels.

The balance between photosynthesis and respiration

All living organisms respire as explained in Chapter 1. In plant respiration the glucose produced in photosynthesis is broken down to release energy. Plants require oxygen to respire and they produce carbon dioxide as a waste product. These gases enter the leaves through tiny pores called **stomata**.

During the night when there is no light for photosynthesis, respiration will be the only process involving gas exchange that takes place. Therefore oxygen will enter the leaf and carbon dioxide will leave. However, during the day when photosynthesis is occurring both processes will take place. When the light intensity is high the rate of photosynthesis will exceed the rate of respiration. When this happens carbon dioxide enters the leaves and oxygen moves out. There will be times during the day when the light intensity is low, causing photosynthesis to take place very slowly. At these points, usually at dawn and dusk, the rates of respiration and photosynthesis are equal and there will be no overall, or net, gas exchange.

The movement of carbon dioxide and oxygen into and out of plants can be determined using hydrogencarbonate indicator. Hydrogencarbonate indicator is bright red in normal atmospheric carbon dioxide levels. If there is an increase in carbon dioxide levels the indicator will change colour to yellow. A decrease in carbon dioxide levels will turn the indicator purple. Figure 4 shows how the indicator can be used to show gas exchange in plants.

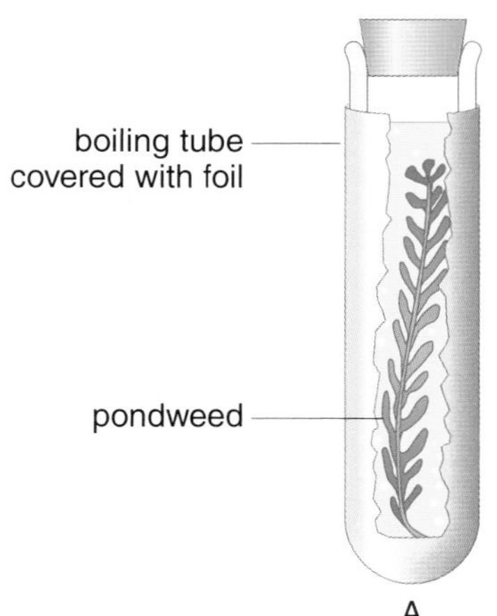

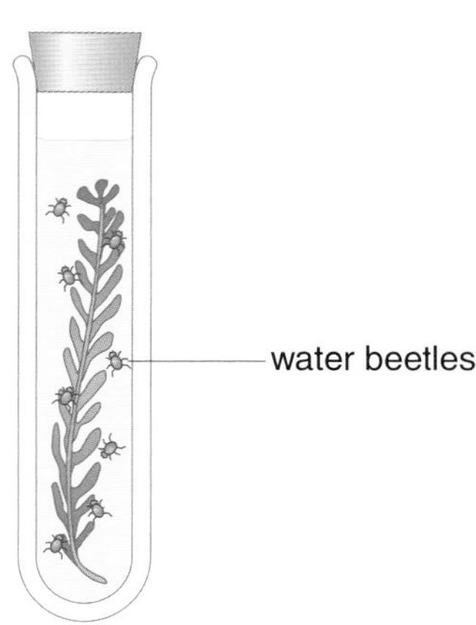

Figure 4 The effect of photosynthesis and respiration on gas exchange. Each boiling tube was filled with hydrogen carbonate indicator and placed in bright light for one hour

The results are explained in the following table.

Tube	Colour at start	Colour at end	Reason for change
A	Red	Yellow	The foil strip stops light entering and photosynthesis occurring. Respiration increases carbon dioxide levels
B	Red	Purple	Both photosynthesis and respiration are taking place in the pondweed. As the rate of photosynthesis is faster than the rate of respiration more carbon dioxide enters the plant than is produced
C	Red	Yellow	The water beetles produce more carbon dioxide in respiration than the pondweed takes in for photosynthesis

Questions

Suggest what colour change you would expect if the following changes were made. Explain your answers in each case.

4 There was only partial shading in tube A allowing some light to enter. Muslin and other similar materials provide partial shade.

5 More pondweed was introduced into tube C.

Using the products of photosynthesis

The glucose that is produced in photosynthesis can be converted into a range of products that the plant requires. As already stated the glucose is usually converted quickly into starch for storage in the leaves. The starch is converted back to sugar when needed and transported to other parts of the plant. The sugar can be used in respiration or converted into other essential plant products. These include:

- **Cellulose.** This is the main component of plant cell walls. Cellulose is a very tough carbohydrate which helps give the cell walls their strength.
- **Amino acids** and **lipids** (fats and oils). The glucose that is produced can be converted into amino acids and eventually proteins by a series of reactions in the plant cells. This is essential because amino acids are needed in plants for growth and repair in the same way as they are used in animals. Lipids can be used as an energy store.
- **Starch** – in the storage parts of the plant, for example the roots, the sugar can be converted back to starch for long-term storage. Many of our most important food products such as potatoes, carrots and parsnips are specialised roots with large quantities of stored food.

Questions

6 Why do many seeds have high levels of stored lipid within them?

Minerals

Plants also require a number of mineral ions or salts to function properly and stay healthy. The most important minerals include:

- **Nitrates** – these are required as a source of nitrogen to make amino acids. The amino acids are converted into proteins for growth.
- **Calcium** – this is required to make cellulose, an important component of cell walls.
- **Magnesium** – this is required to make chlorophyll.

Questions

7 Why do some plants growing in magnesium deficient soils have yellow coloured leaves?

Nitrates, calcium, magnesium and other mineral ions are absorbed by the plant roots. When they are absorbed against the concentration gradient active uptake is involved. Normally these ions will be present in the soil in sufficient concentration for normal plant growth, but occasionally it is necessary to fertilise the soil with one or more of these minerals.

Factors affecting the rate of photosynthesis

The rate at which photosynthesis occurs depends on the availability of the raw materials needed for the process. Levels of carbon dioxide and light will directly affect the rate of photosynthesis, as will the availability of water to some extent. As temperature affects the rate of all reactions it will influence the rate at which photosynthesis takes place.

When photosynthesis is taking place at its maximum rate all of these environmental factors must be present at peak or optimum levels. However, if one (or more) factor is in short supply the rate of photosynthesis will be limited. These raw materials become **limiting factors** and the rate of photosynthesis will be determined by whichever factor is in shortest supply.

Figure 5a shows the effect of light intensity on the rate of photosynthesis. It also shows how temperature (cold and hot days) can further influence the rate.

As light intensity increases, irrespective of temperature, the rate of photosynthesis increases up to a point where the graph begins to level off and forms a plateau. As an increase in light intensity causes an increase in photosynthesis at the lower light levels, the amount of light must be limiting the rate at which photosynthesis occurs. Within the plateau part of the graph further increases in light intensity do not lead to an increase in photosynthesis, therefore something else must be limiting the rate.

The effect of temperature can be explained by comparing the rates of photosynthesis on the cold and hot days. On the hot day photosynthesis occurs at a higher rate at higher light intensities when compared to the cooler day. Therefore we can conclude that temperature is limiting the rate at the higher light intensities on the cooler day.

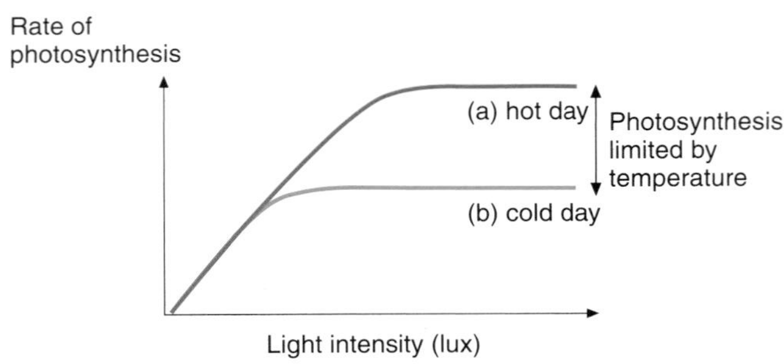

Figure 5a This graph shows how the rate of photosynthesis is affected by increasing light intensity on a) a hot and b) cold day

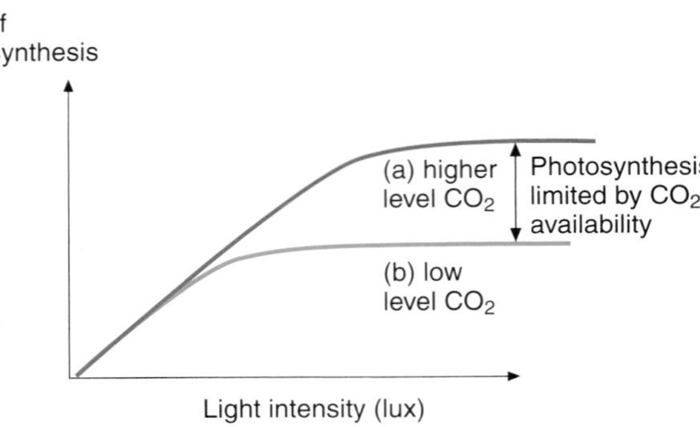

Figure 5b This graph shows how the rate of photosynthesis is affected by increasing light intensity at a) high and b) low carbon dioxide concentrations

It is possible that the rate of photosynthesis may still not be at its maximum where the rate has plateaued on the hot day at the highest light intensities. It is possible that carbon dioxide could be a limiting factor in these conditions. To test this we would need to increase carbon dioxide levels to see if this has any effect.

Figure 5b shows how light intensity affects the rate of photosynthesis at different carbon dioxide levels.

Again light intensity is limiting the rate of photosynthesis at low light levels. The fact that an increased carbon dioxide level leads to a higher rate of photosynthesis at higher light intensities shows that the low carbon dioxide level was a limiting factor once light levels had ceased to be limiting.

Questions

8 The graphs in Figure 5 show that the raw materials for photosynthesis interact with each other and that while some of the essential materials can be present in abundance it only takes one to be in short supply to limit the rate. Which of the factors discussed above do you think might limit the rate of photosynthesis in the following situations?

a) During a bright winter afternoon in a British grassland.

b) In a cornfield in mid-summer sunshine in Southern France.

In the natural environment the rates of photosynthesis and growth depend on environmental conditions. In crop production it is sometimes possible and profitable to control the environmental factors that affect photosynthesis. Controlling the environment to increase productivity is discussed in the next section.

Photosynthesis and crop production

To maximise crop production it is important that photosynthesis takes place at its optimum rate. The availability of the raw materials can be increased, if necessary, to ensure that they do not limit the rate of photosynthesis and hence production. It is much easier to control the environmental factors that affect photosynthesis in a glasshouse than in an open field.

Examples of increasing or enhancing environmental factors include:

- increasing temperature
- increasing carbon dioxide levels
- increasing light intensity
- increasing fertiliser applications
- increasing water availability

Figure 6 Environmental factors are carefully controlled in glasshouses to ensure a bumper crop

Increasing any of these environmental factors will increase the rate of photosynthesis if that factor is limiting. Paraffin heaters can be used to increase both temperature and carbon dioxide levels. It is also possible to pipe carbon dioxide into the glasshouse. Water sprinklers and artificial lighting are also frequently used to create ideal conditions. The use of sensors allows the environment to be controlled to within very strict limits. However, enhancing environmental factors has cost implications and maximum profit will be achieved when there is a balance between increasing essential raw materials and increased productivity.

The leaf – the centre of photosynthesis

In most plants the process of photosynthesis takes place in the leaves. Leaves come in many shapes and sizes but to allow photosynthesis to take place efficiently they are usually highly adapted for:

- light absorption
- gas exchange

The way in which leaves are arranged on a plant ensures that each leaf can absorb as much light as possible and that as far as possible each leaf is not in the shade of other leaves. The section through a leaf shown in Figure 7 shows many other ways in which a leaf is designed to aid light absorption and encourage gas exchange.

Light absorption in a leaf is maximised by:

- The short distance from top to bottom which allows all the cells to receive light.
- The large surface area.
- The thin transparent **cuticle** that reduces water loss by evaporation, but does not prevent light entering the leaf.
- The presence of chloroplasts rich in the pigment chlorophyll that absorbs light.
- The regular structure of the **palisade layer**, which ensures that many cells rich in chloroplasts are packed together near the upper surface of the leaf.

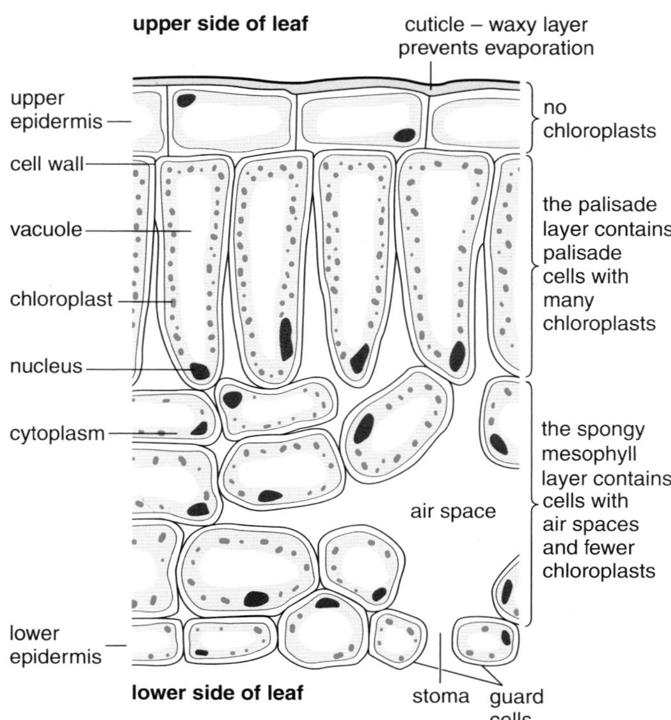

Figure 7 Cross section of a leaf

Gas exchange in a leaf is maximised by:

- The **intercellular air spaces** in the **spongy mesophyll** which allow carbon dioxide to enter, and oxygen to leave the photosynthesising cells that are mainly concentrated in the palisade layer.
- Carbon dioxide and oxygen can enter and leave the leaf through the stomata. Stomata are small pores that occur between cells on the bottom surface of leaves. Each stoma is surrounded by two **guard cells** that regulate the opening and closing of stomata. In many plants the stomata are open during the day and closed at night.

In some plants stomata can occur on both the upper and the lower leaf surface. Some plants have all their stomata on their upper leaf surfaces.

Questions

9 Why do some plants, such as water lilies, only have stomata on their upper leaf surfaces?

The chloroplast – the site of photosynthesis

The chloroplast is a small organelle found in the cytoplasm of cells that can photosynthesise. The chloroplasts contain pigments that can trap light energy and convert it into chemical energy during the process of photosynthesis. In green plants the most common pigment for trapping light is chlorophyll and it is this pigment that gives the plant its green colour. The chlorophyll appears green because it reflects the green part of the visible spectrum and it absorbs the red and blue parts. Usually chloroplasts also contain other pigments that absorb slightly different wavelengths of light from chlorophyll. In this way as much of the available light as possible can be absorbed with relatively little light reflected or passing through the chloroplast.

Note: Some plants such as seaweeds have a different range of **photosynthetic pigments** compared to most land plants. This is partially due to the fact that some wavelengths of light penetrate water better than others. Therefore the pigments in seaweeds have become adapted to absorb the wavelengths of light that reach them.

Figure 8 summarises the energy changes that take place in the chloroplast.

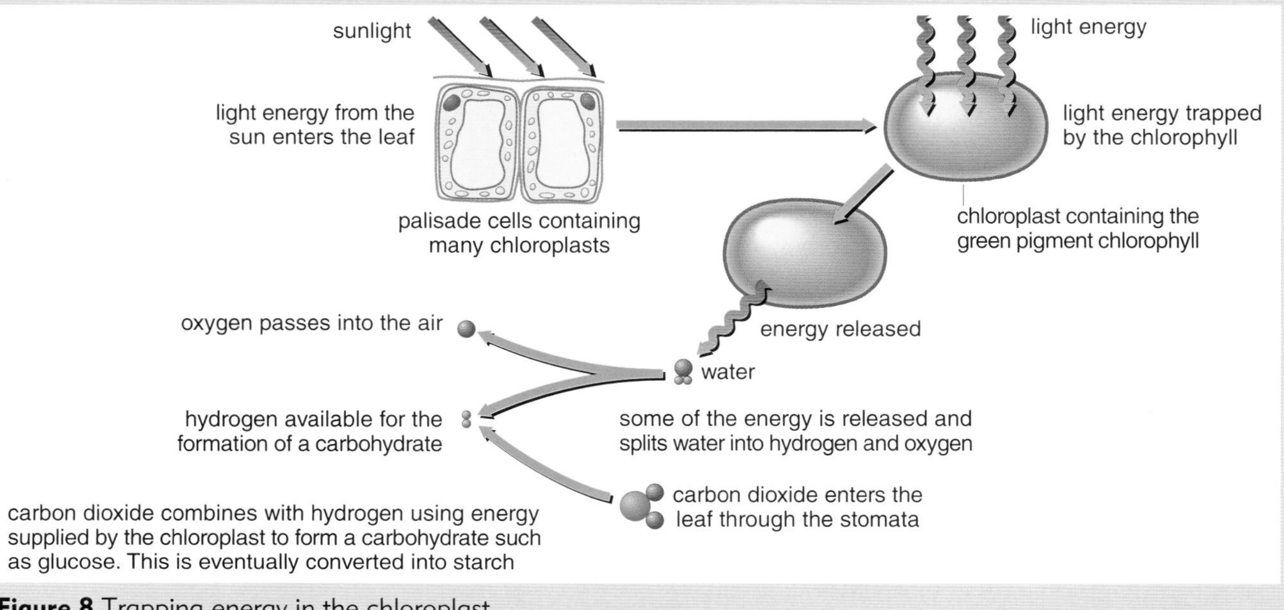

Figure 8 Trapping energy in the chloroplast

Websites

http://www.learn.co.uk
The science section at Key Stage 4 contains useful revision material including summaries of some of the experiments listed above.

http://www.darvill.clara.net
Attempt the virtual experiment on factors affecting the rate of photosynthesis.

http://www.purchon.com/biology/leaf.htm
Excellent diagram of leaf structure and associated notes.

http://www.revise.it/reviseit/content/GCSE/Biology/
Good summary of photosynthesis

You can do your own searching on the Internet. Try using criteria such as photosynthesis + experiments.

Exam questions

1 This experiment was set up to find out if carbon dioxide is needed for photosynthesis. The plant was destarched then left in a warm, sunny place for a few days after which both Leaf A and Leaf B were tested for starch.

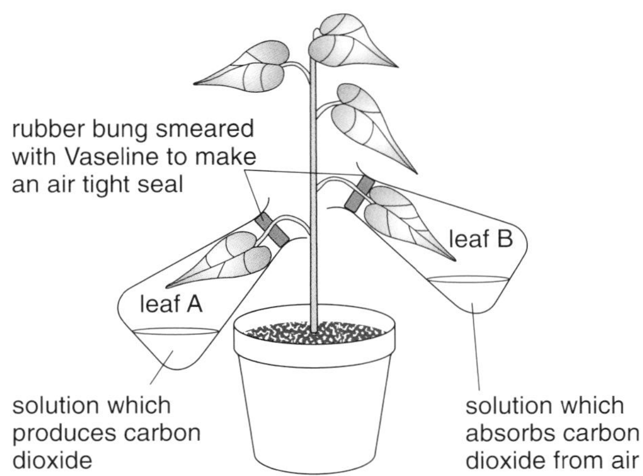

a) When carrying out the starch test on the leaf, explain how the:

(i) leaf is killed *(1 mark)*

(ii) chlorophyll is removed from the leaf. *(1 mark)*

b) After testing with iodine, describe the colour you would expect for each leaf. *(2 marks)*

2 Describe how you would use the apparatus shown to investigate the effect of light intensity on the rate of photosynthesis.

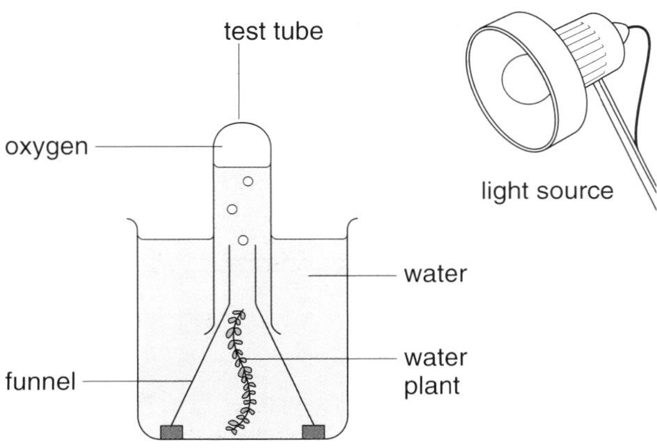

(4 marks)

3 The diagram represents the movement of carbon dioxide in and out of the air.

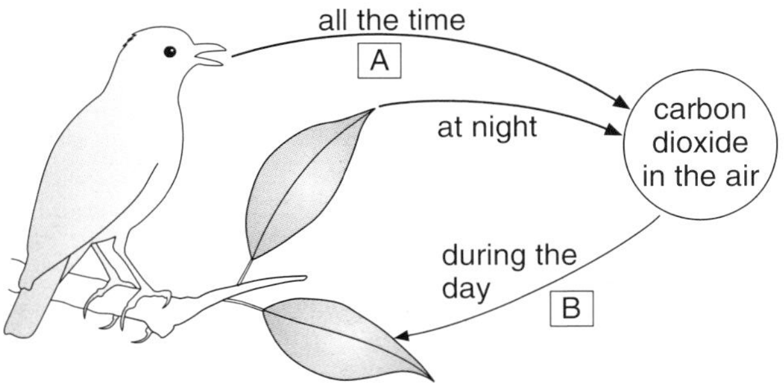

a) Name processes A and B. *(2 marks)*

b) An experiment was set up as shown in the diagram.

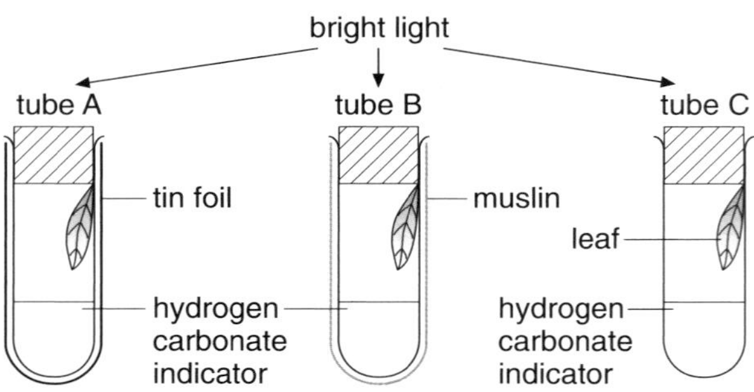

(i) Copy and complete the results table.

Tube	Indicator colour at start	Indicator colour after 24 hours
A	Red	
B	Red	Red
C	Red	

(2 marks)

(ii) Use **one** of the statements, listed below, to describe why there is no change in the colour of the indicator in tube B after 24 hours.

Carbon dioxide concentration:

[A] higher than before;

[B] less than before;

[C] same as before.

(1 mark)

4 The graph shows the rates of carbon dioxide release and uptake in some plants. The plants were placed for 12 hours in the dark followed by 12 hours in the light in a laboratory.

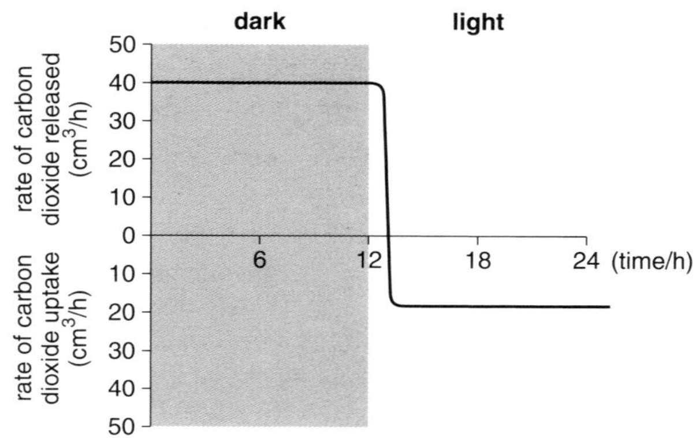

a) What process affecting gas exchange takes place in the plants during the 12 hours of darkness? *(1 mark)*

b) Explain the change that occurs when the plants are in the light. *(2 marks)*

5 The graph shows the yield of tomato plants grown in different percentages of carbon dioxide.

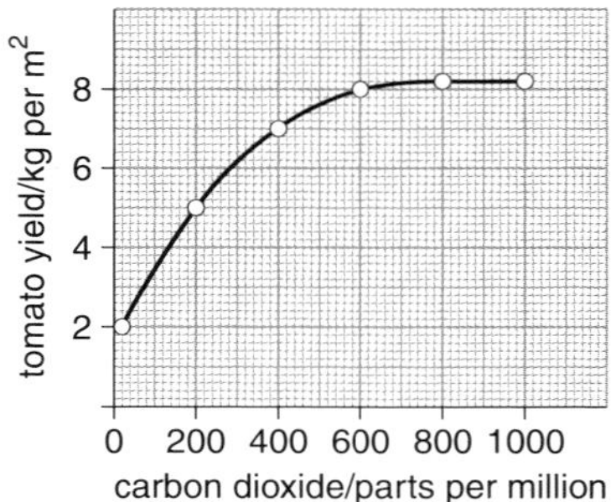

a) What is the tomato yield at a carbon dioxide concentration of 300 parts per million? *(1 mark)*

b) Explain the result obtained when the carbon dioxide concentration was increased from 800 to 1000 parts per million. *(2 marks)*

c) Why is it important to keep the light intensity constant for all the tomato plants? *(2 marks)*

d) When growing tomatoes for sale, what would a gardener have to consider before providing extra carbon dioxide for the plants? *(2 marks)*

6 The graph shows the effect of adjusting environmental conditions on the rate of photosynthesis in tomato plants in a glasshouse.

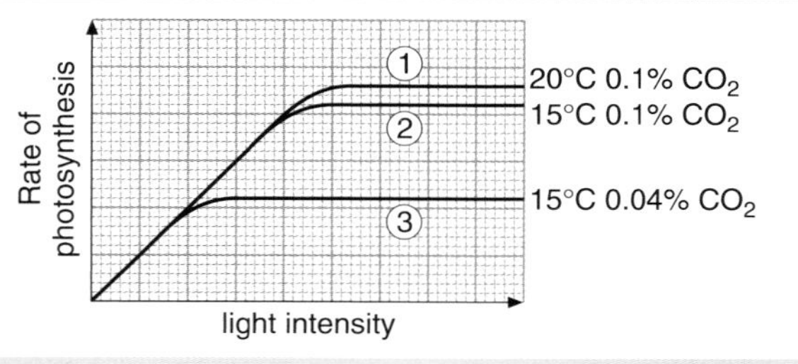

a) Use the graph to explain why carbon dioxide levels are not artificially increased on a cloudy, overcast day. *(1 mark)*

b) Use the graph to explain why it is more economical to increase carbon dioxide levels rather than the glasshouse temperature. *(2 marks)*

c) Very high carbon dioxide levels (0.5 % and above) are not used in glasshouses as these levels cause the stomata of the tomato plants to decrease in size. Explain why this would result in a lower yield. *(2 marks)*

7 a) The diagram shows part of a cross section through a leaf.

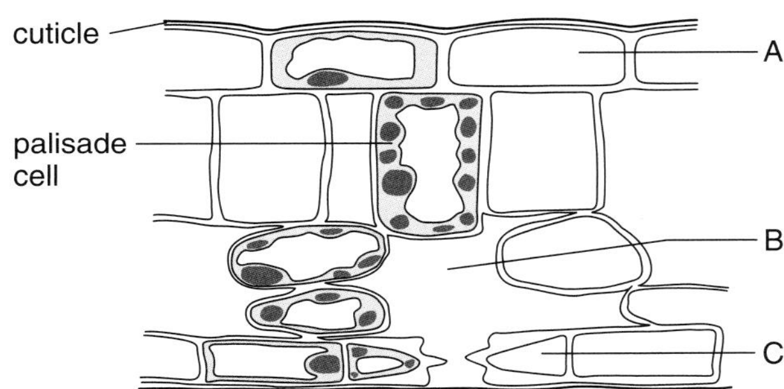

(i) Name A, B and C. *(3 marks)*

(ii) Copy the diagram and **use arrows** to show the pathway taken by a molecule of carbon dioxide from the air into the palisade cell. *(3 marks)*

(iii) Why is it an advantage for leaves to have a large surface area? *(1 mark)*

8 a) (i) Copy and complete the word equation for photosynthesis.

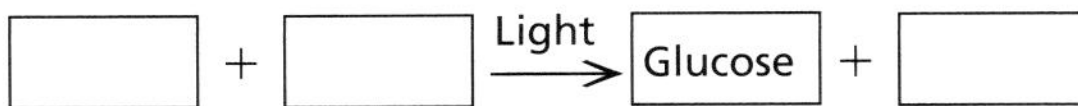

(3 marks)

(ii) Name the chemical, found in green leaves, which absorbs light. *(1 mark)*

b) Two variegated geranium plants were destarched before a photosynthesis experiment.
These variegated leaves are green in the middle and white round the edges.
A leaf from each plant was then removed and tested to show that no starch was present.
The diagrams show how to test a leaf for starch.

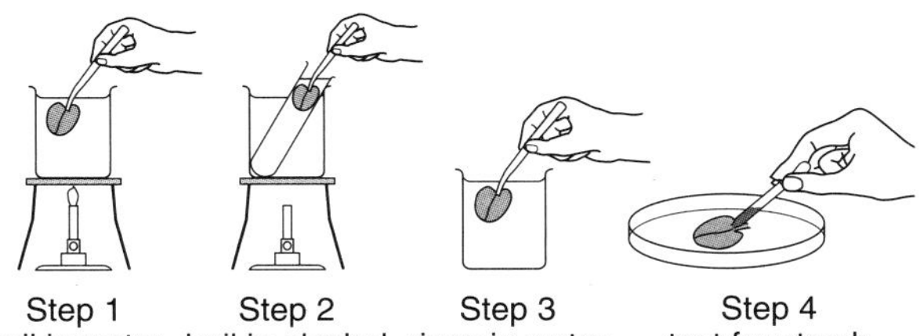

(i) Explain why the leaf was boiled in:
[A] water. *(1 mark)*
[B] alcohol. *(1 mark)*

(ii) One of the destarched plants was placed in bright light while the other was placed in the dark.
A leaf from each plant was then tested for starch.

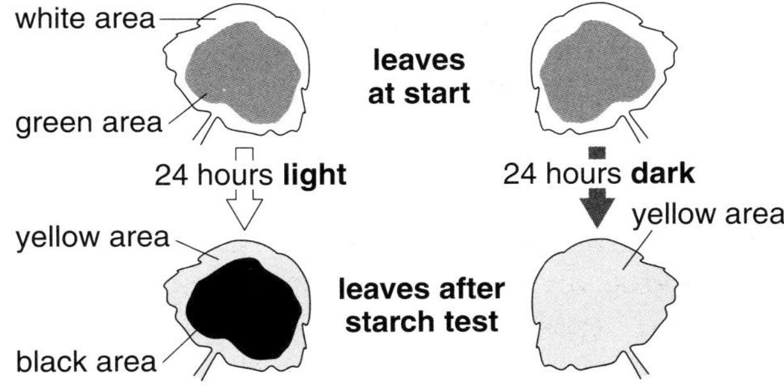

Explain how these results show that
[A] light is needed for photosynthesis. *(2 marks)*

[B] chlorophyll is needed for photosynthesis. *(2 marks)*

Chapter 5

Animal Nutrition

Learning objectives

By the end of this chapter you should:

- Be able to state the components of a balanced diet and their functions in the diet
- Be able to state the roles of calcium and iron in the diet
- Be able to state that an unhealthy diet may lead to the development of heart disease
- Be able to explain the difference between malnutrition and starvation
- Be able to describe how to carry out food tests on starch, sugars, proteins and vitamin C
- Be able to identify the regions of a tooth
- Be able to state how to take care of teeth and the argument for and against addition of fluoride to the water supply
- Be able to state how bacteria and sugar lead to tooth decay

The role of food

Humans need to take in food to survive. Food provides us with energy to carry out the activities and reactions of the body. Food also provides the materials for growth and protection against disease. Generally we need a **balanced diet**, which includes enough of all the following groups of substances – carbohydrates, fats, proteins, vitamins (especially C and D), minerals (especially calcium and iron) and water. However too much of these nutrients over a period of time, with insufficient exercise can lead to health problems including obesity and heart disease. Figure 1 shows examples of the main food groups.

a)

b)

c)

Figure 1 These foods are high in a) carbohydrates, b) protein and c) fibre

Fats are a useful source of energy since they contain a lot of stored energy, but it takes some time for this energy to become available to the body. Fats are also used for insulation and protection of some body organs. **Carbohydrates**, especially simple sugars, provide us with a quick source of energy, but they do not contain as much energy as fats. **Proteins** are needed to provide us with the materials for growth of the body and repair of cells. Fats and carbohydrates both contain the elements carbon, hydrogen and oxygen but in different proportions.

Proteins in addition always contain nitrogen and usually sulphur as well. **Vitamins** and **minerals** are needed for various functions in the cells. Vitamin C is needed for healthy skin and gums. Lack of vitamin C produces a disease called scurvy. Vitamin D is needed for bone formation, if not enough is present in the diet it can lead to rickets.

Vitamin	Best sources	Essential for	Symptoms of deficiency
A (fat-soluble)	Fish liver oils, liver and kidney, green and yellow vegetables, butter, egg yolk	Growth, good eyesight, healthy skin and mucous-membranes	Retarded growth, night blindness, viral infections
C (water-soluble)	Vegetables, citrus fruit, blackcurrants	Growth, maintaining strength of blood vessels, development of teeth and gums	Scurvy (sore gums and bleeding around bones and from intestine)
D (fat-soluble)	Fish liver oil, liver, milk, eggs	Growth, regulating use of calcium and phosphorus for making bones and teeth	Rickets (soft bones and dental decay)

a)

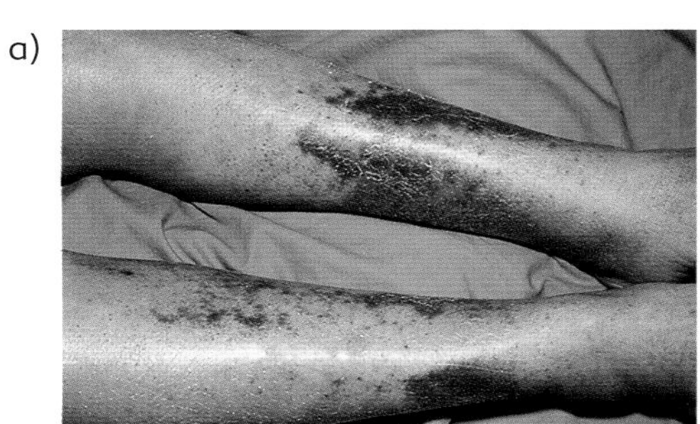

b)

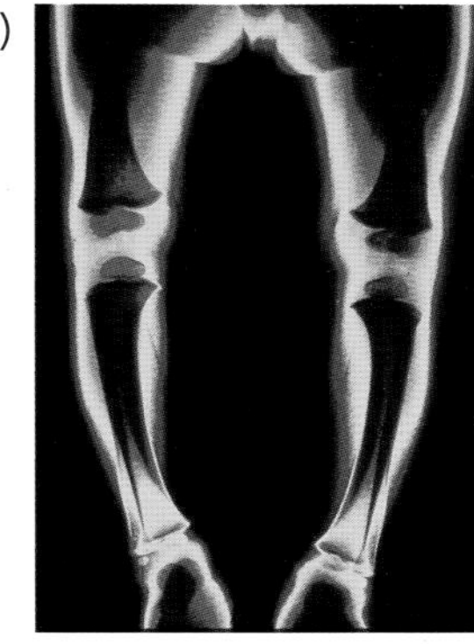

Figure 2 These photographs show a) scurvy and b) rickets

Calcium is needed for bones and teeth and the mineral iron is needed for blood. Iron is found in red blood cells in a substance called **haemoglobin** which enables these cells to transport oxygen around the body.

The amounts of these substances which we need to stay healthy vary during our lifetime. It depends on our level of **activity**, **gender** and **age**. A child will require more nutrients than a person who does little activity. Figure 3 shows some examples. If a person eats too much and exercises too little then they will become **obese**. This leads to an increased risk of heart disease and strokes.

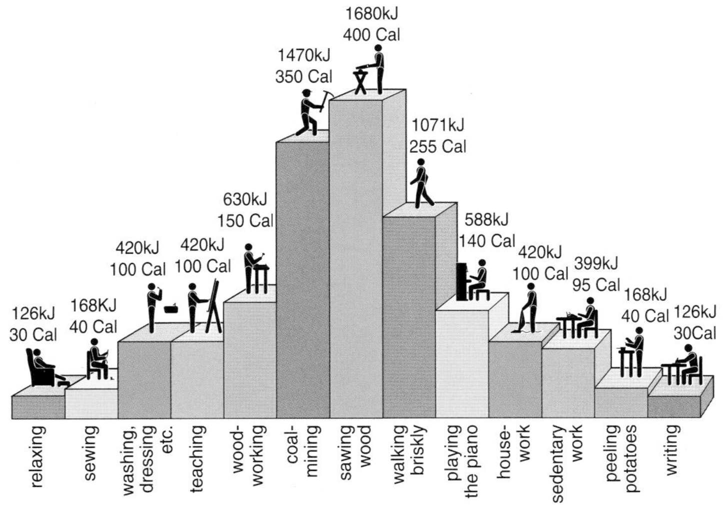

Figure 3 How energy needs vary with activity

Questions

1 What nutrients in particular should a pregnant woman make sure she has in her diet to ensure the healthy growth of her baby?

Water

This makes up a large proportion of our cells and blood is 92 % water. Water is needed:

- in our cells as a solvent
- to help us regulate body temperature
- to help transport substances around the body in the digestive, blood, tissue fluid and lymph systems
- to help in excretion.

As we lose water, or if we do not take in enough water, then we suffer from dehydration where the cells start to shrivel and cannot function properly.

Figure 4 shows some of the methods of water gain and loss in the body.

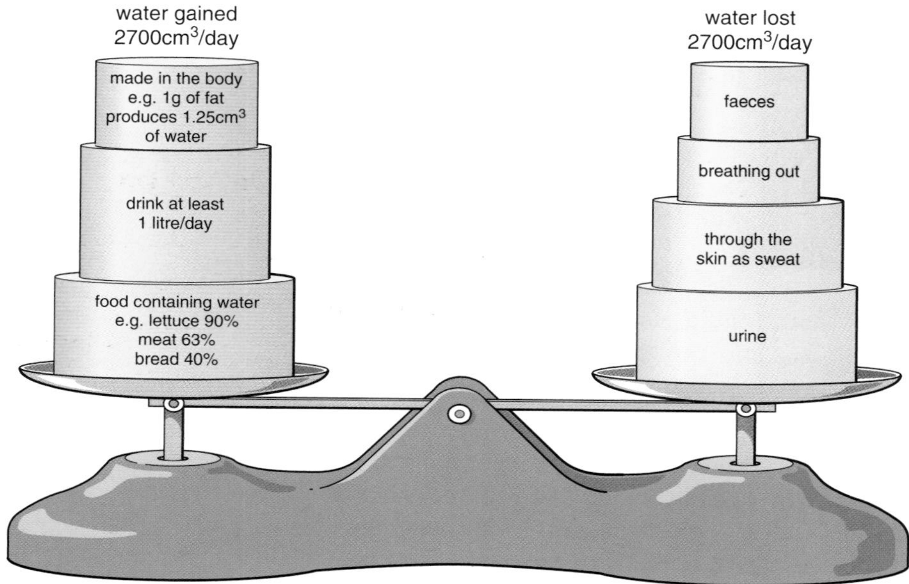

Figure 4 Water gain and loss in the body

Fibre

This comes from cellulose in plants. Humans cannot digest cellulose but it helps to keep food moving through the digestive system and prevents constipation and bowel cancer.

Starvation and malnutrition

In many countries in the world people do not have enough to eat. This is called **starvation**. In other areas they may have a reasonable quantity of food to eat, but it may consist mostly of one food type. This is called **malnutrition**.

Figure 5 This family is suffering from starvation

Questions

2 Why is it important to drink more fluid than normal if you are in a warm climate?

3 Why do many people, especially in underdeveloped countries not have enough to eat?

Food tests

These tests can be carried out to identify what substances are present in different foods. The food may need to be crushed in a pestle and mortar and a little water added to it. It is then filtered and the solution divided between several test tubes. Each solution is then tested for a different food group.

SAFETY – WEAR GOGGLES WHEN CARRYING OUT THESE EXPERMENTS.

1 Test for simple sugar

Add 2 cm^3 of Benedict's solution and heat carefully in a water bath.

If the solution changes from a blue to green and then to orange/red colour then sugar is present.

2 Test for starch

Add iodine to the solution in the test tube.

If the solution changes from a yellow/red colour to a blue/black colour, starch is present.

3 Test for protein

Add 2 cm^3 of sodium hydroxide to the solution (WARNING – THIS IS ALKALI AND CAUSTIC – DO NOT GET IN EYES, ON SKIN OR CLOTHES).

Then add 2 cm^3 of copper sulphate solution. (These two solutions are sometimes already added together and called the Biuret solution.)

If the solution changes from a blue colour to a purple colour then there is protein present.

4 Test for vitamin C

Add DCPIP solution drop by drop to the solution in the test tube.

If the solution changes from a blue colour to clear then there is vitamin C present. (The fewer the drops of DCPIP solution needed for the colour change, the more vitamin C is present in the food.)

a) starch test

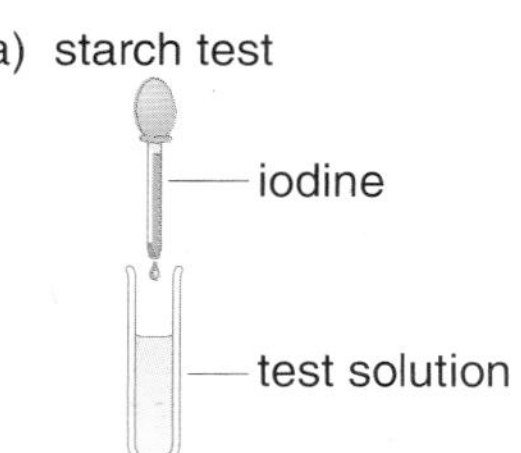

b) simple sugar test

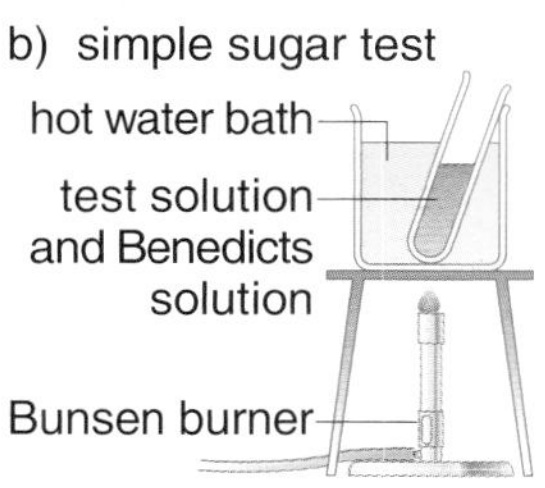

c) protein test

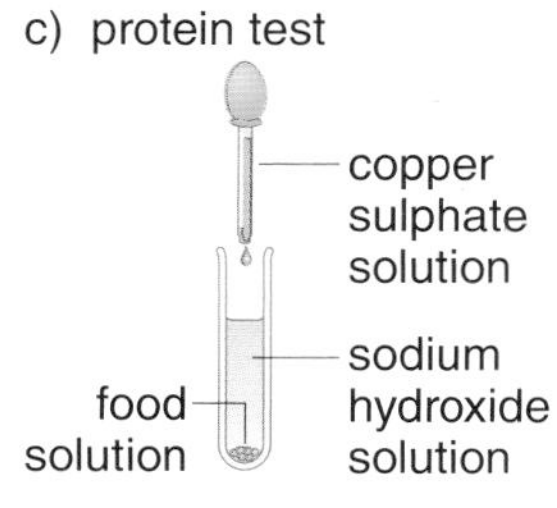

Figure 6 Food tests

Teeth

Humans produce two sets of teeth during their lifetime. The first set are called the **milk teeth** and these are later replaced and added to, to produce the permanent teeth. Teeth help to chop and grind the food so that it can be easily swallowed and digested.

Figure 7 shows the structure of teeth and gives some information about their composition.

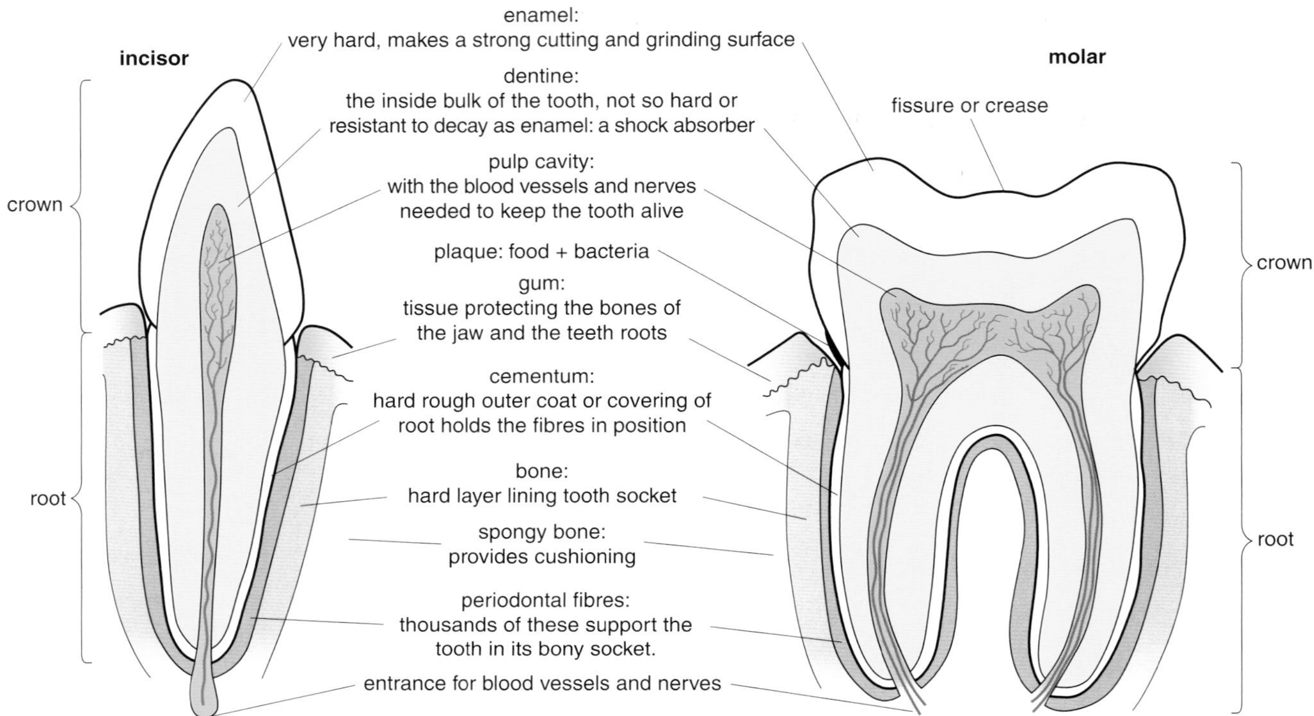

Figure 7 The structure of teeth

Tooth decay

This is brought about when acids produced by bacteria in the mouth attack the enamel of the teeth. The bacteria use sugar from foods for respiration and produce acid. If the acid eats away at the enamel the person starts to feel pain as the process of decay spreads into the dentine and pulp cavity where the nerves are.

bacteria in plaque produce acid which eats into the enamel

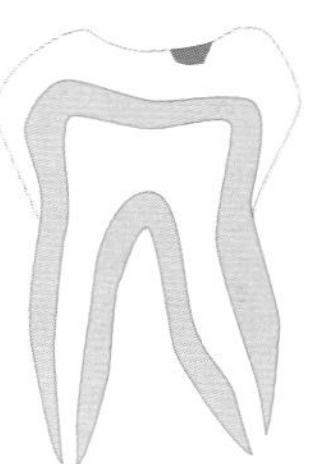

once decay gets into the dentine it progresses much more quickly

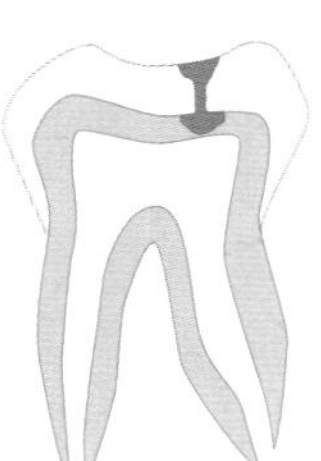

when the decay reaches the pulp it spreads very quickly. It affects the nerve and causes toothache. Decay like this often means that the tooth must be extracted

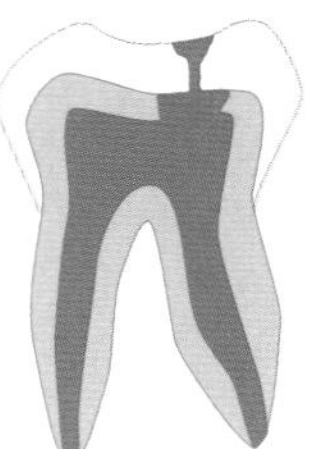

Figure 8 Tooth decay

A healthy diet, brushing and flossing of the teeth, as well as regular visits to the dentist all help to reduce the chances of tooth decay.

In some areas fluoride is added to the water supply in the form of sodium fluoride. This is because it has been found that certain levels of fluoride help strengthen the enamel in teeth. However there is controversy surrounding this process since some people object to having anything added to the water supply. They are also concerned about the levels of fluoride that are added and how safe the process is since too much fluoride can actually damage teeth.

Figure 9 shows the results of a study of how tooth decay is reduced when fluoride is added to the water.

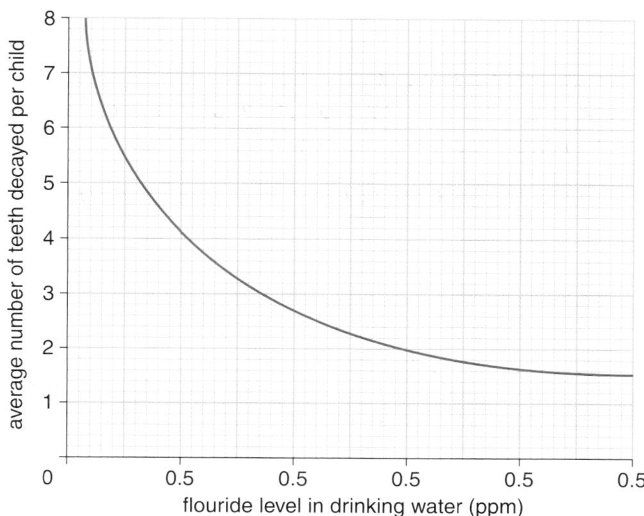

Figure 9

Questions

4 What level of fluoride should be added to the water supply based on the evidence from the graph shown in Figure 9?

Websites

http://www.bbc.co.uk/food/healthyeating
Includes advice on healthy eating and a diet quiz.
Also in same site, healthy living/nutrition.
More informatiion about dietary requirements and fitness.

http://www.nutrition.co.uk/information/dietandhealth
Sections of information on balanced diet, healthy teeth, diet, cancer and heart disease, and diabetes.

Exam questions

1 The table lists some nutrients in a healthy diet.

a) Copy and complete the table.

Nutrient	Food high in nutrient	Deficiency disease
Calcium		poor bones and teeth
Vitamin C		
	oily fish	rickets

(4 marks)

A balanced diet also requires water.

b) Give **two** functions of water in the body. *(2 marks)*

2 a) The diagram shows a tooth.

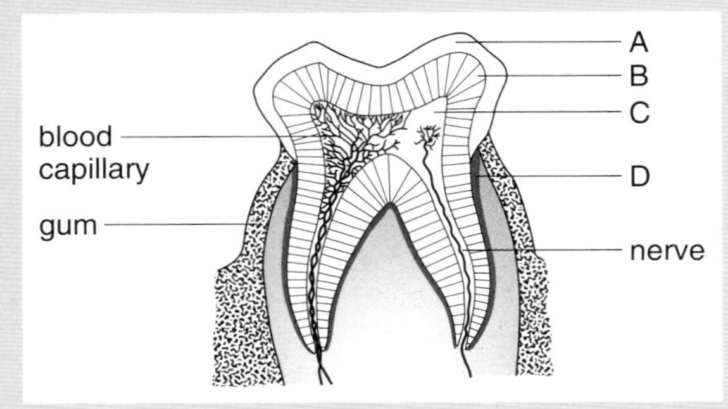

(i) Name A, B, C and D. *(4 marks)*

Sugars play an important role in tooth decay.

(ii) Describe the test for simple sugars. *(2 marks)*

The diagram shows a decaying tooth.

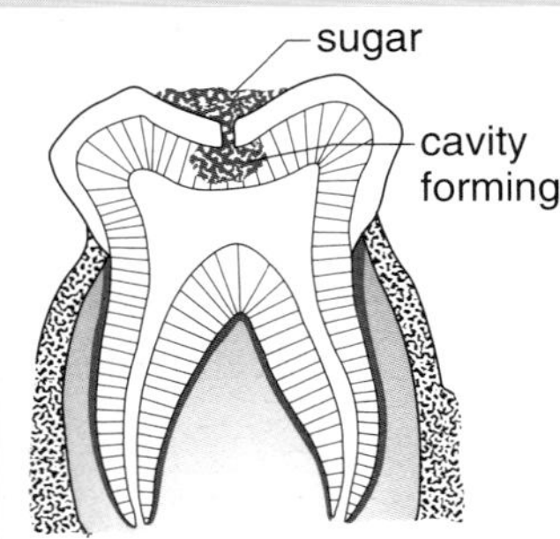

(iii) Use the diagram to help explain how eating sugary food can lead to tooth decay. *(3 marks)*

b) The graph shows the average number of decayed teeth of 5-year-old children.

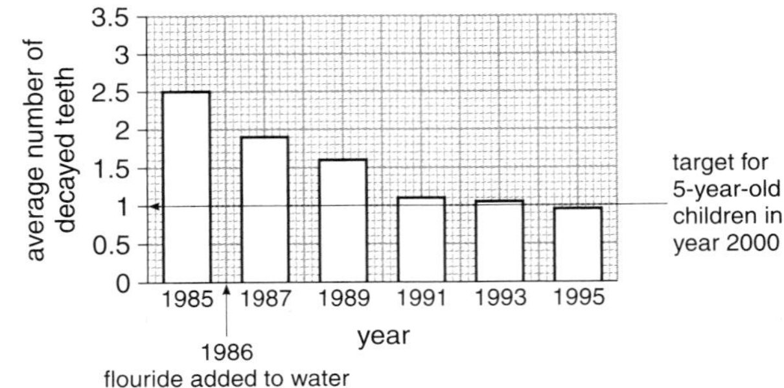

(i) Give the **average** number of decayed teeth of 5-year-old children in 1985. *(1 mark)*

(ii) Describe the changes in tooth decay from 1985. *(1 mark)*

(iii) Suggest a reason for the changes in the average number of decayed teeth. *(1 mark)*

In 1995 the average number of decayed teeth of 5-year-old children from Northern Ireland was 3.76.

(iv) How does this compare with the target on the graph? *(1 mark)*

(v) Name **one** other mineral, present in the diet, which is required for healthy teeth. *(1 mark)*

c) The food label shows the ingredients of yoghurt.

(i) Name **two** nutrients, missing from yoghurt, which are needed in a balanced diet. *(2 marks)*

Water is an important ingredient of yoghurt.

(ii) Give **three** uses of water in the body. *(3 marks)*

Chapter 6

Enzymes

Learning objectives

By the end of this chapter you should:

- Be able to state the role of amylase, lipase, and protease in digestion – their substrates and products
- Be able to state that enzymes are biological catalysts
- Be able to state that enzymes are not only involved in the breakdown of larger molecules, but that some enzymes catalyse reactions where molecules are assembled (e.g. starch)
- Be able to explain what substrate specificity means and how it is related to the shape of molecules
- Be able to explain how temperature and pH affect enzyme activity

Digestive enzymes

The following table shows the names of the different digestive enzymes, the substance they act upon and what is produced as a result. The substance that an enzyme works on is called its **substrate**. Notice that the names of most enzymes end in -ase, for example amylase which breaks down starch.

Place of digestion	Glands	Secretion	Enzymes	Digestive action
mouth	salivary	saliva	amylase	starch to glucose
stomach	gastric	gastric juice	protease (pepsin)	proteins to amino acids
		hydrochloric acid		activates pepsin; kills bacteria
small intestine	liver	bile		emulsifies fats
	pancreas	pancreatic juice	protease (trypsin)	proteins to amino acids
			amylase	starch to glucose
			lipase	fats to fatty acids and glycerol
	intestinal	intestinal juice	protease	proteins to amino acids
			amylase	starch to glucose
			lipase	fats to fatty acids and glycerol

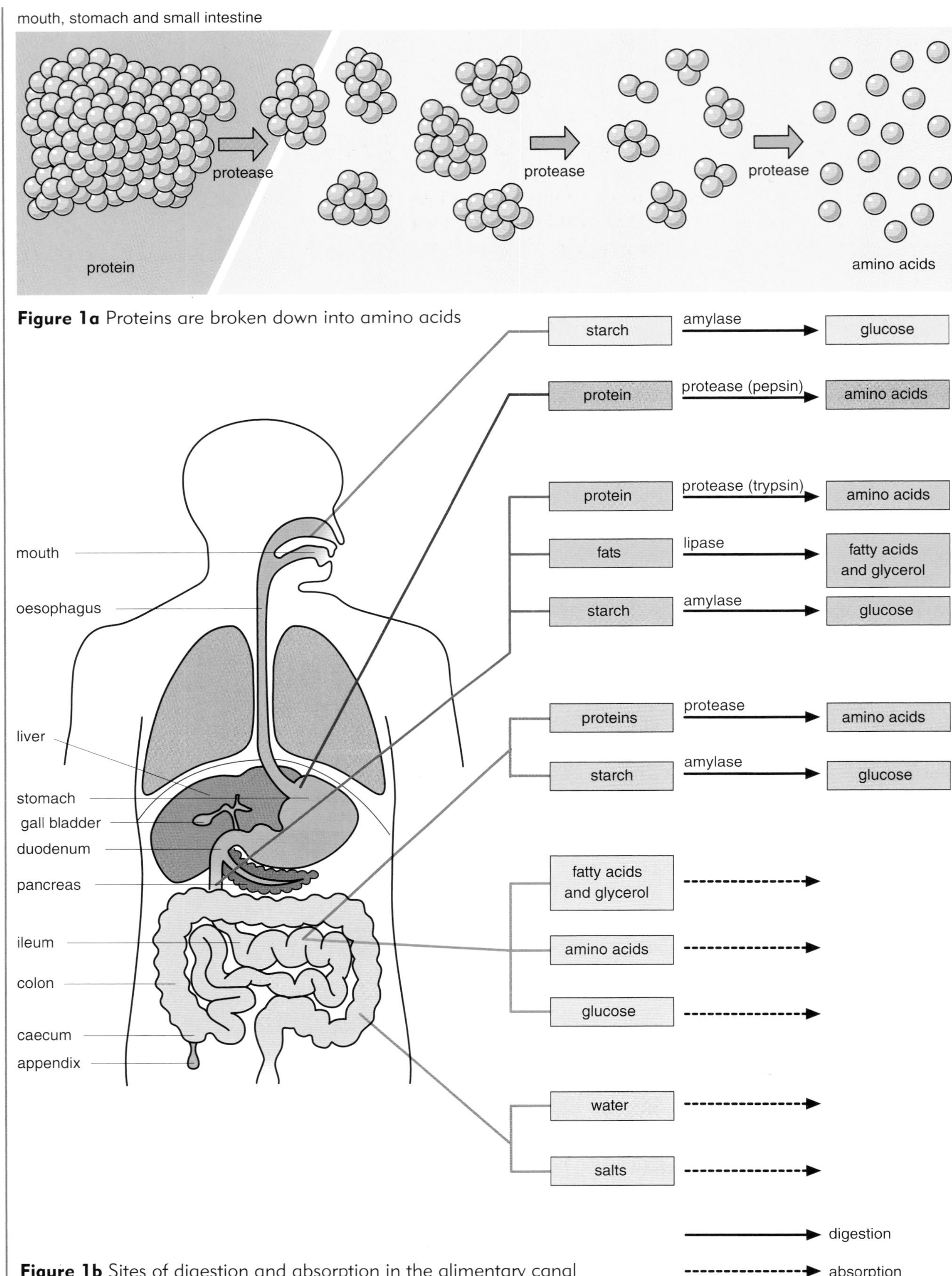

Figure 1a Proteins are broken down into amino acids

Figure 1b Sites of digestion and absorption in the alimentary canal

Practical activity

WEAR SAFETY GOGGLES WHEN HEATING THE AMYLASE SOLUTION

1 Place 30 ml of starch solution in a boiling tube in a water bath at 30°C for 5 minutes.

2 Boil 5 ml of amylase solution, cool it and then place in a waterbath at 30°C for 5 minutes.

3 Take three boiling tubes and place 10 ml of starch into each boiling tube. Then add 5 ml of either amylase, boiled amylase or water as shown in the diagram, mix and put them back in the waterbath. (You will need small measuring cylinders to measure out the liquids.)

5 Just after you have placed the boiling tubes in the waterbath remove a drop of the contents of each boiling tube with a clean teat pipette and place the drop on a white spotting tile. Add a drop of iodine solution to each solution on the spotting tile to test for starch. Record the results in a table similar to the one shown.

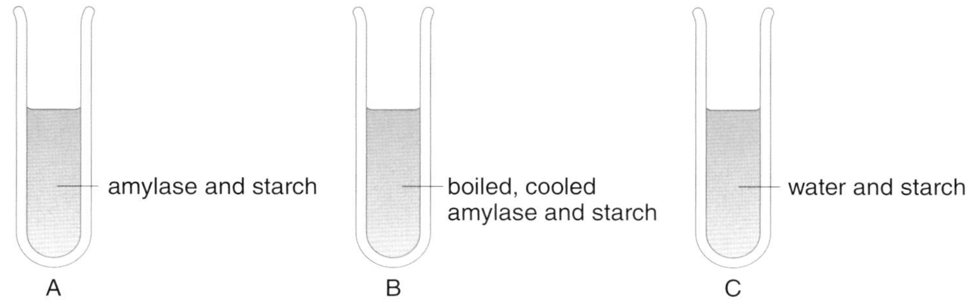

Time/min	Result of starch test Test tube A	Test tube B	Test tube C
0 (start)			
10			
20			

6 Repeat the last step again after 10 and 20 minutes.

Properties of enzymes

Enzymic breakdown takes place in the mouth, stomach and small intestine during digestion, but enzymes are also involved in assembling or synthesising molecules. Enzymes are chemicals which act as **biological catalysts** – they speed up the rate at which reactions occur. Without them most of the reactions in the human body, or in any living organism, would occur too slowly for organisms to function. Most enzymes work best in neutral conditions but some work better in acid conditions, for example protease found in the stomach. Those found in the human body work best at normal body temperature.

Enzymes, pH and temperature

Most enzymes work best in neutral conditions, however some work in acid conditions, for example protease in the stomach. Those enzymes found in the human body work best at normal body temperature. The temperature at which an enzyme works best is called its optimum temperature.

Enzymes are proteins and their shape is very important for their activity.

Changes in pH and temperature affect the bonds holding the protein structure together. If these bonds are broken the enzyme can no longer function. If the temperature is lowered the enzyme will become less active, but it will resume activity once the temperature is raised to normal ranges. However if the temperature is increased then the enzyme becomes **denatured** – for many enzymes found in our bodies this is at about 50–60°C. This means that its structure has been changed so much that it can no longer function.

Enzymes are **substrate specific**. This means that each enzyme will only react with one or a small group of substances, i.e. each enzyme is specific to its substrate. For example lipase will only react with lipids – it will have no effect on proteins.

The reasons for this are again linked to the importance of shape in enzyme molecules. Lipase has a particular shape which allows it to fit together with lipid molecules. This shape is completely unsuitable for proteins and so lipase will not react with proteins. This mechanism of enzyme action is called the **lock and key theory** – based on the model that different locks need different keys depending on shape.

Enzymes are involved in reactions where they break down larger molecules into smaller molecules. The reactions where enzymes break down molecules occur in digestion, for example amylase breaks down starch.

$$\text{starch} \xrightarrow{\text{amylase}} \text{glucose}$$

An example of enzymes building up molecules is that of making glycogen from glucose in the liver.

Questions

1 Why would living organisms not be able to function without enzymes?

2 Explain why shape is important in the functioning of proteins.

Websites

http://web.ukonline.co.uk/webwise/spinneret/
How enzymes work.

http://bbc.co.uk/schools/gcsebitesize/biology/humans/enzymesrev1.shtml
Information about enzymes, how they work and their uses.

Exam questions

1 The diagrams show the effect of enzymes on different food types.

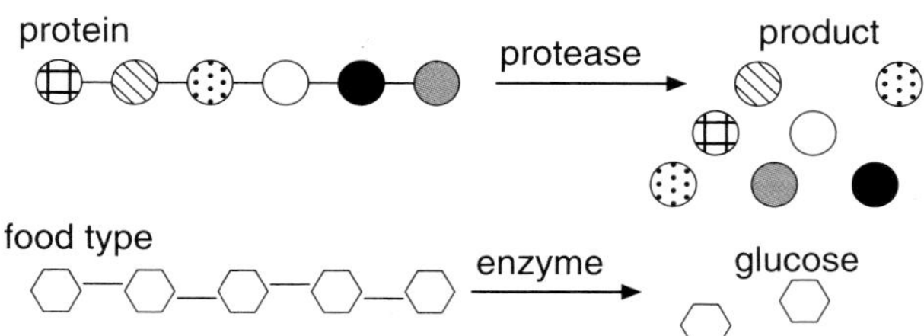

a) Copy and complete the table.

Food type	Enzyme	Product
protein	protease	
starch		glucose

(*2 marks*)

2 a) (i) What is an enzyme? (*1 mark*)

(ii) An investigation was carried out using starch solution and amylase solutions which were kept separately in a waterbath at 20°C for five minutes. After this time the investigation was started by mixing the solutions as shown in the diagram.

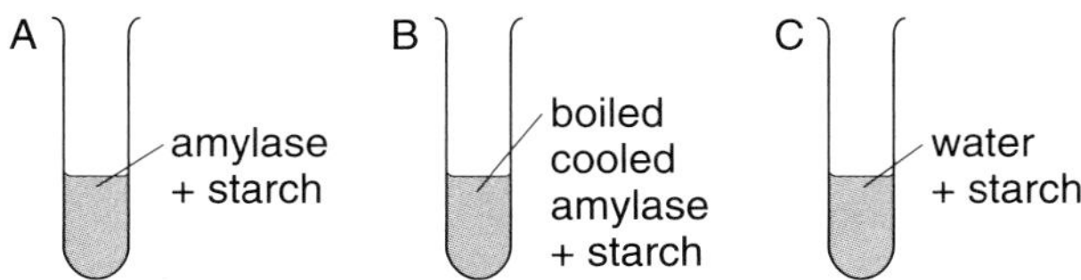

At ten minute intervals one drop of the contents of each test tube was removed and added to one drop of iodine to test for starch. The results are shown in the table.

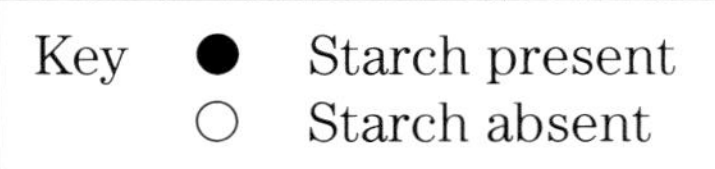

Time/min	Result of starch test: Test tube A	Test tube B	Test tube C
0 (start)	●	●	●
10	●	●	●
20	○	●	●

Why should the starch solution and the amylase solutions be kept separately in the waterbath for five minutes before the investigation begins?

(*1 mark*)

(iii) What do the results at the start of the investigation show? (*1 mark*)

(iv) Explain the results in test tube A after 20 minutes. (*2 marks*)

(v) Name the substance produced when starch is broken down. (*3 marks*)

(vi) Explain the results for test tube B. (*2 marks*)

(vii) Explain the results for test tube C. (*1 mark*)

b) The effect of pH on the enzyme protease, which is found in the stomach, was investigated.

(i) What substance does the enzyme protease break down in the stomach? (*1 mark*)

(ii) What is produced when protease has acted in the stomach? (*1 mark*)

Stomach protease can be used to remove the backing from a strip of photographic film.

Three test tubes were set up with different pH conditions as shown in the diagram.

The same amount of protease was added to each.

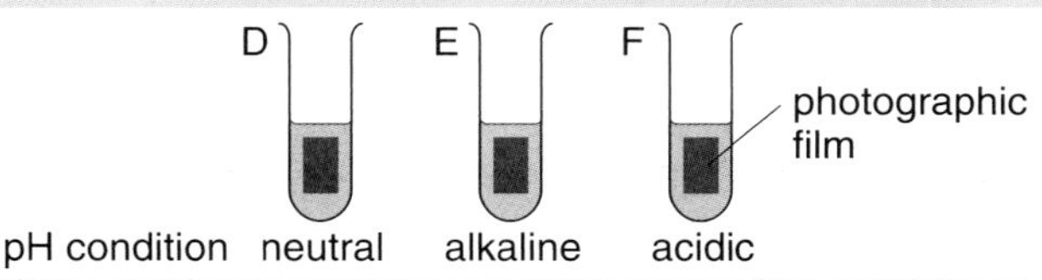

(iii) In which test tube will the backing be removed most quickly from the film? Explain your answer. (*2 marks*)

Chapter 7

The Digestive System

Learning objectives

By the end of this chapter you should:

- Be able to identify and state the functions of the various parts of the digestive system.
- Be able to state definitions for the processes of ingestion, digestion, absorption, assimilation and egestion
- Be able to explain peristalsis
- Be able to give the source of bile and its action
- Be able to state how the small intestine is adapted for its function
- Be able to state the function of the colon
- Be able to state where digestive enzymes are produced and their substrates
- Be able to explain the role of the liver in the assimilation of glucose

The structure of the digestive system

The digestive system is composed of the **alimentary canal** which is one long tube with several organs attached to it. Varying in size throughout the body it starts with the mouth and ends in the anus. The function of this system is to break down large insoluble molecules into smaller soluble ones (digestion), so that these smaller soluble molecules can pass across the wall of the digestive system and into the blood (absorption). Without these processes much of what we eat would pass out through the anus before the body had a chance to absorb the nutrients in the food.

The main processes that take place in the digestive system are ingestion, digestion, absorption and egestion.

- **Ingestion** is the process of taking in food and occurs in the mouth.
- **Digestion** is the process of breaking down large insoluble molecules into smaller soluble ones and occurs in the mouth, stomach and small intestine.
- **Absorption** is the process of small soluble molecules passing across the wall of the small intestine (especially the ileum) and into the blood or lymph systems.
- **Assimilation** is the process where digested food molecules are absorbed into body cells.
- **Egestion** is the process of passing out undigested material (the faeces) from the anus.

The parts of the digestive system are organised so that different processes take place in the different regions. Therefore by the time the food reaches the ileum it has been broken up so that any useful substances from it can be passed across the ileum wall. The food is first physically broken up into smaller pieces and then chemicals called enzymes break it up further into smaller molecules.

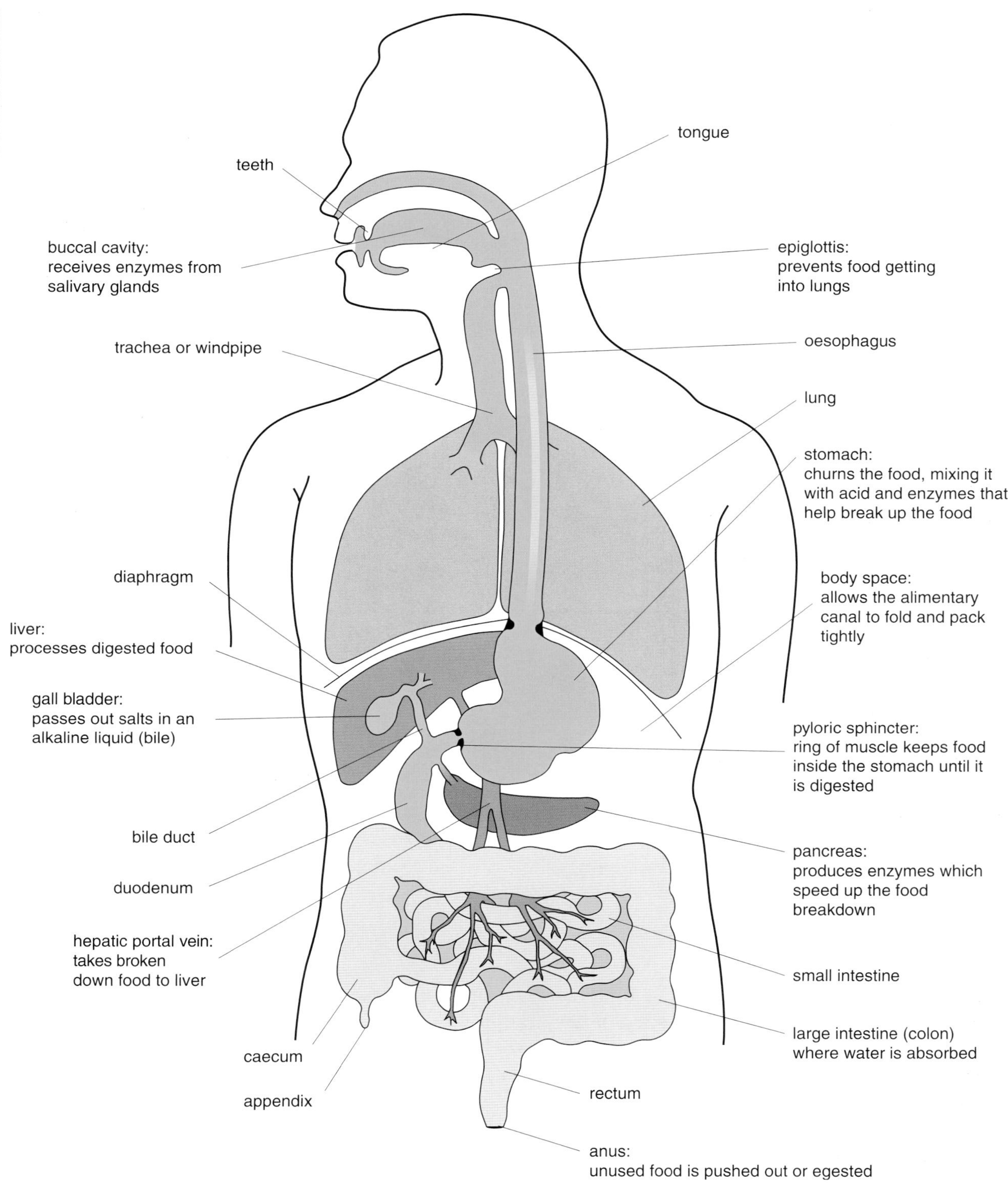

Figure 1 The human digestive system

Physical digestion

The physical breakdown of food begins in the mouth with the action of chewing and grinding by the teeth. Further down the digestive system physical digestion continues as the food is mixed up and churned in the stomach.

The mouth (buccal cavity)

In the mouth the food is physically broken down and saliva is added to it. The saliva contains the enzyme amylase which breaks down starch into maltose and then into glucose. The ball of food that is swallowed is called the **bolus**.

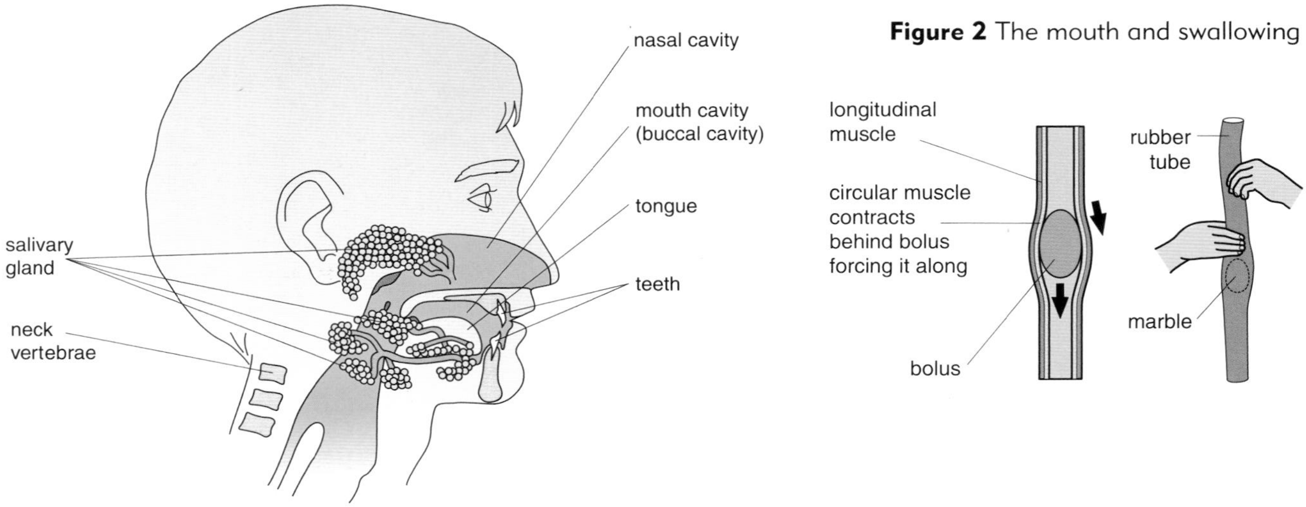

Figure 2 The mouth and swallowing

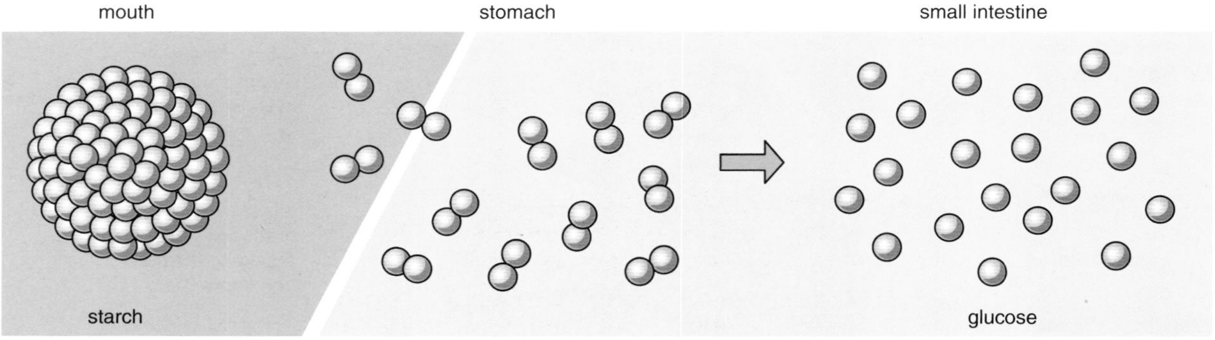

Figure 3 The breakdown of starch

The oesophagus

This is the tube at the back of the throat that the food passes down.

The stomach

In the stomach the food is held for a period of time whilst it is mixed thoroughly. In addition gastric juice produced by the stomach is added. Gastric juice contains two substances that help digestion, acid (hydrochloric) and a protease enzyme (pepsin). The protease breaks down protein into amino acids. This enzyme works best in an acid environment such as exists in the stomach.

The small intestine

Duodenum

The duodenum is the first part of the small intestine. It receives bile from the gall bladder and pancreatic juice from the pancreas to help further digestion of the food.

Bile is produced in the liver and stored in the gall bladder. It contains bile salts that emulsify fats and break them into smaller droplets. This makes it easier for the lipase enzymes produced by the pancreas to break down fats into fatty acids and glycerol. Bile also contains alkali to help neutralise the acid from the stomach.

Pancreatic juice contains three types of enzymes. In addition to lipase it also contains protease to break down proteins, and amylase to break down starch.

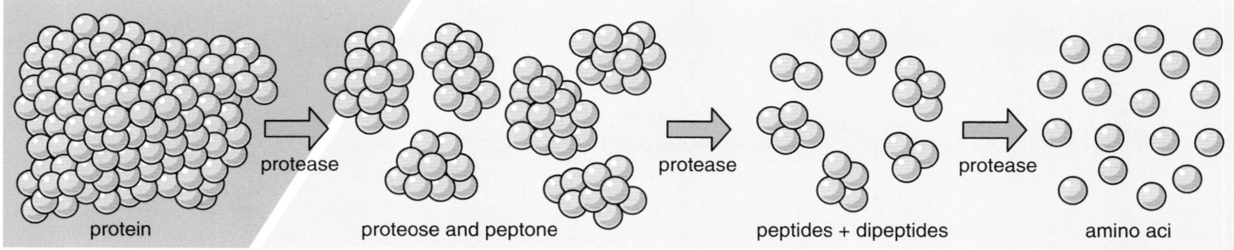

Figure 4 The breakdown of protein

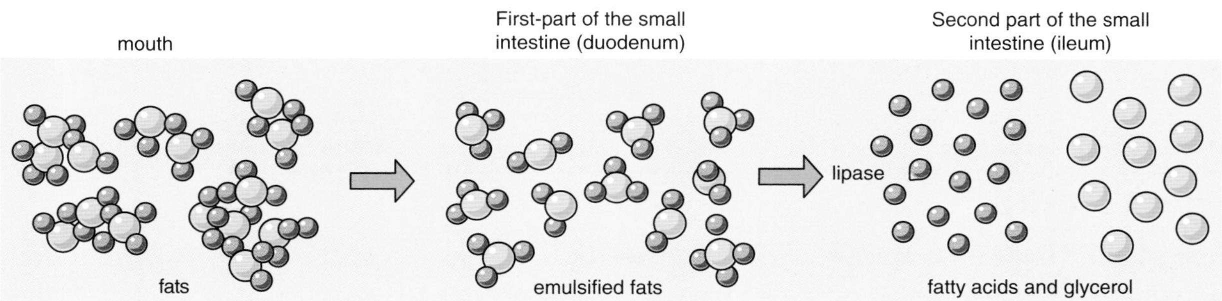

Figure 5 The breakdown of fat

Ileum

This is the second part of the small intestine. It produces all the same enzymes as are produced in the pancreatic juice: amylase, protease and lipase. These are present to make sure that any remaining undigested starch, proteins and fats are broken down. The structure of the ileum is modified to aid absorption of all the products of digestion.

The structure of the ileum

This part of the small intestine is modified to produce a greater surface area for absorption of digested food and allows it to pass quickly into the blood or lymph. The ileum is **long** and has folds and structures called **villi** (see Figure 6) which increases the surface area for absorption. Within the villi there are **capillaries** to carry the digested food molecules away to the liver. The surface of the villi is thin to allow easy diffusion of molecules into the blood capillaries. Also near the centre of each villus is a structure called a **lacteal** leading to the lymph system. Some of the products of fat digestion such as fatty acids pass into this system instead of going straight into the blood. They are modified as they travel through this system and after this modification they then enter the blood.

Following absorption the digested food molecules such as glucose, amino acids, vitamins and minerals are transported from the blood capillaries in the villi to the **hepatic portal vein** and then to the liver. The liver stores, breaks down or distributes these molecules to the rest of the body as necessary.

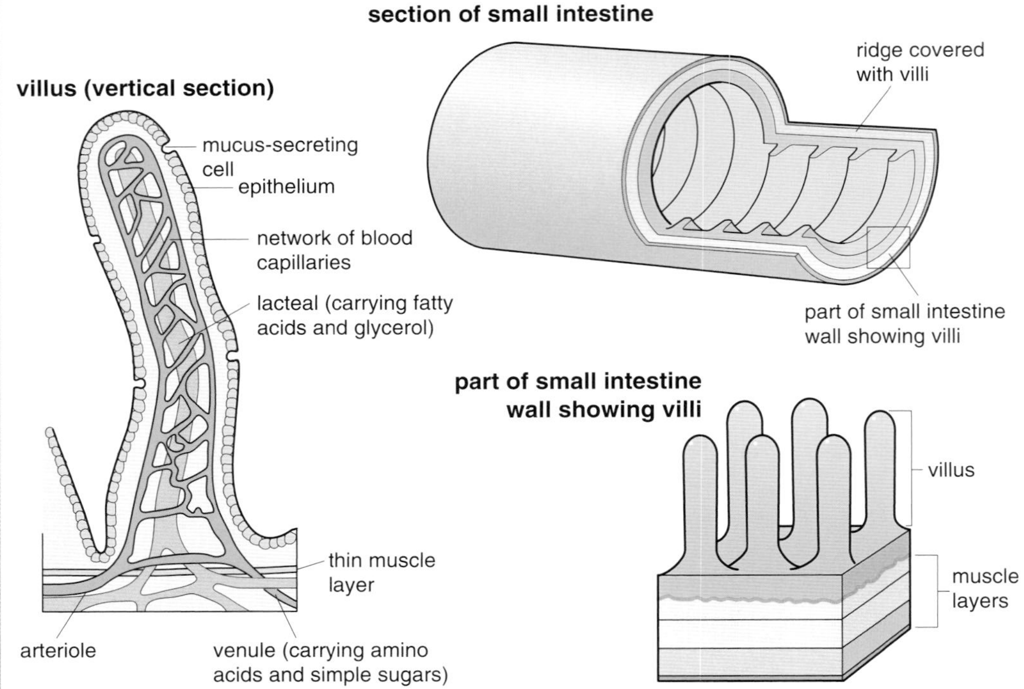

Figure 6 The small intestine

Practical activity

WEAR SAFETY GOGGLES WHEN TESTING FOR GLUCOSE

1 Carefully half fill the visking tube with the starch/glucose mixture. Tie the top of the visking tube. Rinse the outside of the tube under a tap to make sure there is no starch or glucose on the outside.

2 Half fill a beaker with distilled water and place the visking tube into the beaker.

3 Test the water in the beaker straight away for starch or glucose. Record your results in a table, like the one below.

4 After 15 minutes test the water in the beaker again for starch and glucose.

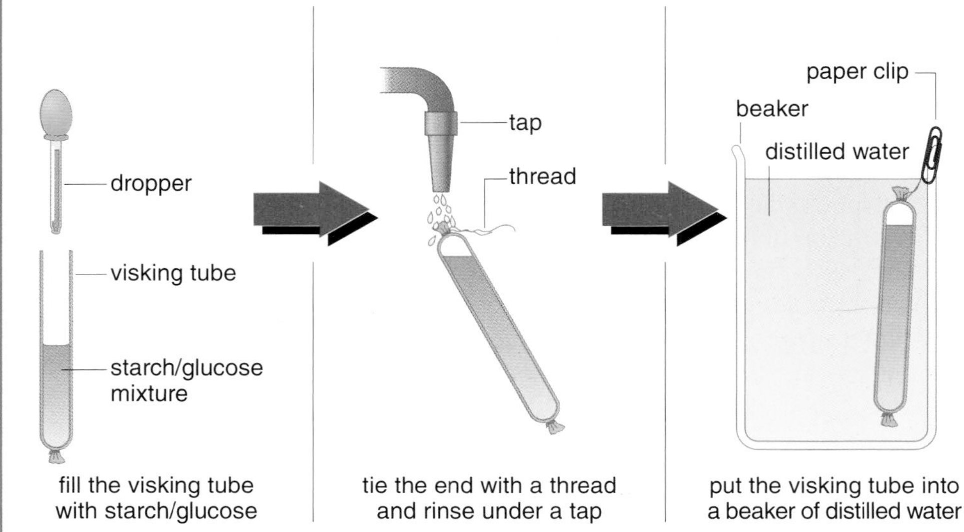

	Starch	Glucose
Test on the water immediately after the visking tube was added		
Test on the water 15 minutes later		

Questions

1 Did starch pass through the visking tube?

2 Did glucose pass through it?

3 What structure would the visking tubing represent in the gut?

The large intestine

This transports the undigested material, largely fibre from plant material, along the colon to the rectum where it is stored and then egested from the anus. Water is removed from this material as it is turned into faeces, and absorbed back into the blood. The presence of fibre in the food helps its progress as it passes along the length of the alimentary canal. Muscles in the wall of the alimentary canal contract in a process called **peristalsis** to push the food along the length of the intestine. Without fibre in the food these muscles cannot work as effectively.

Questions

4 List the ways in which the ileum is adapted for its function.

5 What is absorbed from the large intestine into the blood?

The liver

Following digestion the digested food molecules travel in the blood to the liver. In the liver excess amino acids are broken down and converted into **urea** which is sent to the kidneys for excretion. If there is too much glucose in the blood then the liver, under the influence of the hormone insulin, will absorb more glucose from the blood and will store it as glycogen. If blood glucose levels drop then the stored glycogen will be broken down to release glucose back into the blood (see Chapter 14).

Websites

http://library.thinkquest.org/10348/find/content/digestive.html
Information about the digestive system and a game to play.

www.bbc.co.uk/science/humanbody
Digestive system. Also a quiz.

Exam questions

1 Food is broken down as it passes through the digestive system. The table below shows where the food substances are digested. Copy and complete the table by placing a tick in the correct boxes.

Region of digestive system	Food substance		
	Starch	Protein	Fat
Mouth (buccal cavity)			
Stomach			
Small intestine			
Large intestine			

(5 marks)

2 The diagram shows food being swallowed.

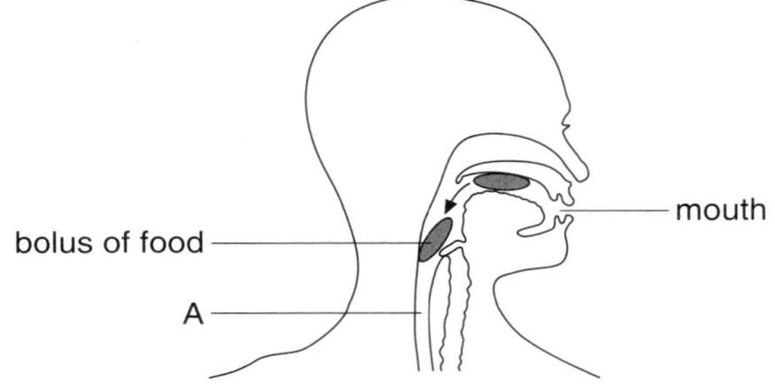

a) Name the process of taking food into the mouth. *(1 mark)*

b) Name part A. *(1 mark)*

The bolus of food is moved along part A to the stomach by muscular contractions.

c) Give the term used to describe these muscular contractions. *(1 mark)*

d) The graph shows the effect of chewing on the amount of starch remaining in the bolus.

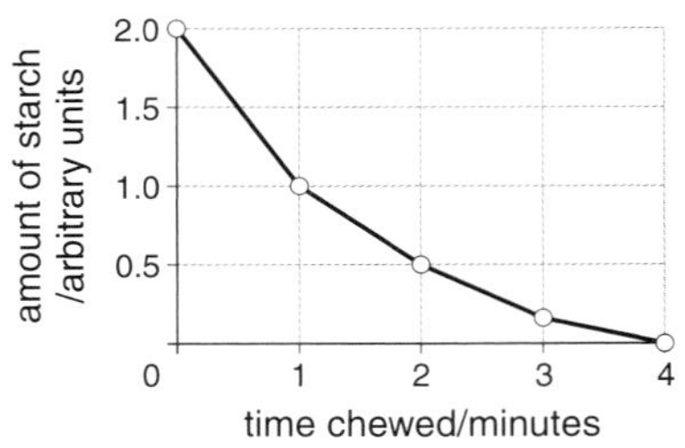

(i) Give the amount of starch present after 2 minutes. *(1 mark)*

(ii) Describe the effect of chewing on the amount of starch remaining in the bolus. *(1 mark)*

(iii) Name the enzyme, present in saliva, which brings about this change. *(1 mark)*

Chapter 8

Respiration

Learning objectives

By the end of this chapter you should:

- Be able to identify and state the functions of the respiratory system in humans
- Be able to explain the mechanism of breathing
- Be able to state how the respiratory surfaces are adapted both in animals and plants
- Be able to state that aerobic respiration depends on the presence of oxygen and anaerobic respiration takes place without oxygen
- **Be able to compare the energy production from aerobic and anaerobic respiration**
- Be able to state how nicotine, tar, and carbon monoxide in cigarette smoke cause health problems
- Be able to state some arguments about smoking in public places

Respiration in animals

Respiratory systems in animals are designed to deliver oxygen to a surface so that it can be absorbed and then transported to the individual cells of the body. Here the oxygen is used in cell respiration to provide large amounts of **energy**.

glucose + oxygen → carbon dioxide + water + energy

Waste products such as carbon dioxide and water need to be delivered back to the respiratory surface so that they can be removed. This system requires a very large surface area so that gas exchange can take place at a fast enough rate to supply the cells of the body with enough oxygen. This is achieved by having lungs with many small air sacs called **alveoli** which have folded surfaces to increase their area. In addition the ventilation mechanism, which moves the lungs, ensures the fresh, frequent supply of air and the maintenance of a concentration gradient for the diffusion of gases.

In humans, the respiratory system consists of a series of tubes – the nasal passages, the **trachea**, the **bronchi** and **bronchioles** – which carry the gases to and from the lungs. The nasal passages are covered in hairs, which help to filter the air that enters the lungs, and along with the production of mucus they trap entering micro-organisms. The trachea is kept open during all the changes in pressure by the presence of rings of cartilage in its walls. There is a dense network of capillaries beside the alveoli, allowing the gases to pass across into the blood which carries them away. This helps maintain a concentration gradient for diffusion of gases across the alveoli.

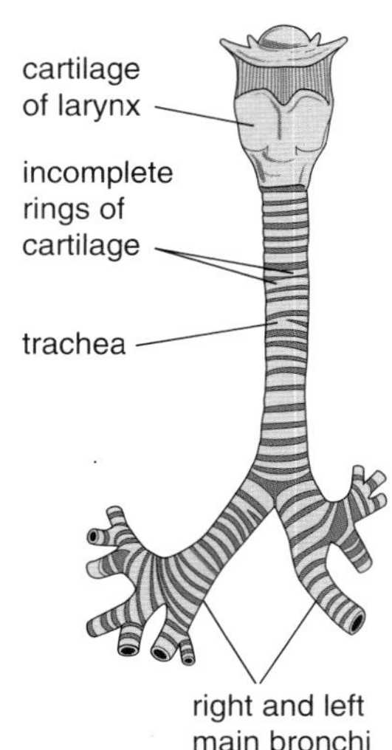

Figure 1 The trachea

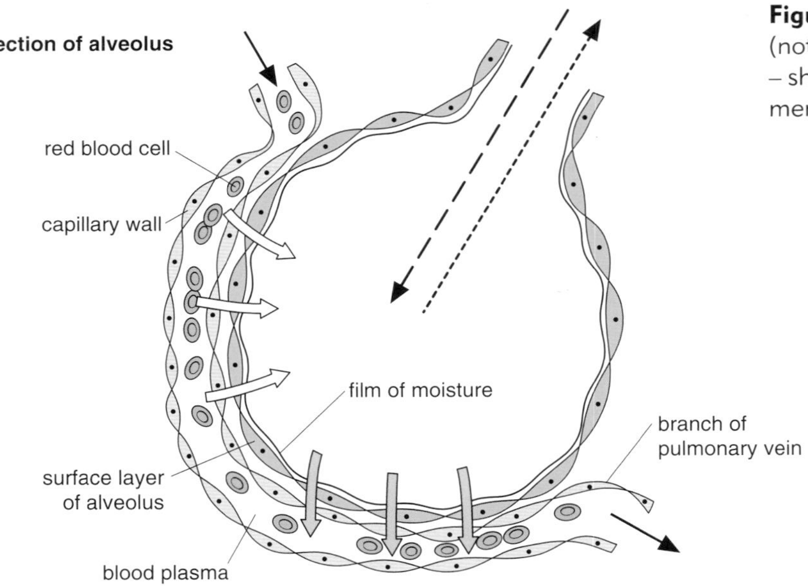

Figure 2 Gas exchange in an alveolus (notice adaptations for gas exchange – short diffusion pathways, thin membranes and large surface area)

Breathing

The movement of the ribs and lungs during breathing is called **ventilation**. The lungs are soft tissue and are protected from outside injury by ribs. During the breathing process the lungs are protected from rubbing against the ribs by membranes called the pleural membranes and fluid.

Inspiration begins when the **diaphragm**, a sheet of muscle at the bottom of the thorax, contracts and moves down. At the same time the **intercostal muscles** between the ribs contract and move the ribs up and out. These two processes increase the volume inside the thoracic cavity and cause a decrease in air pressure inside the cavity. The air pressure inside the thorax is now lower than the air pressure outside the lungs and air moves in by a process of diffusion.

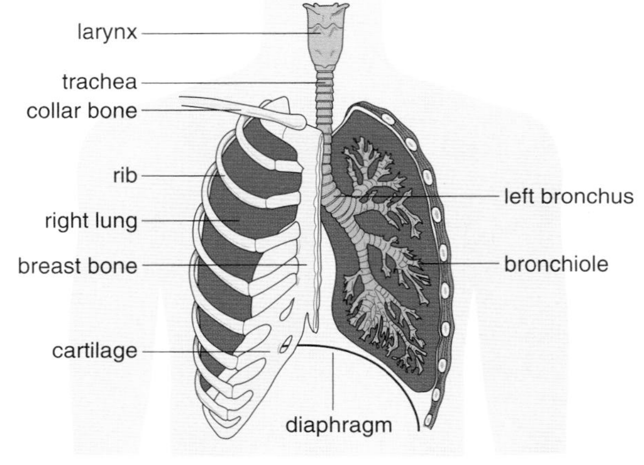

Figure 3 The breathing system

During **expiration** the reverse of these processes occurs. The diaphragm relaxes and moves up. The intercostals muscles between the ribs now relax and the ribs and lungs move down and in, decreasing the volume in the thorax and therefore increasing the pressure in this cavity. The air pressure inside is now greater than that outside and the air moves out by diffusion. The table shows the composition of gases in inhaled and exhaled air.

Gas	% in inhaled air	% in exhaled air
oxygen	21	16
carbon dioxide	0.04	4
nitrogen	79	79

Respiration in plants

To gain energy plants must also respire. To carry out this process they use some of the glucose, that has been produced during photosynthesis, and oxygen.

Plant leaves are designed to aid diffusion of gases since their leaves are thin and the cells in the leaves have many air spaces between them. The leaves have large numbers of pores or stomata on their lower surfaces surrounded by guard cells, which can open or close to allow more gases to enter the leaf.

At night the leaf may absorb some oxygen from the air enabling it to carry out respiration. The leaf cells each have a large surface area to aid the diffusion of gases.

Smoking and health

Smoking cigarettes leads to a variety of illnesses caused by the different chemicals present including nicotine. This is one of the reasons people find it hard to give up this habit, as **nicotine** is addictive. In addition to this, nicotine also causes an increased risk of blood clotting and irregular heartbeat. The **tar** in cigarettes increases the risk of lung cancers and other cancers of the respiratory system. The incidence of bronchitis is also much greater in smokers. Smoking causes inflammation in the passageways of the respiratory system due to the cilia being damaged, and so mucus and other materials collect in the tubes.

In the lungs the **carbon monoxide** in cigarette smoke competes with oxygen to bind with haemoglobin in the red blood cells. This means that less oxygen is absorbed into the blood and so the cells of the body will not receive as much oxygen. This can cause long-term damage to some areas of the body. The greater the number of cigarettes smoked and the longer the person has smoked, the greater the risk to their health. Giving up smoking reduces the risk to health.

In recent years evidence has indicated that the health of people who do not smoke may be affected if they are exposed to cigarette smoke from others. This is called **passive smoking**. This evidence has led to the banning of smoking in many public places, but the evidence and the consequences of passive smoking are still a matter of controversy.

Questions

1 Why do people find it difficult to give up smoking?

2 Suggest some things that people could do to help themselves give up smoking.

Aerobic and anaerobic respiration

When respiration is carried out in air or oxygen it is called **aerobic**. However, some organisms can carry out respiration without oxygen. This type of respiration is called **anaerobic**. This releases only a fraction of the energy produced in aerobic respiration. Organisms such as yeast respire in this way.

glucose → alcohol (ethanol) + carbon dioxide + small amount energy

Practical activity – Anaerobic respiration in yeast

WEAR GOGGLES

Figure 4

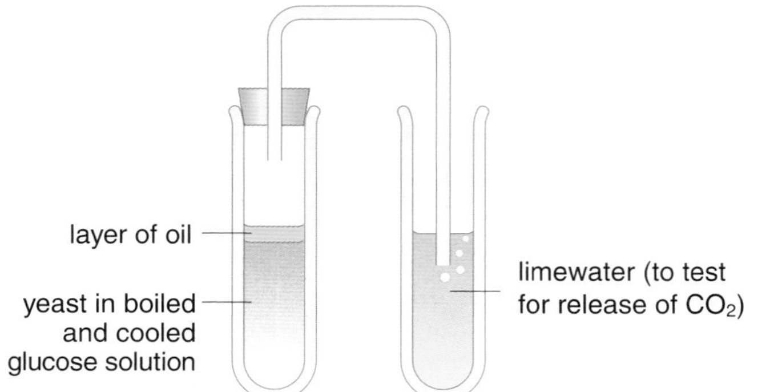

1 Put a 10 % solution of glucose into a boiling tube to a depth of 2 cm.
2 Boil the glucose solution to remove any oxygen present.
3 Cool it, then add a little yeast.
4 Pour a thin layer of liquid paraffin on top of the glucose solution to stop oxygen getting to the yeast.
5 Set up the boiling tube as shown in the diagram.
6 Set up a second boiling tube exactly like the first one, but do not add any yeast to the glucose. This is your control.
7 Leave the boiling tubes in a warm place for at least an hour. Then examine them.

Questions

3 Has the lime water gone cloudy? If it has, carbon dioxide has been given off.

4 Sniff the contents of the boiling tubes. Does either smell of alcohol?

5 Feel the two boiling tubes. Is one warmer than the other?

6 What conclusions do you draw from this experiment?

Websites

http://www.innerbody.com
Animation of the lungs.

http://www.howstuffworks.com
How your lungs work.

http://www.biology.arizona.edu
Information about tobacco smoke and lung development.

Exam questions

1 The diagram shows part of the human respiratory system.

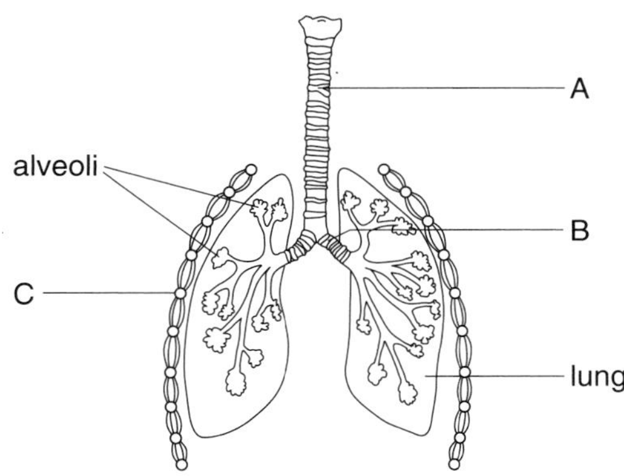

a) Name parts A, B and C. *(3 marks)*

b) Give **one** function of alveoli. *(1 mark)*

c) The table shows the composition of inhaled and exhaled air.

	Percentage in inhaled air	Percentage in exhaled air
Oxygen	21	16
Carbon dioxide	0.04	4
Nitrogen	79	79

Describe **two** differences in the composition of inhaled and exhaled air. *(2 marks)*

2 Copy and complete the word equation for aerobic respiration.

Glucose + ☐ → ☐ + Water + ☐

(3 marks)

3 The table shows the results of a survey into the smoking habits of 1000 lung cancer patients.

Number of cigarettes smoked per day	Number of lung cancer patients
0	3
1–4	51
5–14	259
15–24	302
more than 24	385

a) What trend is shown by these results? *(1 mark)*

b) What do the results show about non-smokers? *(1 mark)*

c) Name one other disease that can be caused by smoking. *(1 mark)*

4 The apparatus is used to show anaerobic respiration in yeast.

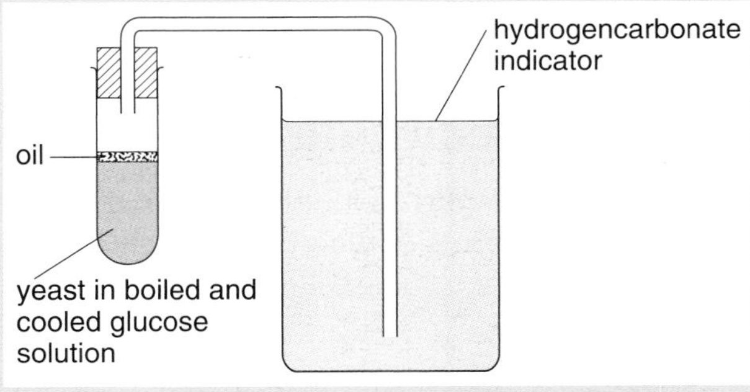

a) Name the gas produced by the respiring yeast. *(1 mark)*

b) Explain how anaerobic conditions are achieved by

(i) boiling the glucose solution. *(1 mark)*

(ii) adding a layer of oil. *(1 mark)*

c) Give **two** differences between the products of anaerobic and aerobic respiration. *(2 marks)*

Chapter 9

Transport in Animals

Learning objectives

By the end of this chapter you should:

- Be able to state the functions of blood
- Be able to state the composition of blood and the roles of the different components of blood
- Be able to identify the regions of the heart and its blood vessels
- Be able to state the function of the heart
- Be able to state the sequence in which blood passes through the heart
- Be able to name the different types of blood vessels and their roles
- Be able to identify cross sections of the different blood vessels and explain how their structure is related to their function
- Be able to identify the main blood vessels in the general circulation
- Be able to explain how a heart attack occurs and some of the risk factors associated with this condition
- Be able to explain some of the beneficial effects of fitness on the heart
- Be able to explain why blood pressure is used to monitor the health of the circulatory system
- Be able to explain what tissue fluid and lymph are, their roles and how they are formed

Blood and circulation

Blood is the transport medium of the body in many animals. Humans usually have about five litres of blood. It consists of a pale yellow liquid called **plasma** which carries many substances dissolved within it as well as some cells.

Its functions are:

- To carry substances around the body including oxygen, carbon dioxide, food materials and urea.
- To maintain body temperature since heat is transported with the blood.
- To protect the body from damage by clotting and to produce white blood cells and antibodies which fight invading microbes.

Many of these functions are carried out by two types of cells – the **red blood cells** and the **white blood cells**, as well as cell fragments called **platelets**.

Platelets produce substances that are involved in clotting the blood which reduces blood loss in the case of a cut. At the same time the body sends white blood cells to the site of injury since they are involved in defence and their increased numbers will help prevent microbes entering at the injured site and causing infection.

White blood cells are normally fewer in number than red blood cells but their numbers increase if the body is cut and microbes such as bacteria or viruses get past the body's first line of defence. White blood cells are large cells with either a very large nucleus or a lobed nucleus. They either produce chemicals called antibodies or engulf the microbes – both methods result in destruction of the microbes.

The red blood cells are smaller than the white, but are normally found in greater numbers. They contain a chemical called haemoglobin which combines with oxygen and carries it around the body to the cells. The red blood cells are biconcave discs. This shape provides a large surface area for the diffusion of gases. They are unusual since they have no nucleus. This enables them to hold more haemoglobin and therefore transport more oxygen.

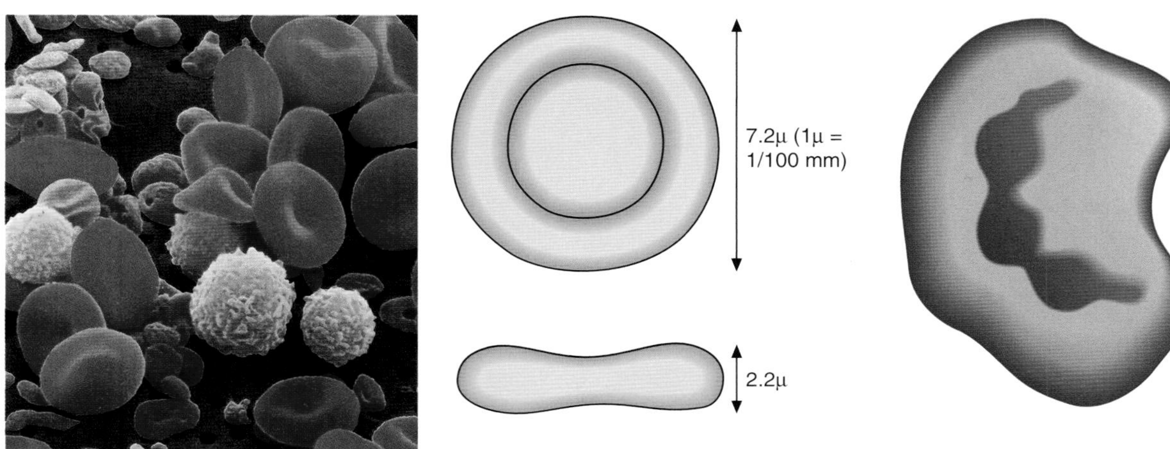

Figure 1 The blood

Figure 2 A red blood cell

Figure 3 A white blood cell

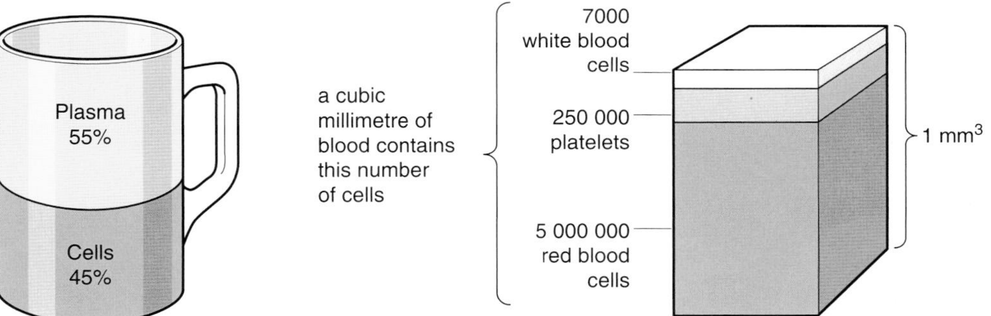

Figure 4 The composition of blood

The heart

The heart is a made of a special type of muscle which can contract regularly. It pumps out the blood it contains into blood vessels which carry the blood either to the lungs or around the body. In one complete circuit of the body the blood goes through the heart twice – once on its way to the lungs to pick up oxygen and then through the heart again to be pumped to the body. This means that the circulation is called a **double circulation**.

The heart is made up of two sides – the right and left sides. The two sides are separated by a wall of muscle called the **septum**. At the top of the heart are the two smaller chambers – the **atria**. The right atrium receives deoxygenated blood from the body and the left atrium receives oxygenated blood from the lungs.

(a)

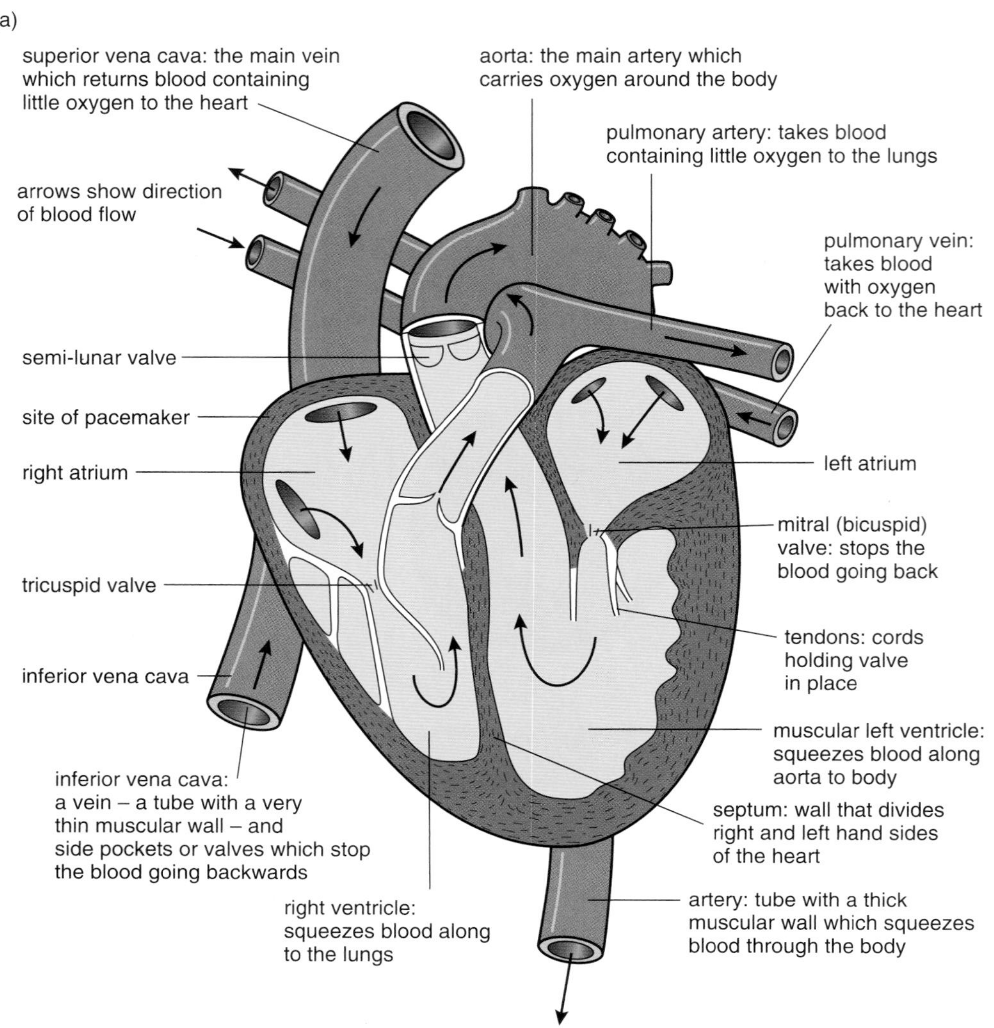

(b)

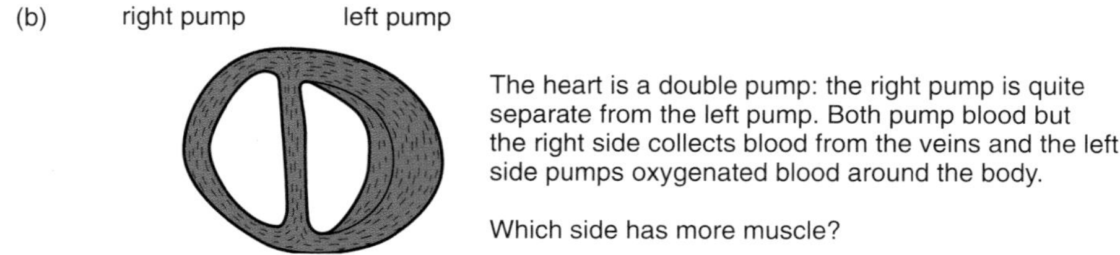

The heart is a double pump: the right pump is quite separate from the left pump. Both pump blood but the right side collects blood from the veins and the left side pumps oxygenated blood around the body.

Which side has more muscle?

Figure 5 The human heart

Below the atria are another two chambers which are much larger – the **ventricles**. These have much thicker muscular walls to pump the blood out of the heart to the lungs and around the body.

To help ensure the correct direction of blood flow and prevent backflow of blood, the heart and some of its attached blood vessels have **valves**. There is a valve on each side of the heart between the atria and the ventricles.

These allow blood to flow through them, but close over when the ventricles are full of blood so that when the ventricles contract the blood is pumped out of the heart, not back up into the atria. On the right hand side of the heart the valve is called the tricuspid valve and on the left hand side the bicuspid valve.

In addition the two blood vessels that carry the blood out of the heart – the pulmonary artery and the aorta – have valves called **semi-lunar valves** which stop the blood flowing backwards into the heart.

Circulation of blood through the heart

This flow diagram gives the pathway of blood through the heart.

Deoxygenated blood

Enters the vena cava
↓
Into the right atrium
↓
Through a valve into the right ventricle
↓
Into the pulmonary artery which branches to the two lungs
↓
Picks up oxygen in the lungs

Oxygenated blood

Pulmonary veins from the lungs
↓
Into the left atrium
↓
Through a valve into the left ventricle
↓
Into the aorta
↓
In arteries to the various parts of the body

Blood vessels

Blood is carried around the body in several types of blood vessels – arteries, veins and capillaries. **Arteries** generally carry oxygenated blood away from the heart whilst **veins** carry deoxygenated blood back to the heart. Linking these larger blood vessels are smaller ones called **capillaries** which are present in all areas of the body. Unlike the larger blood vessels these small vessels are permeable and will let small molecules out or in through their walls. This is how oxygen and molecules such as glucose, minerals, and amino acids are supplied to the cells of the body. Waste products produced by the cells, such as carbon dioxide, pass back into the capillaries. Carbon dioxide is then transported in the blood to the heart and from there to the lungs to be breathed out.

The blood in the arteries is under pressure from the pumping action of the heart and so these blood vessels have a thick layer of smooth muscle and elastic fibres. Veins carry blood back to the heart from around the body and the blood in them is not under as much pressure, therefore they have a thinner layer of muscle and elastic fibres and a wider lumen (which is the area for the blood to pass through). Because the blood in the veins is not under high pressure the veins have valves to prevent the backflow of blood. The blood is moved along in the veins by movement of the muscles in the part of the body adjacent to the vein. The capillaries are much smaller vessels with only one thin layer of cells, the endothelial cells, which are permeable to allow substances such as oxygen, glucose, amino acids, and carbon dioxide to pass through them. Figure 6 shows the detailed structure of these blood vessels.

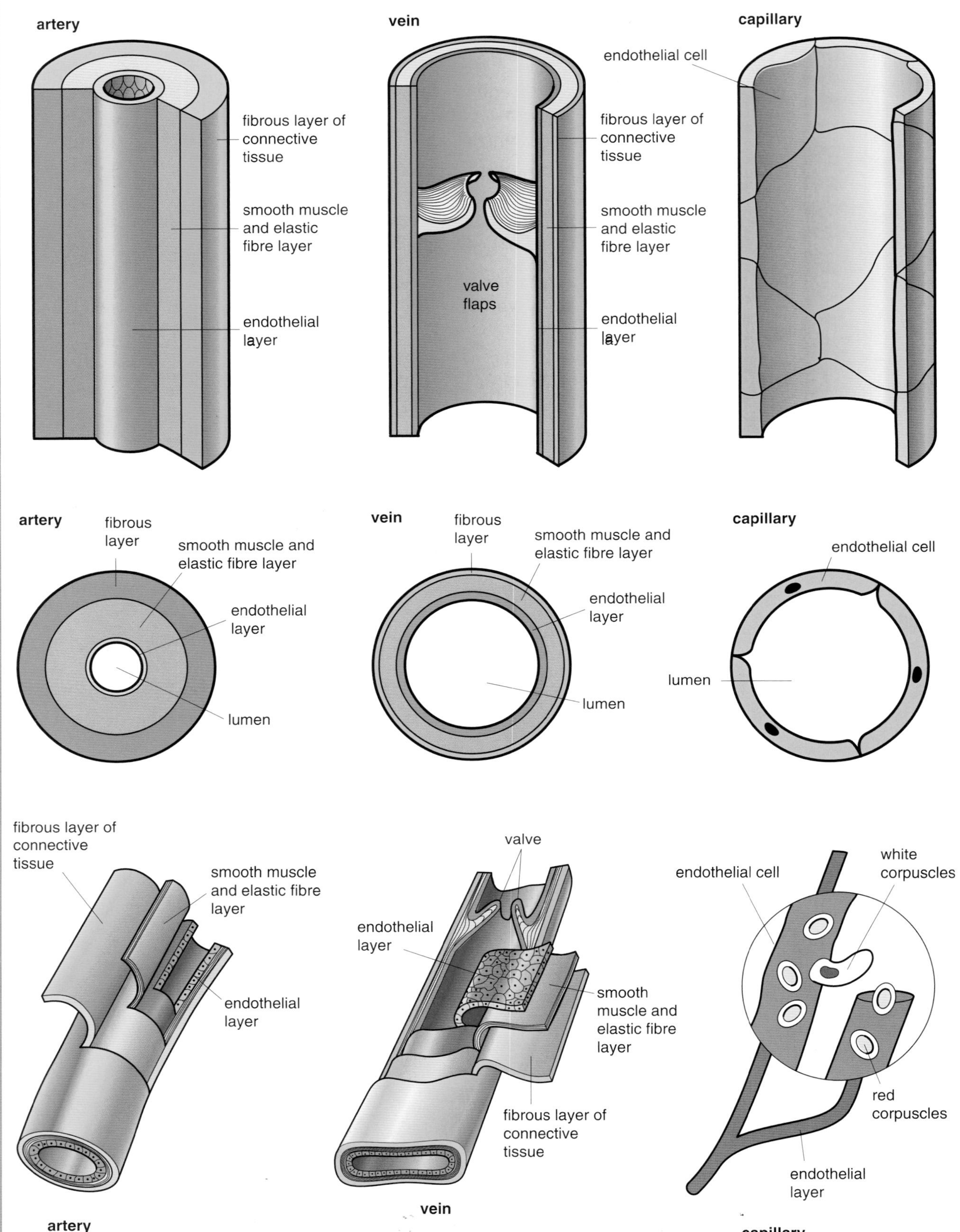

Figure 6 The structure of blood vessels

Circulation through the body

The blood vessels that supply the heart itself are called the **coronary arteries** which branch into capillaries to supply the heart muscle cells with oxygen and nutrients, including glucose. The coronary veins collect the blood on its way back from the heart muscle cells. Other important blood vessels include the **renal artery** which supplies the kidneys, the **hepatic artery** which supplies the liver, and the **mesenteric artery** which supplies the intestines. In each case the blood is collected from the organs by a vein with the same name as the artery that supplied that organ (e.g. renal vein). These veins empty their blood back into the vena cava on the right hand side of the heart. The pulmonary vessels are unusual in that the **pulmonary artery** carries deoxygenated blood to the lungs, and the **pulmonary vein** carries oxygenated blood from the lungs to the heart. **The hepatic portal vein** carries blood with digested food from the small intestine to the liver. The **aorta** is the main artery of the body carrying oxygenated blood from the heart to the body whilst the **vena cava** carries deoxygenated blood back to the heart.

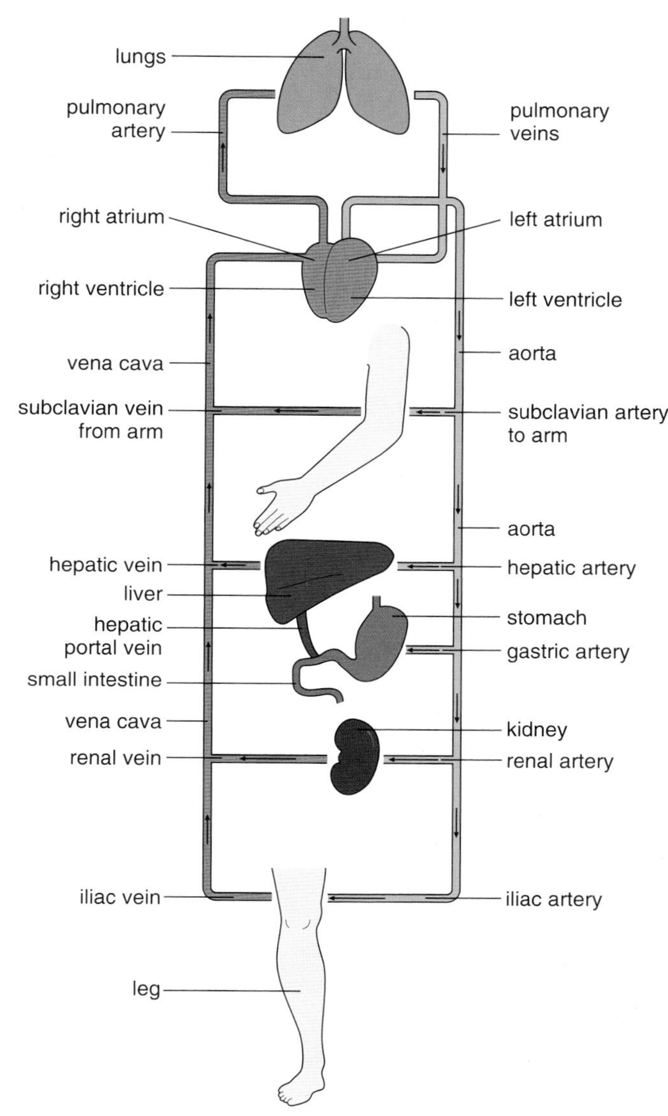

Figure 7 The main blood vessels in the human body

Blood clotting

This is a process involving many steps that take place in a particular sequence. Most of the substances needed for the process are already present in the blood, but they are in one form and need to be converted to a different form during the process.This conversion is necessary so that these substances only form a clot when there is a cut, otherwise the blood vessels could be blocked. When there is a cut the process is initiated by the platelets which produce a 'factor' which starts the chain of reactions.

The final stage in the process occurs when a protein called **fibrinogen** which is soluble and present in the blood all the time, is converted into insoluble fibres of **fibrin**.

The fibrin fibres produced by this chain of reactions form a mesh which traps the blood cells to form a clot. At the same time more white blood cells are sent to the site of injury to help deal with any bacteria or viruses that have entered the blood at the cut.

Tissue fluid and lymph

When blood flows in the capillaries, smaller molecules such as water, glucose, minerals, amino acids and hormones pass out through the permeable walls of these blood vessels. The liquid that is formed surrounds the cells and carries these useful substances to them from the blood. Some of this fluid leaks back into the far end of the capillaries and carries with it the waste products from the cells. Excess tissue fluid that does not go back into the far end of the capillaries drains into structures called lymphatics. From here this fluid called lymph is transported through another system of vessels called lymph vessels. These collect at lymph nodes in several places in the body including the groin, under the arm pits and in the neck. Eventually this fluid is emptied back into a blood vessel just above the heart, but on its journey it has been changed in various ways. White blood cells in the lymph system will deal with any microbes that they find in the lymph and in addition some of the fats that have been carried from digested food will be changed so that they are made more soluble before they enter the blood.

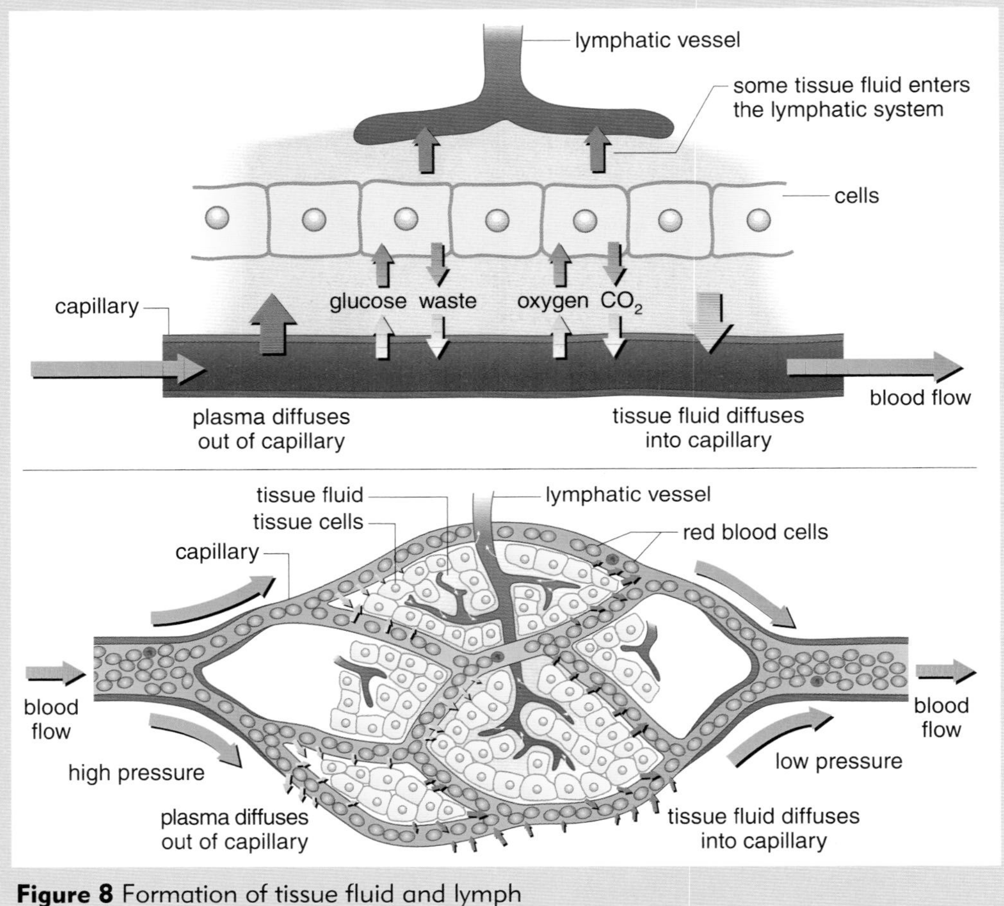

Figure 8 Formation of tissue fluid and lymph

Diet, fitness and heart disease

Heart attacks

These are caused when a coronary artery, or one of its branches, becomes blocked, usually with deposits of fat. This cuts the blood supply to the heart muscle cells. Since they cannot receive oxygen or glucose these cells cannot respire to produce energy and so they cannot contract and the heart will not beat.

For a short time these heart muscle cells will switch to anaerobic respiration using small amounts of glucose they already have and this will give them a little energy for a short time. However this process produces lactic acid and cramp and it is this that causes the pain in a heart attack. Lack of exercise and a diet rich in sugars and fats can cause obesity and high blood pressure and lead to an increased risk of developing heart disease. Other factors such as smoking, stress and a family history of heart disease may also cause increased risk.

Fitness

At rest in a normal individual the heart beats about 70 times a minute and pumps between four and six litres of blood each minute. In a person who trains this blood flow can be increased to about 30 litres a minute during exercise. This is brought about by an increase in the heart rate and the amount of blood that is pumped with each beat. In a fit person after exercise this increase will return to normal levels more quickly than in an unfit individual. A fit person usually has a lower resting heart rate because their training has strengthened the heart muscle so that it can pump out more blood with each beat, but this training needs to be gradual since very sudden demands on the heart in an unfit person can be dangerous and lead to heart attacks.

Blood pressure

Blood pressure is a measure of the amount and the force of blood against the walls of blood vessels. The pressure in the arteries needs to be at a certain level to help to force some of the contents of the blood into the tissue fluid . A weakened heart may produce a low blood pressure and affect the composition of tissue fluid and the amount of substances delivered to the cells of the body. High blood pressure is often produced as a result of the build up of fat deposits in some of the arteries. Therefore monitoring of blood pressure can give an indication of the health of the circulatory system.

Questions

1 What are the main functions of blood?

2 What are the functions of arteries, veins and capillaries?

Websites

http://www.pba.org/wgbh/nova/heart/heartmap.html
The heart and blood flow with animation.

http://www.howstuffworks.com
How your heart works.

http://www.innerbody.com
The heart and circulation in action.

Exam questions

1 Copy and complete the table which gives information about the components of blood.

Component	Structure	Function
Plasma	water containing substances in solution	transport of food and waste in solution
Red blood cells		transport oxygen
	large cell with nucleus	1 engulf and destroy bacteria 2 make antibodies
Platelets	cell fragments, no nucleus	

(3 marks)

2 a) The diagram shows a human blood smear.

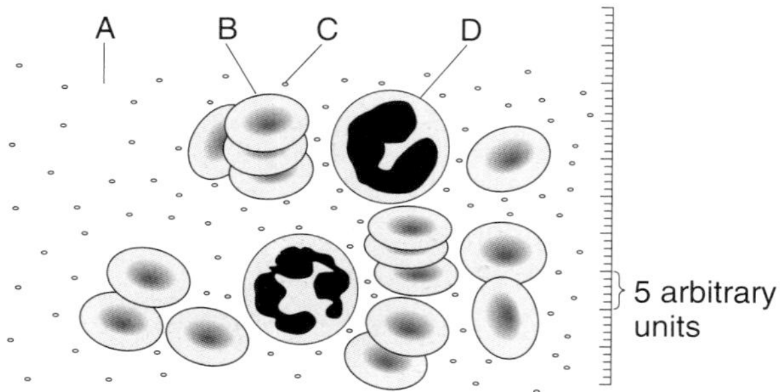

Use the diagram and your knowledge to copy and complete the table.

	Blood component			
	A	**B**	**C**	**D**
Name		red blood cell		white blood cell
Diameter/ arbitrary units				
Function				

(4 marks)

b) The diagram represents the lungs, heart and body organs.

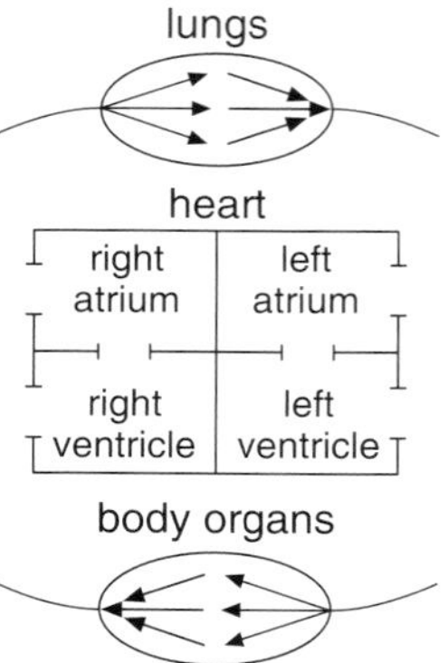

Copy the diagram and draw lines to link the lungs, heart and body organs, showing the **direction** of the blood flow.

(4 marks)

3 The diagram shows part of the human circulatory system.

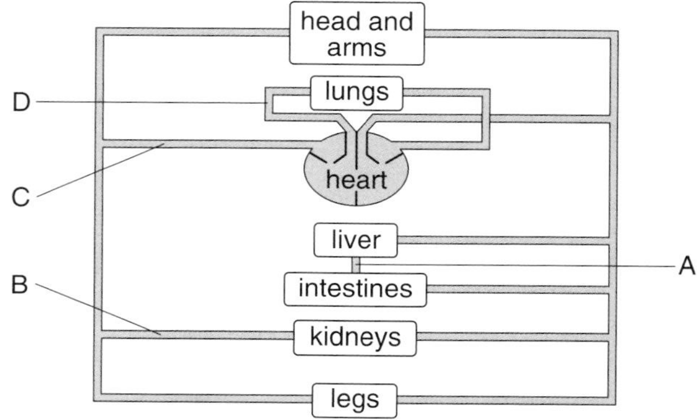

a) Copy the liver and intestine part of the diagram and **draw an arrow**, beside vessel A, to show the direction of the blood flow.

(1 mark)

b) Name the blood vessels B, C and D.

(3 marks)

c) Give **one** difference between blood and plasma.

(1 mark)

Chapter 10

Disease, Immunity and Microbes

Learning objectives

By the end of this chapter you should:

- Be able to state how the body defends itself against infections including the role of mucous membranes, the skin and blood clotting
- Be able to state how active and passive immunity protect the body against pathogens
- Be able to explain what antigens and antibodies are and their roles
- Be able to state that diseases can be caused by
  - Viruses – AIDS
  - Bacteria – gonorrhoea, salmonella, TB
  - Fungi – athlete's foot
- Be able to explain how the first vaccination against smallpox was developed by Jenner
- Be able to explain the theory of spontaneous generation and the results of Pasteur's swan neck experiment
- Be able to explain how bacteria and fungi are used to produce bread, alcohol and yoghurt
- Be able to explain the reasons underlying aseptic techniques
- Be able to state that bacteria and fungi are important in the decomposition of foodstuffs and plant leaves and explain the key factors needed for decay
- Be able to explain various methods of food preservation and how they enable food to be kept for longer
- Be able to describe the action of antiseptics (phenol) and antibiotics (penicillin)
- Be able to describe the discovery of penicillin by Sir Alexander Fleming
- Be able to explain the use of a simple biodigester, for example in the manufacture of drugs such as penicillin

Defence against disease

The cells of the body all have proteins on their surface that are unique to the individual. These proteins are called **antigens**. In this way the body is able to identify its own cells. Micro-organisms that cause disease are called **pathogens**. To protect itself against foreign micro-organisms the body has several lines of defence. The initial protection is provided by the skin, which acts as a barrier to prevent entry of micro-organisms.

Protection is also provided by the cilia in the nose and respiratory tracts, along with the mucus produced in these passageways, which trap dust and micro-organisms and transport them to the back of the throat, from where they are swallowed. The acid in the stomach, along with the digestive juices in the intestine, break the micro-organisms down and any remains are passed out with any undigested food. Only if micro-organisms get past these systems of defence does the immune system of the body come into operation as a second line of defence. One of these mechanisms is clotting. Clotting of the blood when the skin is cut is also a defence mechanism (see Chapter 9). It prevents loss of blood, further entry of microbes and at the same time phagocytic white blood cells are sent to the site of the cut to destroy any micro-organisms that have already entered the blood. Clotting is brought about when platelets in the blood produce chemicals that cause the formation of fibrin fibres. These fibres form a mesh which traps platelets and blood cells.

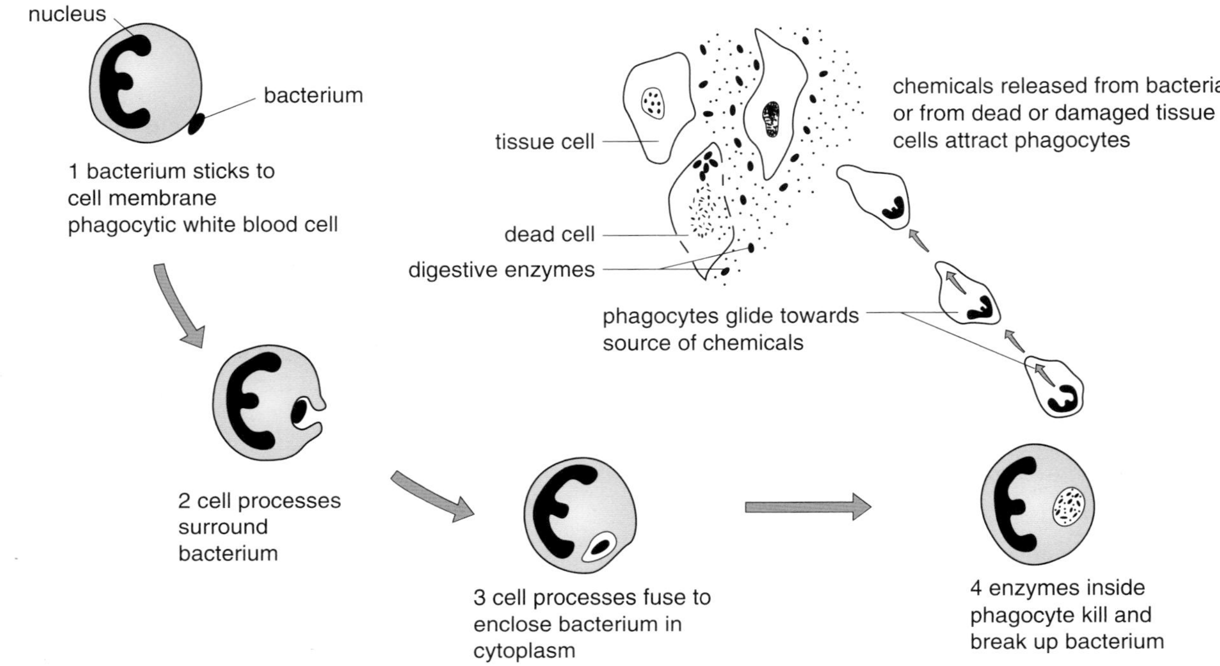

Figure 1 Phagocytosis

The immune system has a variety of methods to help defend the body against attack. During an infection the numbers of white blood cells in the body increases dramatically, for example from 8000/mm^3 to 25 000/mm^3. One type of white blood cell is the **phagocyte**. These cells carry out a process called phagocytosis in which they surround and engulf pathogens such as bacteria. They move their cytoplasm to surround the pathogen and when it is completely surrounded they use chemicals (enzymes) to digest the pathogen and so destroy it.

In addition other white blood cells produce chemicals called **antibodies** to help fight pathogens. These antibodies are made to match chemicals, called **antigens**, on the surface of the disease-causing micro-organism. It is the presence of the antigens on the pathogens that stimulates antibody production. The antibodies lock onto the antigens. In some cases the antibodies can kill the micro-organism. In other cases they cause clumping of micro-organisms where they become grouped together. This marks out the mico-organisms, making them an easier target for the phagocytic white blood cells that destroy them.

Immunity

This is the level to which the body can protect itself from infections. Some immunity may be natural, while in other cases it is produced by vaccination.

- **Active immunity** involves the body producing its own antibodies to fight infection.
- **Passive immunity** is when the body receives ready-made antibodies against the organism that causes infection.

Natural immunity

Natural immunity can be **innate** or **acquired**.

Innate

This is when antibodies are passed from the mother across the placenta, so that the child is given some protection against disease-causing micro-organims in its first few months of life. The foetus can only be given antibodies against diseases the mother has encountered.

Acquired immunity

This is where the body has immunity from a pathogen because it has produced antibodies to fight the infection before. After a pathogen enters the body, whether you get the symptoms of the disease depends on how quickly your body reacts to the infection. The body produces antibodies to fight the infection and it will also retain some of these antibodies for a period of time. Once these antibodies eventually break down the body will continue to produce small amounts of them and also retain a memory of how to make those particular antibodies. If you are infected by the same pathogen again then very large numbers of the necessary antibodies will be produced very quickly and this gives you immunity to the disease caused by that pathogen. This is called the secondary response.

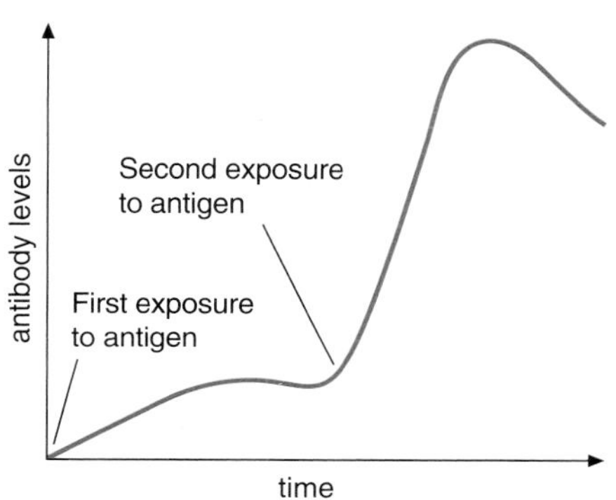

Figure 2

Artificial immunity

This principle of immunity is the basis on which vaccination works. There are two types of **artificial immunity** – active and passive, but they both involve vaccination.

Active immunity

This involves injection with a modified form of the pathogen that has been treated so that it will not actually cause the disease. The body reacts by producing antibodies to fight the pathogen. The antibody levels in the blood will rise and the body will also retain a memory of how to make these antibodies if it comes across this pathogen again. In some cases a series of vaccinations are given to ensure that the antibody levels remain high enough over a long period of time. Most of the vaccinations we receive as a child and throughout our lives are this type of vaccine. This process provides long-term protection from many diseases.

Passive immunity

This also involves a vaccination, but what is contained in the vaccine is different. The vaccine contains ready made antibodies which will fight the pathogen. The advantage of this type of vaccine is that it gives immediate protection against the pathogen. However this immunity is short lived and if the person encounters the disease again, at a later date, the body has no memory of developing antibodies itself. This type of vaccination is only used in a few cases to give quick protection when it is thought the person may already have the disease.

Development of vaccines

The process of developing vaccines is a long one. In most cases the type of vaccine that is preferred is one that will produce active immunity and give long-term protection. However for some diseases it is difficult to culture the pathogens and safely modify them, while in other cases the microbes that cause the disease change very quickly, for example cold and flu viruses, making development of a suitable and effective vaccine difficult.

Questions

1 Why might you be given a tetanus vaccination if you go to hospital with a deep cut?

2 What type of vaccine is used?

Organisms that cause disease

Organisms that cause disease are called pathogens. They are spread by various methods including direct contact, in the air, through body fluids such as blood and semen, through food and water and by various insects and other animals.

The fungal disease athlete's foot lives on the skin in between the toes and can be spread by spores produced by the fungus. These can then be passed on by direct contact in bathing facilities or showers. Many organisms are spread through the air and enter the body via the respiratory passages. These include the diseases influenza (viral) and tuberculosis (bacterial) (more detail is given below on viral and bacterial diseases). Poor ventilation or overcrowding means that the viruses or bacteria that cause these diseases can be spread by droplets in the air especially when an infected person coughs or sneezes.

Some diseases can be spread by blood-to-blood contact. Sexually transmitted diseases such as AIDS and gonorrhoea are spread by body fluids including semen. Other micro-organisms can be passed on through food and water, for example *Salmonella* bacteria present in food can cause food poisoning.

All these organisms cause disease because they interfere with the normal reactions of the body or produce poisonous substances that damage the body's cells.

Viral diseases

Viruses cause disease because they enter the body's cells and use the chemicals within that cell to make copies of themselves, and in so doing disrupt the normal reactions of the cell. AIDS is caused by the HIV virus (human immunodeficiency virus) which gets its name from the fact that it attacks some of the white blood cells of the body which normally help fight infections. The virus enters these cells making them not so capable of defending the body against other invading micro-organisms. As a result people with AIDS often succumb to other infections. The virus can be passed from one person to another by:

1. sexual intercourse with an infected person;
2. shared use of a hypodermic needle with an infected person;
3. infusion or injection with contaminated blood or blood products;
4. an infected mother passing on the virus to the foetus or in her milk.

Now all blood for transfusion is checked for the presence of the HIV virus, but this was not always the case. Before it was understood that the HIV virus caused AIDS, some people contracted the disease through blood transfusion. The use of condoms may limit the transmission of the virus during intercourse as well as helping to prevent transmission of other sexually transmitted diseases. Always using sterile needles during injections also prevents this route of transmission.

Some drugs are now available which help to slow the rate at which the HIV virus multiplies by blocking some of the enzymes the virus produces to help it replicate. The main drug used is AZT (zidovudine).

Questions

3 Give three ways in which viral diseases are combated.

4 Why are viral diseases difficult to treat?

German measles (rubella)

This viral disease can be a problem if a woman who is pregnant catches the disease, since it can damage the developing foetus. To try to prevent this the MMR vaccine is used.

Bacterial diseases

Salmonella food poisoning

This is caused by *Salmonella* bacteria which are rod shaped with flagella. The bacteria are present in the digestive tract of many farm animals and their faeces. These animals, in many cases, get the bacteria from their food. The bacteria can be present in eggs and also in meat that has become contaminated during preparation of the carcasses. Thorough cooking of eggs in which the temperature reaches 80°C, for example by boiling for 10 minutes or frying so that the yolk is solid, kills the bacteria. Meat cooked for a sufficient time at a high enough temperature will not contain bacteria since any present will be killed, but the necessary conditions for this will vary depending on the type and quantity of meat.

Salmonella food poisoning results in vomiting, fever and diarrhoea within 12–24 hours of eating contaminated food. Treatment involves using antibiotics to kill the bacteria and rehydration if the person has lost a lot of fluids.

Tuberculosis

This is a disease caused by bacteria which are spread by airborne droplet infection when someone coughs, speaks or sneezes. The bacteria can also be passed on through infected milk. It infects the lungs although it can also affect other organs. Individuals become very tired, suffer weight loss and coughing. The bacteria prevents areas in the lungs from functioning properly, some blood vessels may also be disrupted and the person may cough up blood. X-rays of the lungs show shadows where the bacteria have damaged the lungs. The BCG vaccine prevents infection against some strains of the TB bacterium. If a person already has TB then treatment is by a combination of drugs including antibiotics. Certain strains of TB bacteria are developing resistance to some antibiotics used to treat the disease.

Jenner and the first vaccination

Edward Jenner (1749–1823) was a doctor in England. He had heard that people such as milkmaids who got cowpox, never suffered from smallpox. Cowpox caused a minor illness, but smallpox could be deadly. He decided to test whether having cowpox really did protect you from smallpox . He scratched pus from a blister of a milkmaid who had cowpox onto the arm of a young boy, James Phipps. The boy contracted cowpox. A few weeks later Jenner repeated the process with the same boy, but used the smallpox virus instead. Fortunately the boy did not get smallpox and the process of vaccination was developed.

Controlling microbes

Other measures involved in the control of microbes that cause disease include:

1 **Antiseptics** – these are chemicals which when applied to the surface of the skin prevent infection by killing or inhibiting the growth of pathogens. The chemical must be mild enough not to cause skin reactions, but at the same time must be strong enough to damage the pathogen. There are a variety of chemicals that are antiseptics, including **phenol**, and they come in various forms including liquids and creams.

2 **Antibiotics** – these are generally produced by fungi and they kill bacteria by stopping the formation of bacterial cell walls. The first antibiotic to be developed was **penicillin** and many more have been developed since. The discovery of antibiotics was one of the great medical advances of the 20th century. More recently some bacteria have begun to develop chemicals to counteract the effects of some antibiotics. This process is described as **antibiotic resistance** and we need to be more careful in our use of antibiotics to try to ensure that this development of resistance is limited, otherwise antibiotics will no longer be effective.

Pasteur and the swan neck experiment

Until an experiment carried out by Louis Pasteur in 1861 it was thought that microbes arose spontaneously from non-living matter. This was called the **spontaneous generation theory**. Most people believed that broth became cloudy because microbes developed in it even if there were no microbes already present. Pasteur had been working with microbes and thought that they were carried about in the air. He carried out experiments using specially designed glass containers. These had a bend in a glass tube, called a swan neck. Pasteur reasoned that if microbes were present in the air then they would be trapped by these bends and not enter the container they were connected to. Pasteur suggested that if the broth was sterilised before the start of the experiment, killing any microbes present in the broth, then those containers with swan necks would not show a change in the broth, because the

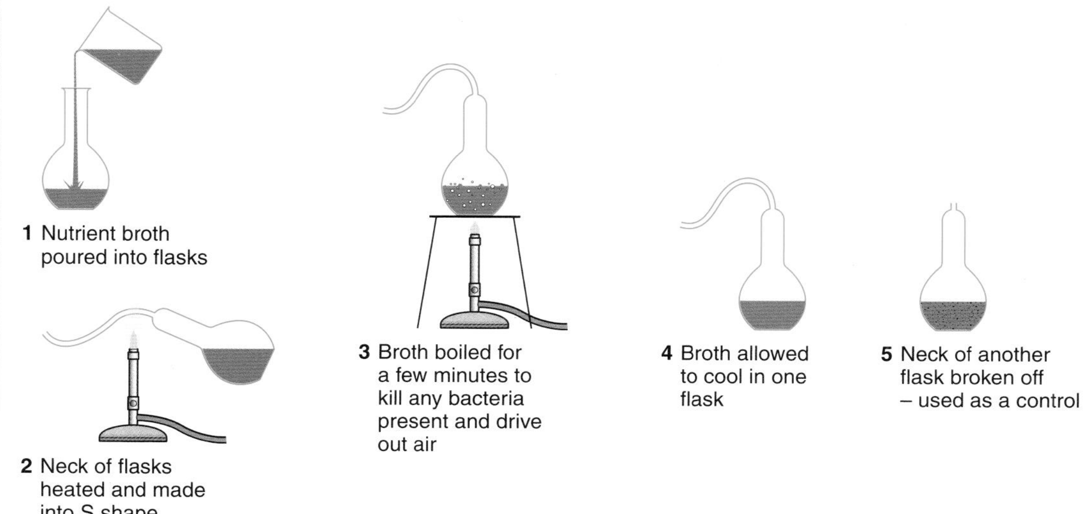
1 Nutrient broth poured into flasks
2 Neck of flasks heated and made into S shape
3 Broth boiled for a few minutes to kill any bacteria present and drive out air
4 Broth allowed to cool in one flask
5 Neck of another flask broken off – used as a control

Figure 4 Pasteur's swan neck experiment

microbes present in the air would be prevented from entering. Other containers that had been left open to the air even though the broth had been sterilised first should become cloudy due to the presence of micro-organisms. The results were consistent with Pasteur's theory that microbes were present in the air, and so the theory of spontaneous generation was disproved. Pasteur also suggested that food goes bad due to microbes that are present in the air.

Aseptic technique

When working with micro-organisms it is usually desirable to study or grow one type of micro-organism while preventing contamination by others. To ensure that this happens a variety of techniques known as **aseptic techniques** are used. These techniques are designed to ensure minimum contamination of the cultures of micro-organisms being studied. Micro-organisms all need water to survive and grow and this is often supplied bound with a jelly like substance called **agar** that can also contain some nutrients.

Growing micro-organisms on agar also enables easy transfer of the micro-organisms for subsequent use.

The techniques outlined here are applied to the growth and culture of bacteria. Other more advanced techniques may be used with viruses or disease causing micro-organisms.

The techniques involved include:

- Swabbing down the bench with alcohol.
- Using sterile utensils such as petri dishes, pipettes, inoculating loops and McCartney bottles.
- Working in an area beside a lit Bunsen burner. (Bunsen flame will kill any microbes in the air.)
- Flaming the neck of bottles of culture. (To kill any microbes on the neck of the flask.)
- Not placing any equipment such as loops etc. on the bench.
- Wearing a laboratory coat.
- Not eating or drinking in the laboratory.

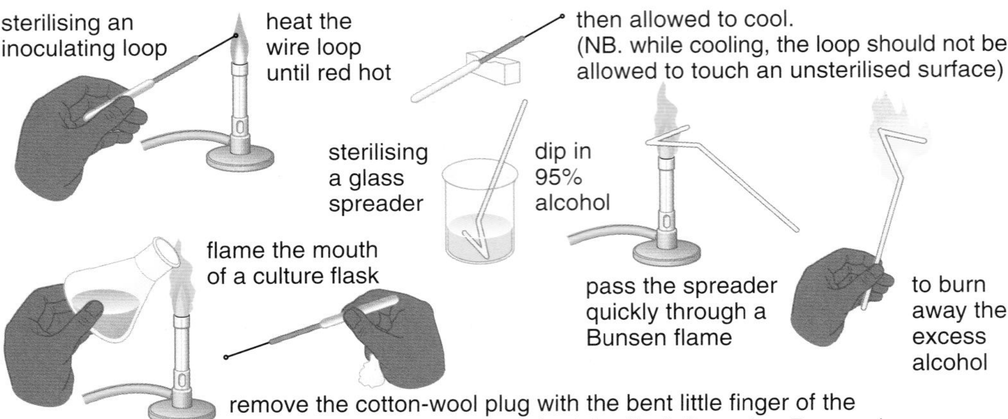
sterilising an inoculating loop
heat the wire loop until red hot
then allowed to cool.
(NB. while cooling, the loop should not be allowed to touch an unsterilised surface)
sterilising a glass spreader
dip in 95% alcohol
pass the spreader quickly through a Bunsen flame
to burn away the excess alcohol
flame the mouth of a culture flask
remove the cotton-wool plug with the bent little finger of the right hand and pass the mouth of the flask through a Bunsen burner

Figure 5 Aseptic techniques

- Washing hands with soap and warm water before and after any work with micro-organisms.
- Placing all equipment in disinfectant after use and sealing any cultures when finished with and heating them in an **autoclave** before disposing of them.
- Examining cultures in their closed containers. (To prevent spread of microbes in the air.)
- Not breathing on the containers of micro-organisms.
- Treating all micro-organisms as potential pathogens.

Sterilisation of agar or equipment can be carried out in a pressure cooker or autoclave. This method produces steam and will kill most micro-organisms if they are heated to 121°C for 15–20 minutes. If agar is sterilised using this method it needs to be cooled before use, but if cooled too much it solidifies. Usually the agar is placed in McCartney bottles in a water bath at about 40°C ready for pouring into sterile agar plates.

Some of the techniques are illustrated in Figures 5 and 6.

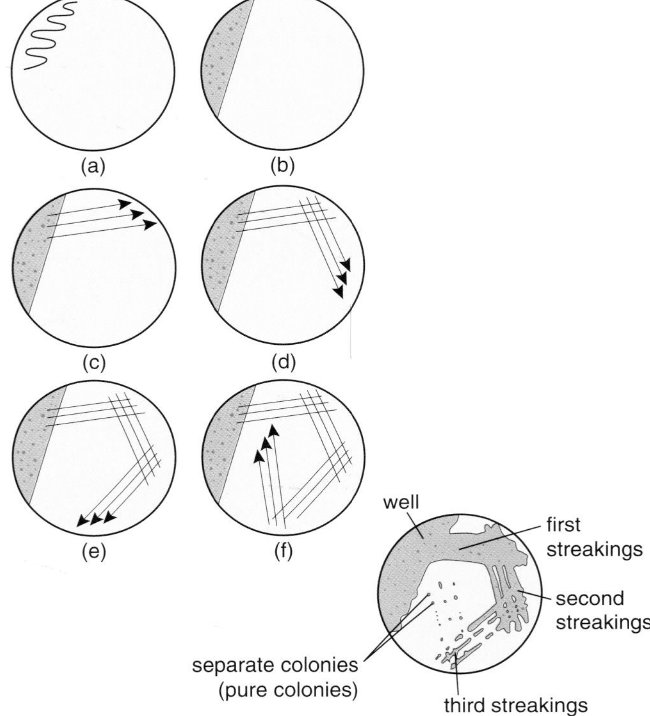
(a)
(b)
(c)
(d)
(e)
(f)
well
first streakings
second streakings
separate colonies (pure colonies)
third streakings

Figure 6 Producing pure colonies of a bacterium

Use of microbes

Manufacture of yoghurt

Yoghurt is produced by fermentation of milk by *Streptococcus* and *Lactobacillus* species of bacteria carrying out anaerobic respiration. The bacteria break down lactose sugar producing lactic acid, this coagulates the proteins in the milk and causes it to thicken.

In yoghurt both types of bacteria are used in equal proportions. The milk is heated to 85–90°C for 15–30 minutes to drive out the air and breaks down the milk proteins. The milk is then cooled and a starter culture of the bacteria is added. The lactic acid produced by the bacteria coagulates the milk proteins and makes the mixture more solid, it also gives the yoghurt its characteristic taste.

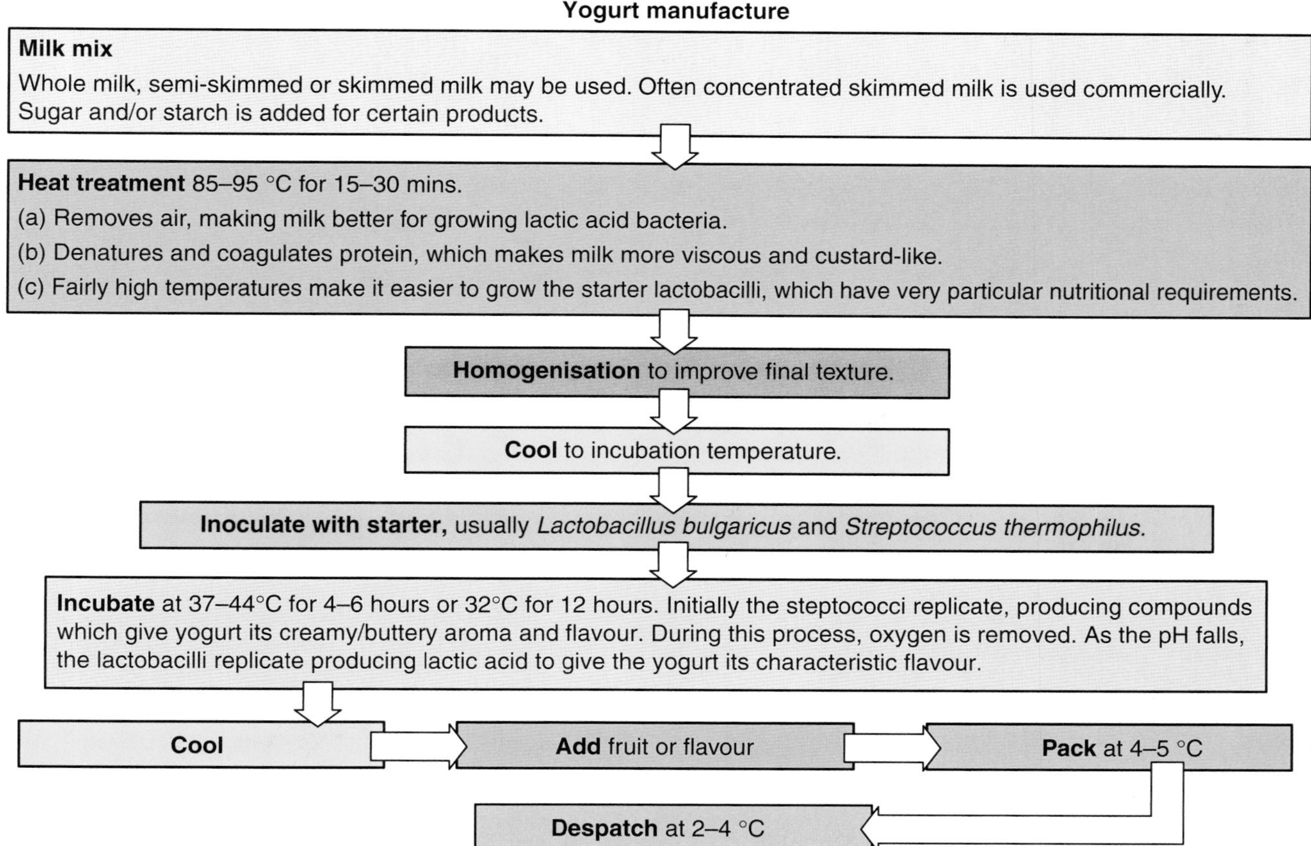

Figure 7 Yoghurt manufacture

Manufacture of bread

The ingredients flour (from wheat), yeast, sugar, salt, fat and vitamin C are mixed and kneaded. The kneading brings about changes in the proteins in the flour which makes it more elastic and allows it to hold the gases produced during fermentation. These gases make the bread rise. The yeast, *Saccharomyces*, reacts with the sugar and breaks it down into ethanol and carbon dioxide. This occurs if the dough is left in a humid atmosphere at about 27°C. The bubbles of carbon dioxide remain trapped in the dough. When it is baked in an oven the alcohol evaporates and the heat kills the yeast and cooks the flour. See Figure 8.

Manufacture of alcohol

This is another fermentation product of yeast. To produce beer, sugars and starch in the seeds of barley or hops are broken down and used as a food source for the yeast. The yeast carries out anaerobic respiration (fermentation) and produces alcohol and carbon dioxide. When fermentation is finished the beer is filtered to remove the yeast, then pasteurised and finally bottled or canned.

Fungi and decay

Fungi and some bacteria bring about decay. Since they do not contain chlorophyll they must get their organic matter by breaking down organic compounds from other organisms. This type of feeding is called **saprophytic nutrition**. The fungi produce and

How bread is made

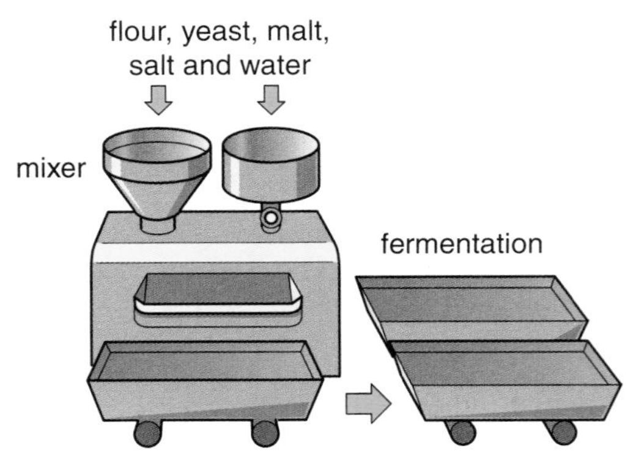

1 A 'sponge' or starting mixture is made which contains only part of the total amount of flour. This is kneaded in a mixer for several minutes. It is then fermented for several hours.

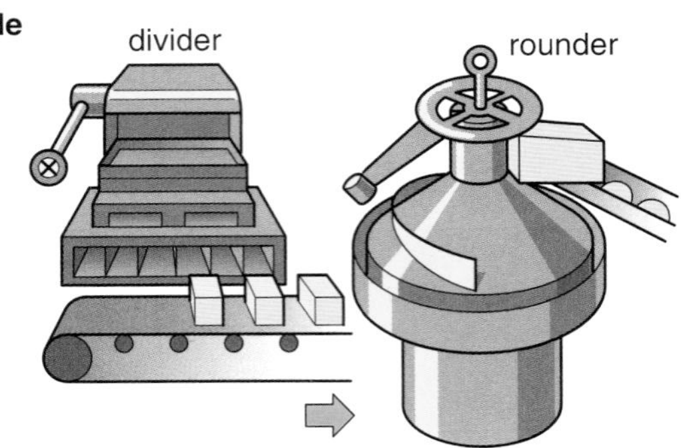

2 The rest of the flour is added and the dough mixed again A divider cuts the dough into loaf-sized pieces. These are shaped by the rounder.

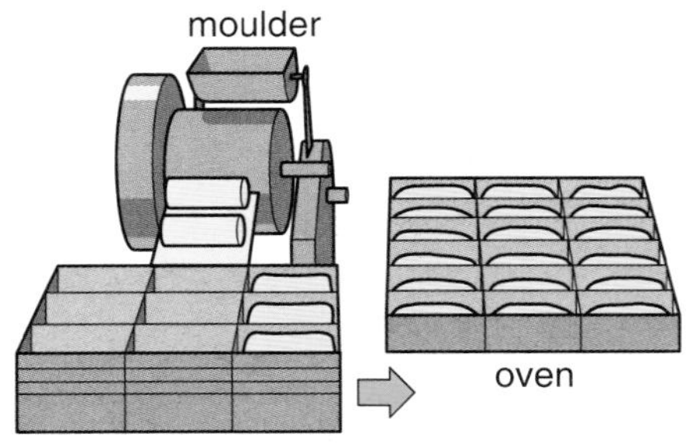

3 A moulder shapes the pieces of dough into cylinders

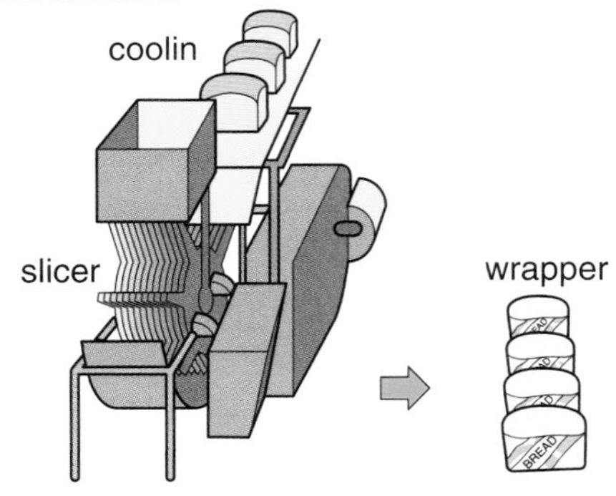

Figure 8 Bread manufacture

secrete enzymes that then break down the organic materials of other organisms, often dead ones, and then absorb the substances to allow them to survive and grow.

In some cases this poses problems since some fungi can cause disease in plants and animals, however they are also valuable since they break down dead organic matter in the soil that has come from dead or decaying plant and animal material, and release minerals into the soil for use by plants. Their action is important in the breakdown of material in compost heaps. Their action also causes the breakdown of food materials, such as bread, especially in moist conditions at a reasonable temperature when the fungi can easily spread and develop.

Figure 9 Bread mould – a type of fungus

Conditions for decay

For decay to take place the conditions need to be right for the bacteria and fungi to survive and grow. They need a certain amount of moisture and a certain temperature, as well as a neutral pH. Figure 10 shows a compost heap where decay would take place. It is better if the organic material is fairly fine when put into the compost heap since it is easier for the microbes to break it down. It is also better if it is not too closely packed since this will allow some circulation of air to supply those microbes that require oxygen with enough of the gas to survive. The microbes needed for the breakdown of organic matter are all present in soil, so some soil needs to be added to the compost heap at the start of the process. The

Figure 10 Compost heap

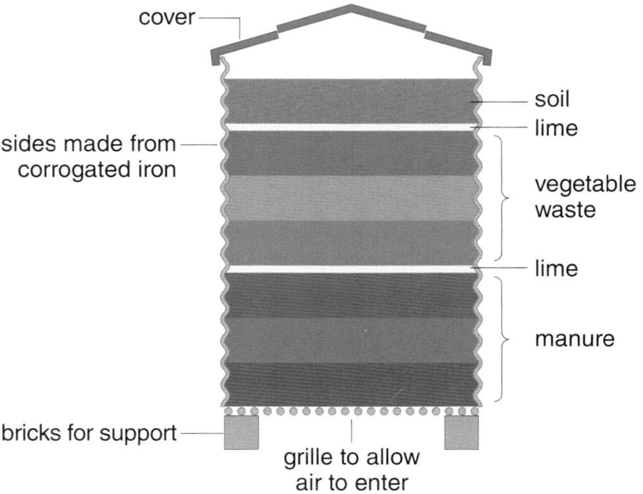

presence of other organisms, such as worms, will aid the decay process since they will help to break down the organic matter into smaller parts so helping the bacteria and fungi.

Food preservation

Food deteriorates when it is broken down by microbes such as bacteria and fungi. These microbes secrete chemicals which break down organic matter in food, and they make the products soluble so that they can be absorbed as their own food source. This spoils the food so that it is no longer edible. To prevent this happening too quickly, and therefore prolong the life of foodstuffs, we use various methods of preservation. All these methods try to deny microbes the sort of conditions they would like to reproduce and grow. They rely on ensuring that the temperature is too low or too high for the microbes to reproduce and grow, for example by storing the food in a refrigerator or freezer, or by **pasteurisation**. Pasteurisation is usually carried out on milk by heating it to 72°C for 15 seconds. Other methods used include drying the food, which removes the water from it and therefore makes it difficult for bacteria and fungi to survive.

What to do	What happens	Useful for
Make them very hot	High temperatures kill bacteria and fungi. After treatment the food is put into a sterile container	Pasteurised milk, sardines, baked beans, UHT milk
Make them very cold	Most bacteria stop growing at 5°C. A refrigerator keeps food below this temperature A freezer reaches −20°C and will keep food for many weeks	Cooked and uncooked meats, butter, milk, cheese, fruit juice, eggs, fish, pastry, cream
Add sugar	Bacteria cannot live in a strong sugar solution. The fluid in their cells is drawn out by osmosis into the sugar solution and they die	Strawberry jam, crystallised fruit
Add salt	Bacteria cannot live in a strong solution of salt because of osmosis	Bacon
Dry them out	Bacteria need water to live. If water is removed from food, bacteria and fungi cannot grow on it	Instant coffee
Add acid	Bacteria do not grow very well in acid solutions. The most commonly used acid is vinegar	Pickled onions, pickled cabbage

Discovery of antibiotics

Antibiotics are chemicals produced by some organisms, particularly fungi, to help them defend themselves against other micro-organisms, i.e. bacteria. The first antibiotic was discovered in 1928 by Sir Alexander Fleming. This antibiotic was penicillin, which is still used to treat bacterial infections in people and animals. Many more antibiotics have been discovered since then.

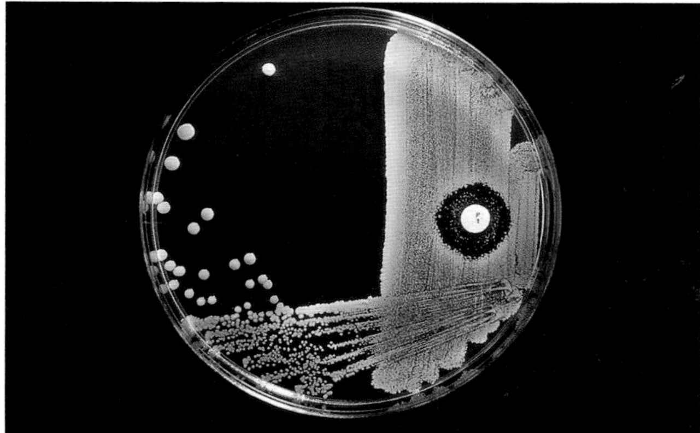

Figure 11 Agar plate showing a clear area where the antibiotic (penicillin) has killed bacteria growing on the plate

Fleming was growing bacteria on agar plates but noticed that on one of them there was a mould (fungi) contaminating the plate. When he looked at the plate he realised that the area around the mould had fewer bacteria growing on it than on the rest of the agar plate. He concluded that the mould was producing a substance which stopped the growth of the bacteria. The mould was *Penicillium* so he named the substance it produced penicillin. Fleming cultured the mould and then extracted a liquid from it, which he injected into mice and rabbits to show that it was not toxic to animals. However Fleming had problems trying to produce a pure form of the antibiotic and after several years abandoned this work.

Figure 12a Fleming

Figure 12b Florey

Figure 12c Chain

It was left to two other British scientists, Florey and Chain, to develop the production of penicillin on a large scale with the aid of American pharmaceutical companies and the American Department of Agriculture. This large-scale production took place in 1941 using a different *Penicillium* mould that produced higher yields of the antibiotic. The antibiotic was then used to treat soldiers injured in the Second World War who otherwise might have died from bacterial infections. This was the first time that large scale production of a microbiological culture using **bioreactors** was undertaken and the techniques developed have been used for the production of many other substances since. In addition the necessary sterilisation techniques for large-scale production of antibiotics have since been applied in other areas.

Figure 13 A commercial fermentation unit

Biodigester/bioreactor

These are large vessels, usually made of stainless steel, which are used to produce large quantities of a certain chemical, often the product of a particular microbe. There are many probes inside the reactor that allow the monitoring of temperature, pH and pressure so that the reaction can be followed and conditions modified if necessary. In addition, they usually have a stirrer to enable efficient mixing of the substances in the biodigester. One example of the use of a biodigester is in the large scale manufacture of the antibiotic penicillin. Once the penicillin has been produced it must be extracted from the reactor, separated from the microbes and purified before it can be used.

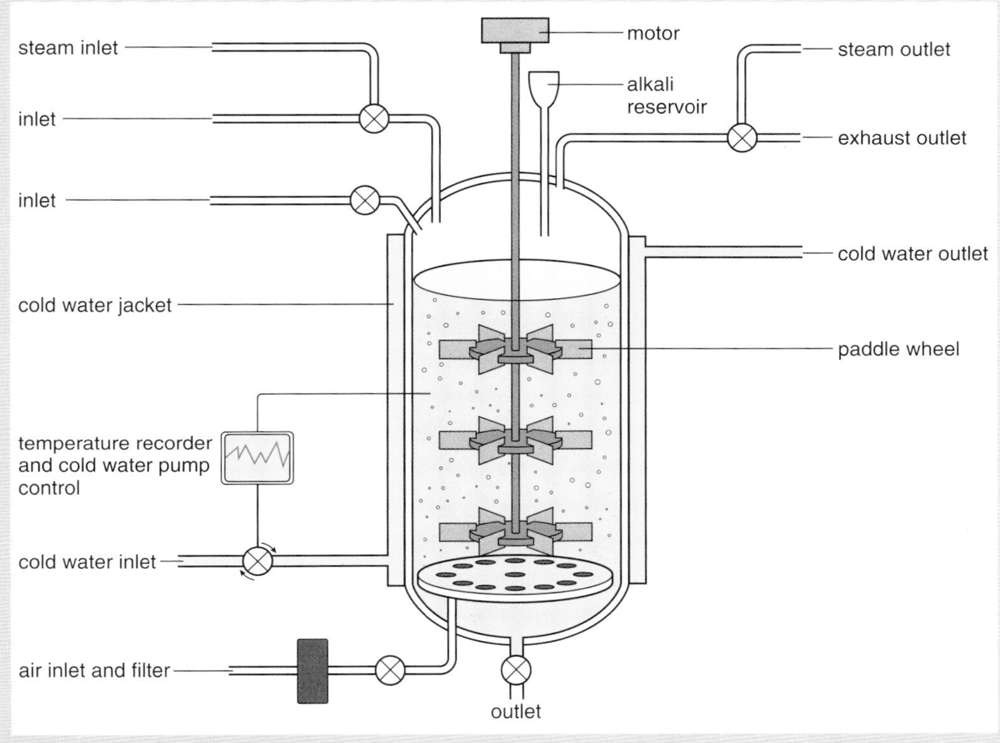

Figure 14 A bioreactor

Questions

5 Explain the aim of using aseptic techniques.

6 Give two examples of manufacturing where microbes are used to produce food products.

Websites

http://www.schoolscience.co.uk
The immune system.

http://www.bbs.org/wgbh/aso/databank/entries/dm79sp.html
Smallpox eradication.

http://library.thinkquest.org/10348/home.html
Immune system.

Exam questions

1 a) Copy and complete the table about some infectious diseases.

Disease	Type of organism	Means of transmission
AIDS	Virus	
Gonorrhoea		Sexual intercourse with infected person
Tuberculosis		
Rubella		Droplet infection

(5 marks)

b) The diagrams show an investigation into which antibiotic was the best at killing bacteria. A multodisk with six different antibiotics, A, B, C, D, E and F was placed on an agar plate containing the bacteria.

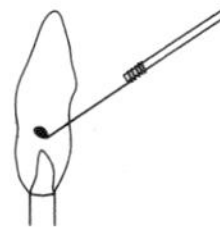

Heat the end of the wire loop in the Bunsen and allow it to cool

Use the loop to transfer a sample of the bacteria onto the agar plate.
Spread the bacteria evenly over the surface

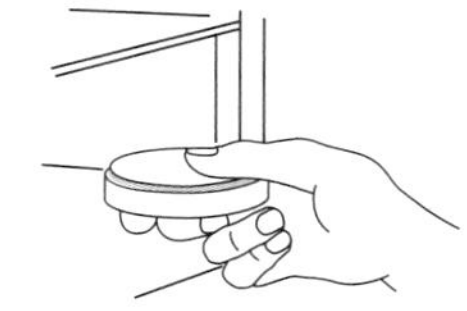

Place the multodisk on the agar plate.
Seal the petri dish with tape.
Incubate at 20 °C for 48 hours

(i) Why was the wire loop heated in the Bunsen flame?

(1 mark)

(ii) Explain why the petri dishes were sealed and not reopened after incubation.

(1 mark)

(iii) Explain why the petri dishes were incubated at 20°C.

(2 marks)

The diagram shows the results of the experiment.

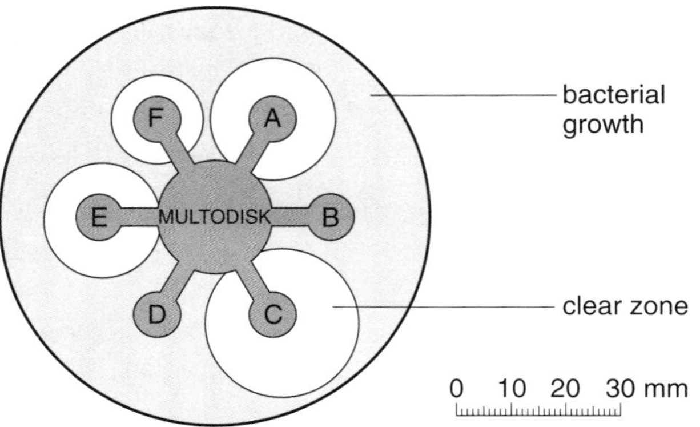

(iv) Copy and complete the table by **giving a heading** for the second column, **measuring the diameter** of the clear zone round antibiotics E and F.

Antibiotic	
A	24
B	0
C	29
D	0
E	
F	

(3 marks)

(v) Explain which antibiotic was the most effective at killing this type of bacterium.

(2 marks)

(vi) What type of organism produces antibiotic?

(1 mark)

c) The diagram shows a simple biodigester used to produce penicillin.

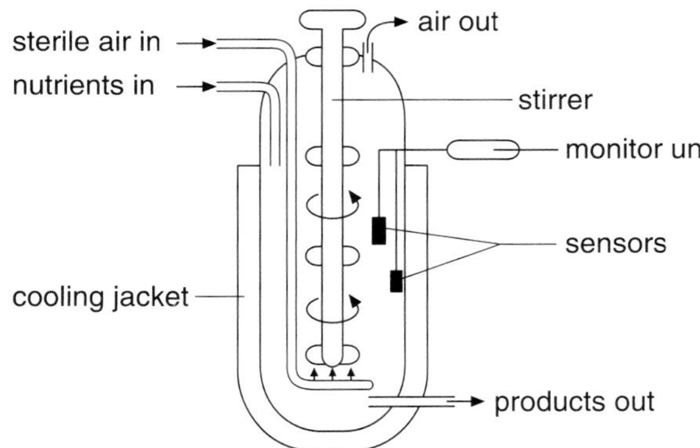

(i) Name **two** conditions, monitored by the sensors, which need to be kept constant. *(2 marks)*

The stirrer is used to mix the contents of the biodigester.

(ii) Explain how this increases the rate of penicillin production. *(3 marks)*

2 The graph shows the body's response to an antigen.

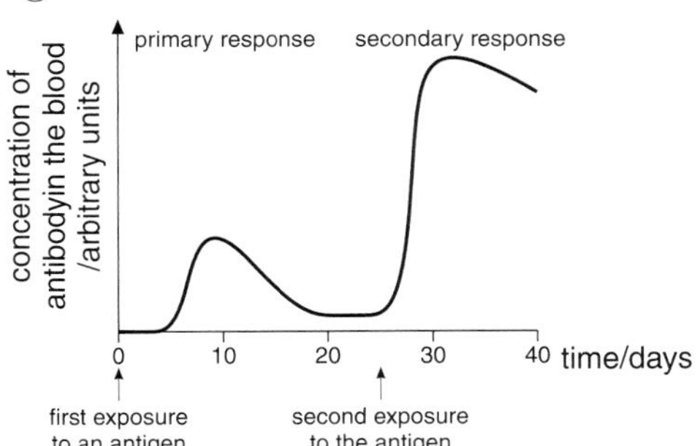

a) What is an antigen? *(2 marks)*

b) Explain why the secondary response is faster than the first. *(2 marks)*

c) Describe one way the body can remove antigens. *(2 marks)*

3 Salmonella, a micro-organism common in uncooked meat, can cause food poisoning.

a) What type of micro-organism is Salmonella? *(1 mark)*

b) Why would cooked meat contain less Salmonella than uncooked meat? *(1 mark)*

c) Explain why cooked meat should **not** be stored in contact with uncooked meat. *(2 marks)*

d) Suggest why meat can be safely stored for long periods when frozen. *(2 marks)*

4 The diagram shows the steps involved in bread making.

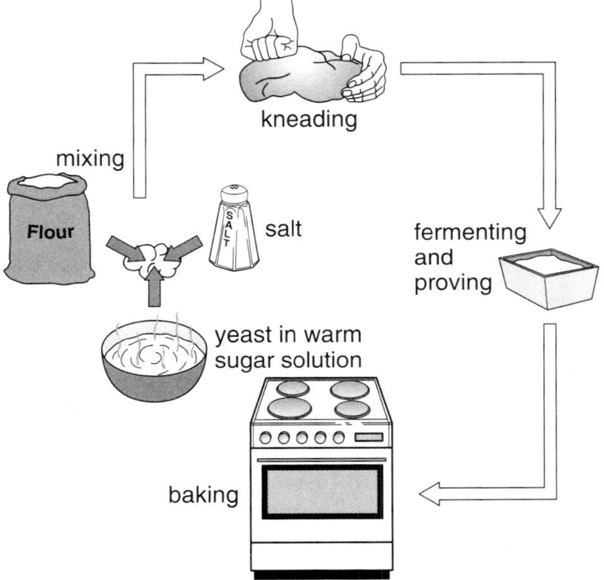

a) Name the micro-organism used to make bread. *(1 mark)*

b) Suggest why bread does not taste sweet when baked. *(1 mark)*

c) Explain why bread rises during fermentation and proving. *(2 marks)*

d) Describe the effect baking has on the

(i) micro-organism. *(1 mark)*

(ii) alcohol. *(1 mark)*

Chapter 11

Transport in Plants

Learning objectives

By the end of this chapter you should know:

- The role of xylem in the transport of water and mineral salts
- The role of water in plants
- The process of transpiration
- **The potometer as a means of measuring water uptake and transpiration**
- **The environmental factors that affect the rate of transpiration**
- The role of phloem in the translocation of soluble food products
- The main structural features of a stem, root and leaf in an herbaceous dicotyledon

The movement of water through a plant

All plants need water to survive. In most plants there is a continuous stream of water into the root, up the stem and into the leaves. Water enters plant root cells by osmosis. This happens because the root cells contain a more concentrated solution than the surrounding soil. Once the water has entered the epidermal cells it passes across the cells of the root, also by osmosis. Figure 1 shows why this happens. When the water enters the epidermal cell (X) it makes the cell more dilute. This cell now becomes less concentrated than the adjacent cell (Y). The water will now move from X to Y by osmosis. Cell Y now becomes more dilute than Z and so on until the water moves across the root as far as the xylem cells.

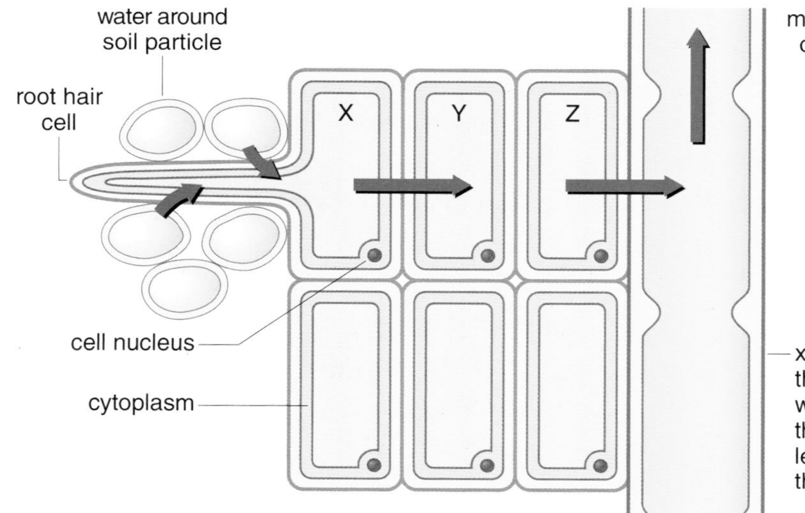

Figure 1 The movement of water into and through the plant root

The **xylem** consists of specialised cells that are adapted to carry water. The most obvious adaptation is the absence of the top and bottom end walls so that a column of xylem cells forms a hollow tube. The xylem cells run in these continuous tubes or vessels from the roots through the stem to the veins of the leaves and form a very effective transport system. The water is pulled or sucked up the xylem in a similar way as would happen when using a drinking straw. As the water is sucked or pulled up the forces of cohesion (attraction) between the water molecules keeps the water moving upwards in a continuous column. When the xylem reaches the leaves it subdivides to form veins.

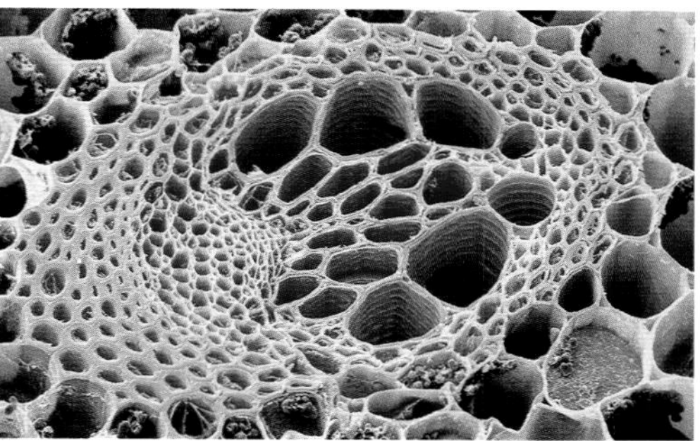

Figure 2 Xylem cells in cross-section

Importance of water to plants

The water that is transported into and through a plant is necessary for many purposes. These include:

- *Photosynthesis* – much of the water that enters the leaves is used as a raw material for photosynthesis.
- *Support* – water is used to keep the plant cells firm or turgid. This is particularly important in non-woody plants.
- As a *solvent* – water is used in many reactions in the plant cells.
- *Transport of mineral ions* – although active uptake may be required to transport ions into plant roots, the ions are transported through the plant by the movement of water.

Transpiration

Much of the water that enters the leaves evaporates into the atmosphere. This loss of water by evaporation is called **transpiration** and the continuous movement of water through the plant is known as the **transpiration stream**. The evaporation of water takes place mainly in plant leaves. This transpiration of water is necessary to ensure that water continually moves up through a plant therefore supplying water and minerals to the leaves. However, as plants cannot afford to lose too much water by transpiration it is important that they have some control over water loss. The stomata are important structures in regulating water loss.

Stomata

Stomata are small pores in the surface of the leaf. These pores allow gases to diffuse in and out of the leaf during the processes of respiration and photosynthesis. As leaves are covered with an impermeable cuticle, through which water cannot evaporate, the stomata are also the route through which most of the water escapes in transpiration. Each stoma consists of a pair of specialised guard cells and an opening or pore between them. The guard cells can open or close the pore by changing shape. Figure 3 shows a stoma in both its open and closed positions.

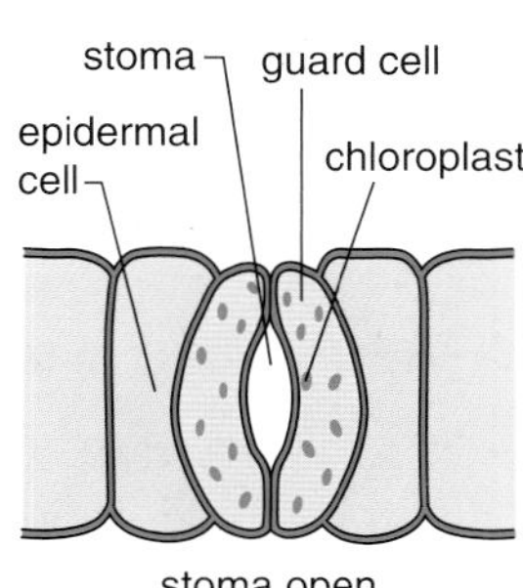

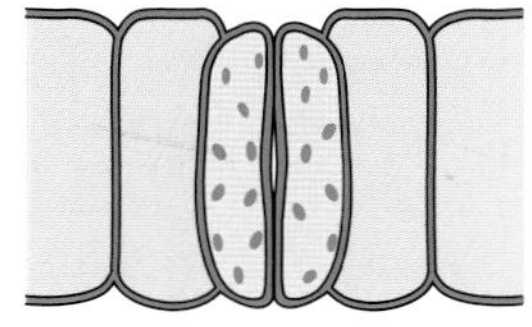

Figure 3 A stoma open and closed

You can make a model of a stoma by blowing up two long balloons that have their ends tied together. As the balloons blow up they become more rigid and because they are tied together at each end they will twist in such a way that a gap develops between them.

The site of transpiration

Water reaches the leaves through the xylem that spreads into leaves in the form of veins. When water passes out of the veins it moves by osmosis into the cells of the leaf. The leaf cells between the upper and lower epidermis are called mesophyll cells. Mesophyll cells, unlike epidermal cells, are not covered by a waterproof cuticle. Water evaporates from these cells into the surrounding air spaces in the leaf. The water vapour that builds up causes a moisture gradient to develop between the leaf and the surrounding atmosphere. The water vapour then diffuses down this gradient and out through the stomata. Figure 4 shows the route by which water moves through the leaf as part of the transpiration stream.

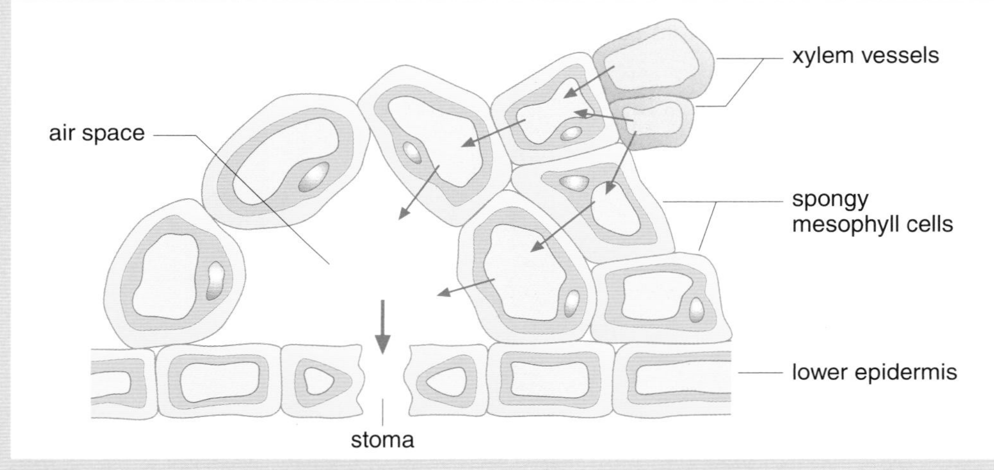

Figure 4 Section through part of a leaf showing the path taken by water during the final stages of transpiration

Measuring water uptake and transpiration in plants

The standard or bubble **potometer** (Figure 5) is designed to measure water uptake in a leafy shoot. As water evaporates out of the leaves of the cut shoot it sucks water up through the potometer. The distance the air bubble travels in a period of time can be used to calculate the **rate** of water uptake. The reservoir allows the apparatus to be reset so that other results can be recorded. As air leaks will hinder the uptake of water into the plant it is important that the potometer apparatus is properly sealed, particularly at the junction between the shoot and the neck of the potometer. To prevent the development of air bubbles in the water column entering the plant it is necessary to assemble the apparatus under water initially.

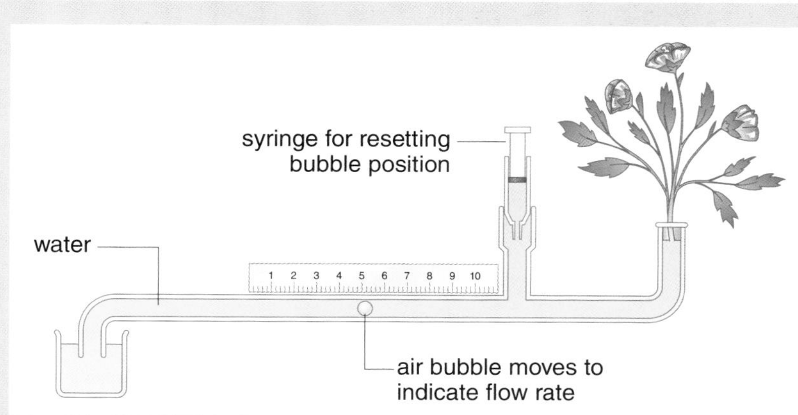

Figure 5 The potometer

The potometer in Figure 5 can accurately measure the volume of water taken up by a shoot but it cannot give an absolute value for transpiration itself. Transpiration is the loss of water by evaporation from the leaves and it is impossible to calculate how much of the water taken up by the plant is actually transpired through the leaf surface. As some of the water will be used in photosynthesis and other reactions, the volume transpired will inevitably be less than the volume taken into the shoot.

However, the potometer can be used to compare rates of transpiration in different environmental conditions. The results obtained in different conditions can identify how transpiration is affected by the environmental conditions.

The apparatus shown in Figure 6, sometimes called a **weight potometer**, can be used to calculate transpiration values. In this apparatus it is possible to work out how much water has evaporated from the leaves in transpiration. The rate of transpiration can be calculated by working out how much water is lost by the plant in a particular period of time.

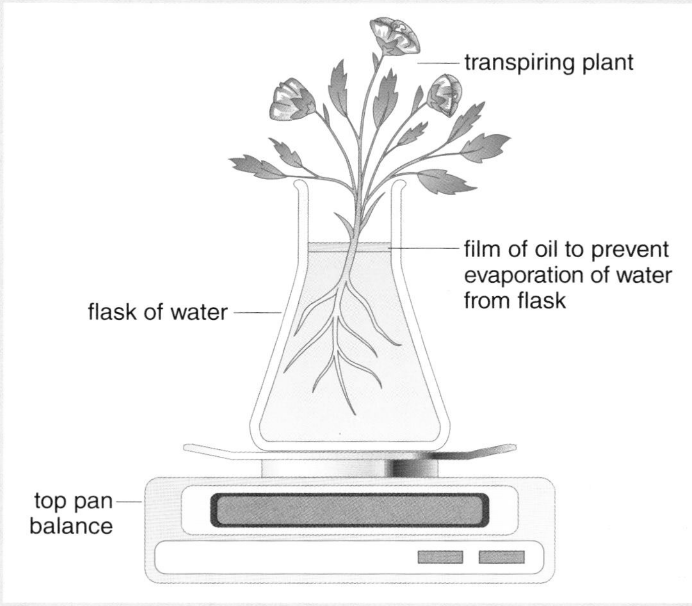

Figure 6 The weight potometer

Environmental factors affecting transpiration rate

The rate of transpiration can be affected by a number of environmental conditions. These include:

- *Temperature* – the warmer the atmosphere surrounding a plant, the faster water will evaporate. Therefore as temperature increases the rate of transpiration will also increase.
- *Wind speed* – wind will help speed up the process of transpiration as the wind will quickly remove evaporating water away from the stomata. This helps make sure that a steep concentration gradient of moisture is maintained between the inside of the leaf and the air surrounding the leaf.
- *Humidity* – evaporation takes place slowly in humid conditions. Transpiration will be at its slowest in moist or humid air.

Although not an environmental factor the surface area of the leaf affects the transpiration rate. Larger leaves will have more stomata than smaller leaves, therefore smaller leaves will tend to lose less water by transpiration. Many plants that grow in very dry areas have leaves that are much reduced in size. This is most obvious in many cacti where the size of the leaves may be reduced so much that they form needles.

Questions

1 It is important to reduce evaporation in many delicate houseplants. Why is it advisable to spray the leaves of these plants with a fine mist of water each day?

Transport of food substances in the plant

The process of photosynthesis makes glucose in the leaves. The glucose can be converted to starch for short term storage in the leaves, but eventually it is converted into sucrose (another sugar) for transport through the plant. The sucrose is transported to storage regions such as the roots or to areas of new growth.

The sucrose is transported in a specialised and complex tissue called **phloem**. The movement of synthesised food products from the leaves through the phloem to other parts of the plant is called **translocation**.

Structure of a plant root and stem

The root and stem are designed to provide stability and support for the plant. Roots and stems are also important in transporting substances up and down the plant. The two types of transport tissue, the xylem and phloem, typically occur together. In stems the xylem and phloem are organised into a number of **vascular bundles** that occur in a ring around the edge of the stem. In roots the vascular tissue occurs in a single central structure. Figure 7 shows cross sections through a root and a stem to show how the xylem and phloem are distributed.

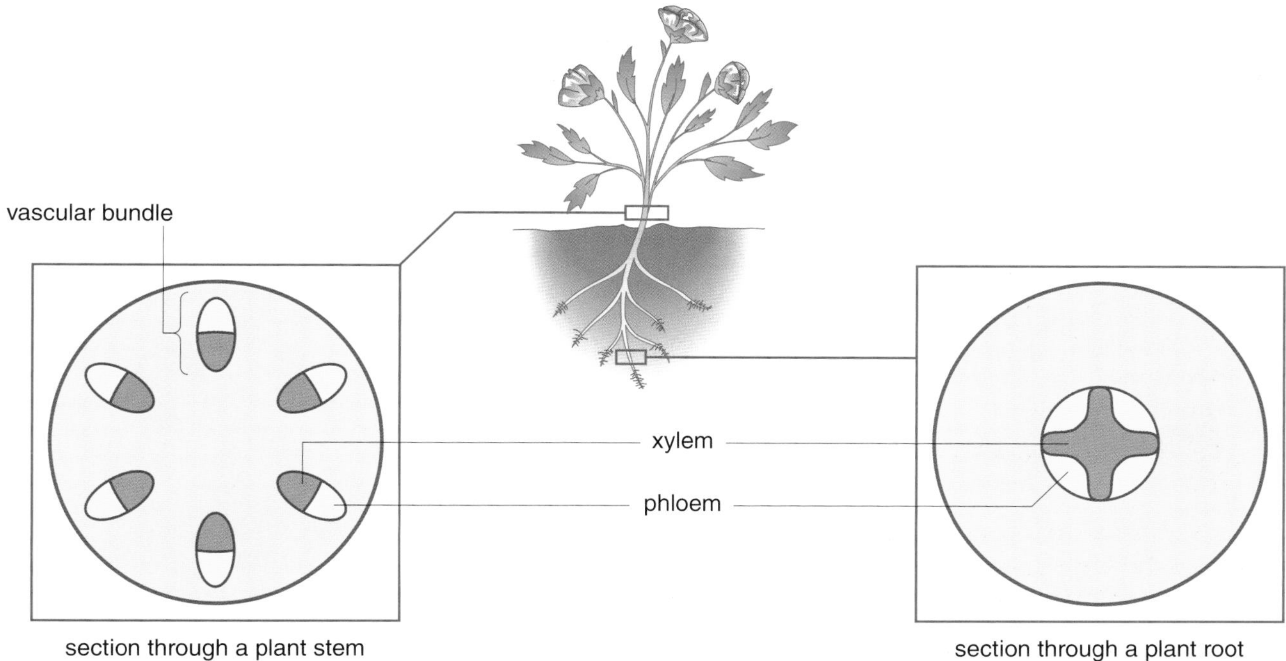

Figure 7 Sections through a plant stem and root to show the distribution of xylem and phloem

Questions

2 Test your knowledge of this chapter by describing the movement of water into, through, and out of a plant. To help you plan your answer it might be worthwhile splitting your answer into three paragraphs or sections. Each paragraph should describe and explain:

a) the movement of water from the soil to the xylem
b) the movement of water up through the root and stem
c) the movement of water through and out of the leaf

In each paragraph it is important to explain not only what happens, but also, why it happens.

Alternatively you could summarise this chapter in the form of a large diagram with detailed labels.

Websites

http://www.learn.co.uk
Contains a summary of transpiration.

http://www.purchon.com/biology/xylem.htm
Look at xylem and phloem in a virtual microscope.

http://www-saps.plantsci.cam.ac.uk

Exam questions

1 The diagram shows the movement of water in a plant.

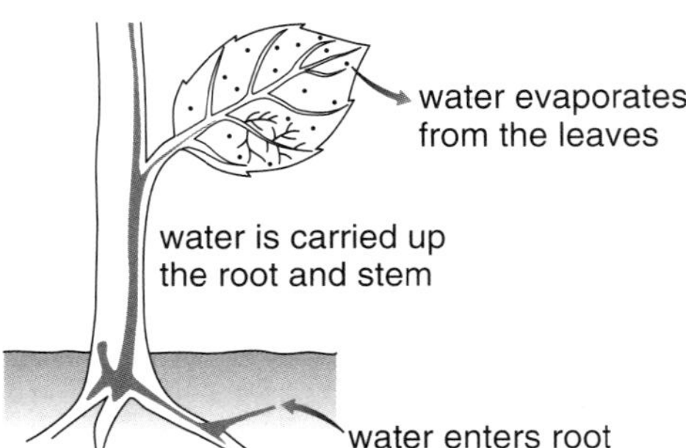

a) What would happen to the plant on a bright breezy day if it lost more water than it could absorb?
(1 mark)

b) What else does the plant take in with the water it absorbs?
(1 mark)

c) Through which type of cell is the water carried in the plant stem?
(1 mark)

2 The diagram shows the movement of water into a plant root.

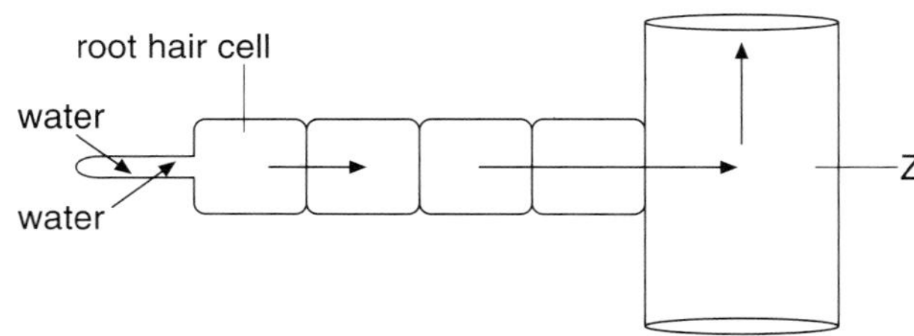

a) Water enters the root hair cell by osmosis.
Explain this process in root hair cells.
(2 marks)

b) Name the type of cell, Z, that transports water to other parts of the plant.
(1 mark)

c) Explain how water can provide support in plants.
(1 mark)

3 A potometer is used to investigate water uptake in a shoot.

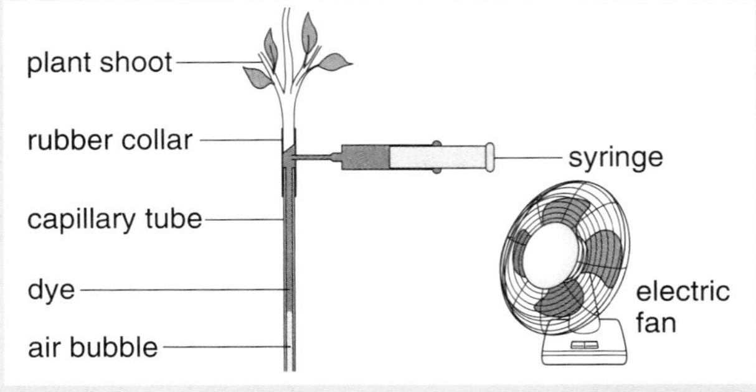

a) What check should be made if the water level in the capillary tube began to fall at the start of the experiment?
(1 mark)

b) Describe clearly how the apparatus in the diagram could be used to investigate the effect of wind speed on water uptake.
(4 marks)

4 A geranium shoot was set up in a potometer as shown.

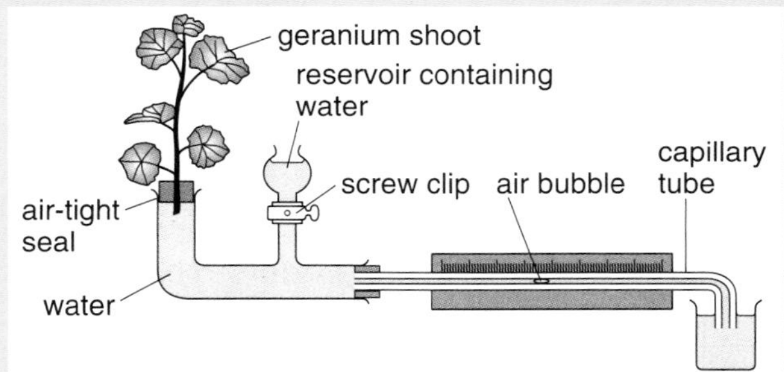

Movement of the air bubble introduced into the capillary tube was recorded over a 2 minute period for each of the five sets of experimental conditions shown in the table below.

Experimental conditions	
A	Still air, leaves untreated
B	Moving air (using a fan), leaves untreated
C	Still air, leaves vaselined on upper surface only
D	Still air, leaves vaselined on lower surface only
E	Still air, leaves vaselined on upper and lower surfaces

Temperature and light intensity were kept constant throughout the experiment.

a) What process is being investigated in this experiment? *(1 mark)*

b) The results of the experiment are shown in the table below.

Copy and complete the table by inserting the letter (experimental conditions, i.e. A, B, C, D or E) which produced each of the results.

Distance (mm) moved by air bubble	Experimental conditions (A, B, C, D or E)
4	
20	
70	
90	
200	

(4 marks)

5 The diagram shows a section through a plant, from the roots to the leaves.

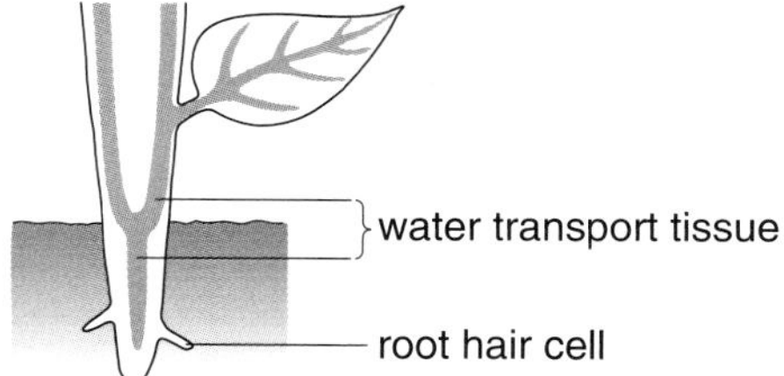

a) (i) Copy the diagram and draw a continuous line to show the passage of water into, and up through the plant. *(2 marks)*

(ii) Name the tissue that transports water. *(1 mark)*

b) The photograph shows a wilted plant.

Explain what has happened to the cells of this plant to make it wilt. *(2 marks)*

c) The diagram shows a weight potometer which can be used to measure the rate of transpiration in a plant.

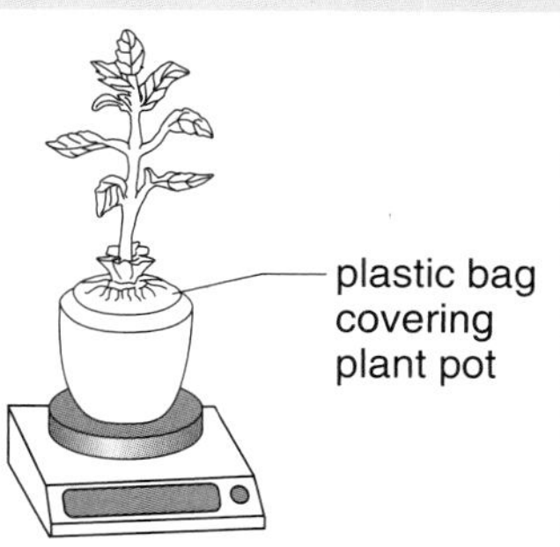

(i) What is the purpose of the plastic bag around the pot? *(1 mark)*

The rate of transpiration is affected by the surface area of the leaves on a plant.

(ii) Describe how you would use the plant and the potometer shown in the diagram to investigate the effect of **reducing** surface area on the rate of transpiration. *(5 marks)*

(iii) What results would you expect when the surface area is reduced? *(1 mark)*

Chapter 12

Excretion

Learning objectives

By the end of this chapter you should know:

- The structure of the kidney and excretory system
- That the kidney is an organ of excretion and regulation
- How kidney transplants and dialysis can be used to treat kidney failure and their relative merits and disadvantages
- How the kidney carries out ultrafiltration of the blood
- The principles of a kidney machine
- That urea is produced from amino acid breakdown in the liver
- That the liver breaks down alcohol to detoxify it

Excretion is the process of producing and getting rid of waste products that have been formed in the cells of the body or taken in from the environment. The main waste products in humans are carbon dioxide, salts, water and urea. The main organs involved are the lungs, skin, liver and kidneys.

The body needs to keep certain substances at a constant level so that all the cells can operate. This process is called **homeostasis**. Excretion of wastes helps to keep this balance. Other processes involved in homeostasis are regulation of blood glucose and temperature (see Chapter 14).

The waste products produced by the body are:

1. *Carbon dioxide* – produced in the cells of the body during cell respiration. It is then carried in the blood to the lungs where it is breathed out.
2. *Water* – essential for the body, but too much can dilute the blood and tissue fluids and cause the cells to swell. Excess water is lost during sweating from the skin, breathing from the lungs, and in the urine.
3. *Salts* – essential in certain quantities, but can cause osmotic (salt and water balance) problems if they are present in larger quantities than necessary. Excess salts are excreted in the urine and in the sweat.
4. *Urea* – a poisonous waste product formed from the breakdown of amino acids in the liver. The amino acids come from proteins that have been digested and are then carried to the liver in the hepatic portal vein. The urea is then transported in the blood to the kidneys where it is turned into urine.

Water balance in the body

Water is taken into the body during eating and drinking. It is lost in sweat, breath, urine and faeces. If the body has too much water then the kidneys will produce large quantities of dilute urine. If the body does not have enough water the kidneys will reduce the amount lost in the urine and so produce small amounts of concentrated urine. Salt levels also need to be controlled. Controlling the water and salt balance in this way is called **osmoregulation** and is one aspect of homeostasis.

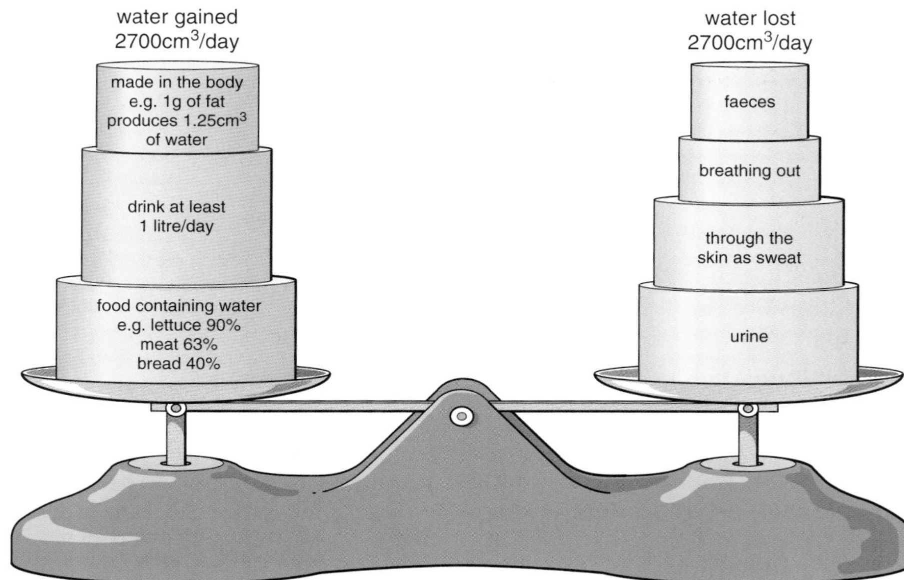

Figure 1 Water gain and loss in the body

Urea production

The amino acids absorbed from digested food in the small intestine are sent to the liver in the hepatic portal vein. The liver will distribute those that are needed back into the blood to go to the heart to be pumped around the body. Excess amino acids cannot be stored and must be broken down. This process of breakdown of excess amino acids in the liver is called **deamination**. Part of the amino acid is separated from the rest of the molecule and turned into **urea**. The liver can use the remains of the amino acid to produce energy. The urea is then carried in the blood to the kidneys where it is turned into urine.

Alcohol detoxification

Alcohol is a small soluble molecule which has a variety of effects on the body. It is absorbed into the blood from the stomach and intestines and is transported to the liver. The liver breaks the alcohol down into less toxic products in a process called **detoxification**. Over-use of alcohol can result in liver damage.

Structure of the urinary system

The urinary system is composed of the kidneys, which are located in the hollow of the back, two **ureters** leading to the bladder and then the **urethra** which carries the urine out of the body.

Figure 2 Excretory system

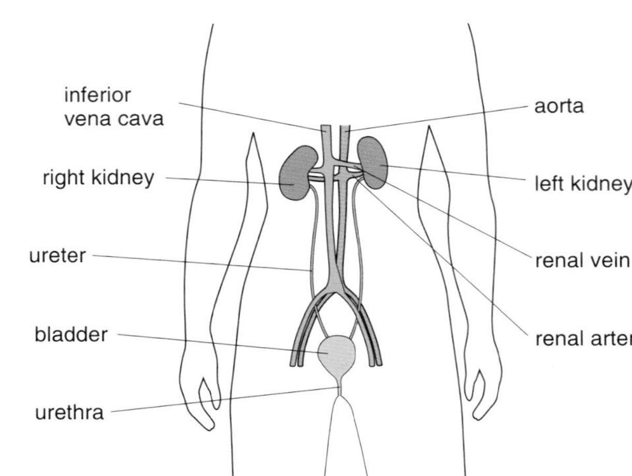

Figure 3 Cross section of the kidney

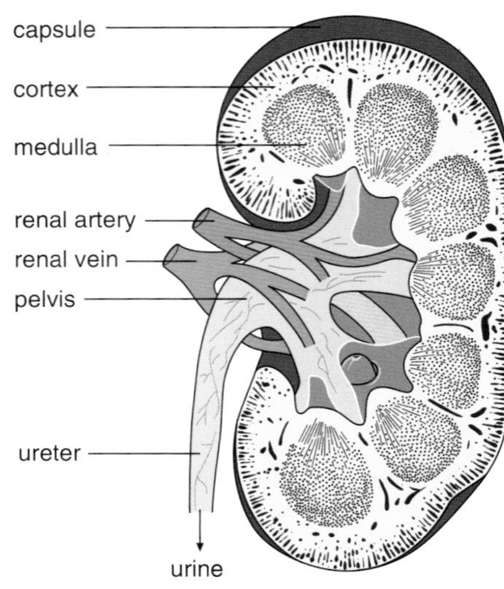

The kidneys carry out **filtration** (ultrafiltration) of the blood. They filter 200 litres of fluid every 24 hours. The filtered liquid passes into tubules in the kidney. As this liquid passes through the tubules useful substances are reabsorbed back into the blood capillaries of the kidney, so that they are not lost in the urine. What remains in the liquid is passed out as urine. It contains water, salts and urea.

The urine travels down the ureters to the **bladder** where it is stored. When the bladder is full the **sphincter muscle** at the base of the bladder relaxes and the urine passes down the urethra and out of the body.

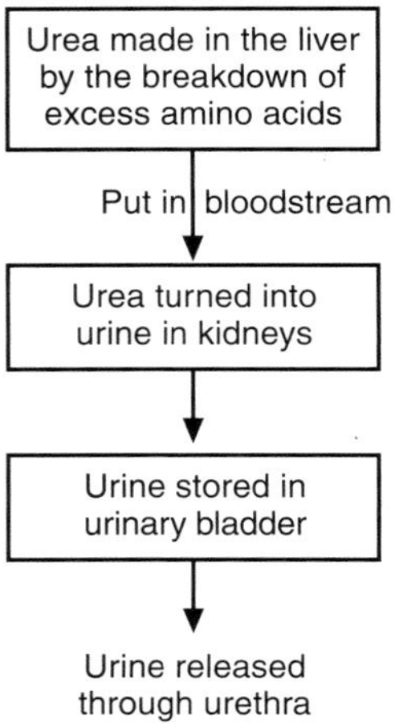

Urea made in the liver by the breakdown of excess amino acids

↓ Put in bloodstream

Urea turned into urine in kidneys

↓

Urine stored in urinary bladder

↓

Urine released through urethra

Figure 4 The process of removal of urea

Urine formation and osmoregulation

The kidneys contain millions of tubules into which blood flows. When blood passes into the kidneys it is filtered through small blood capillaries into these tubules. Only smaller molecules are able to pass across into the tubules of the kidney. Therefore the red blood cells and larger molecules in the blood do not pass across.

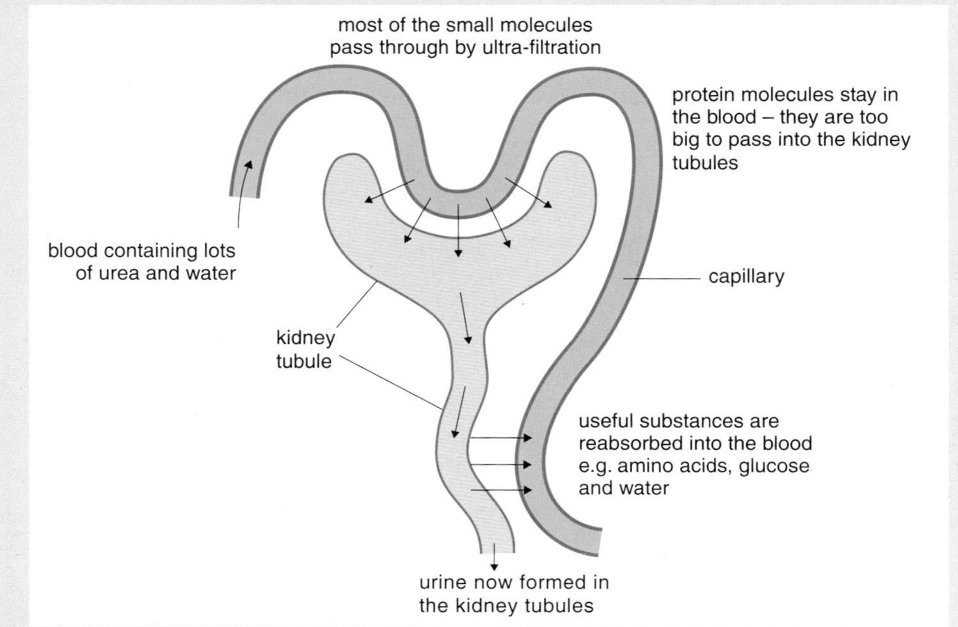

Figure 5 Filtration in the kidney tubules

Small molecules such as water, salts, amino acids, glucose and urea can pass into the kidneys tubules. The useful substances are reabsorbed and the rest is passed out as urine. The amount of water and salt excreted is regulated by hormones working in the kidney in the process of osmoregulation.

Kidney problems and treatment

If the kidneys fail then a person needs to be treated. Otherwise harmful wastes including urea, salts and fluid build up in the body. There are two main methods of treatment – **kidney (renal) dialysis** or a **kidney transplant**.

Usually dialysis is the first type of treatment used. It involves gradually removing the persons blood and filtering it through a machine (dialysis machine) to remove urea. The process needs to be carried out several times a week and each time it takes several hours. In between treatments the person must eat a restricted diet so that they do not build up too much urea in their blood. The problem with dialysis is that it has to be carried out regularly and is time consuming.

The alternative is a kidney transplant. This involves an operation where a kidney from another person is used to replace the defective kidney. However the donor and the recipients cells must be tissue typed i.e. checked to see if they have similar chemicals on their surface. This lessens the chances of the new kidney being rejected by the recipient's immune system. If this happens the new kidney would no longer function. To aid the process of acceptance by the recipient they are given immunosuppressent drugs for a time. These drugs stop the immune system working as efficiently as usual and help the body to adjust to the new organ. Many people recover well from transplant surgery and go on to live normal lives. One of the main problems with this treatment is the shortage of donor organs for transplant.

Figure 6 A dialysis machine

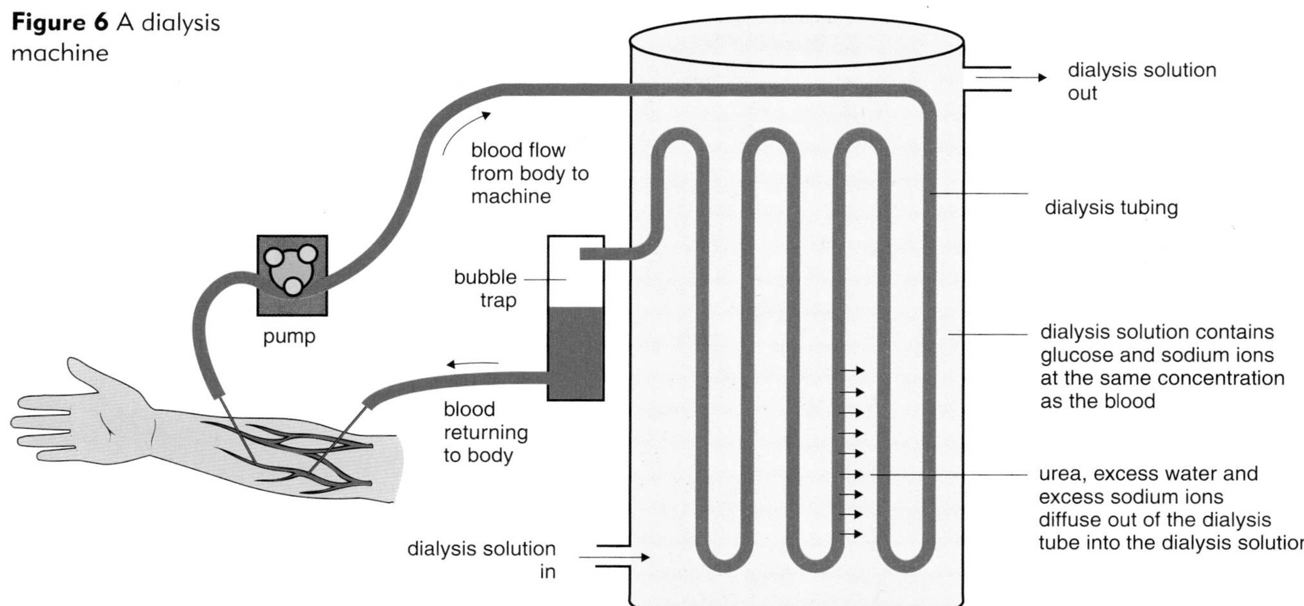

Questions

1 Suggest reasons why many people would prefer to have a kidney transplant rather than continue to have dialysis treatment.

2 Suggest reasons for the shortage of organs available for transplants.

3 Suggest measures that might increase the number of organs available for transplant.

The mechanism of dialysis

Dialysis is the process of filtering the blood using a dialysis machine. It works by filtering out urea which is a poisonous substance in the blood. The process involves passing the blood through tubes that are partially permeable, i.e. they allow small molecules to pass through but not larger molecules. There are large lengths of this tubing in the dialysis machine.

On one side of this tubing is the blood and on the other side of the membrane is a fluid. This fluid picks up the urea as it passes across, down a diffusion gradient. To maintain this diffusion gradient the dialysis fluid must be continually changed and replaced with fresh dialysis fluid which does not contain urea.

In addition to the urea passing across the membrane other small molecules, such as glucose and salts that are useful to the body, could pass across into the dialysis fluid and be lost. To prevent this happening glucose and salts are added to the dialysis fluid at the same concentration as they would be in the blood. This means that there is no diffusion gradient and these substances remain in the blood of the person as it is passed back into their circulation system. During this treatment the blood needs to be kept flowing, at body temperature and be kept free from infection.

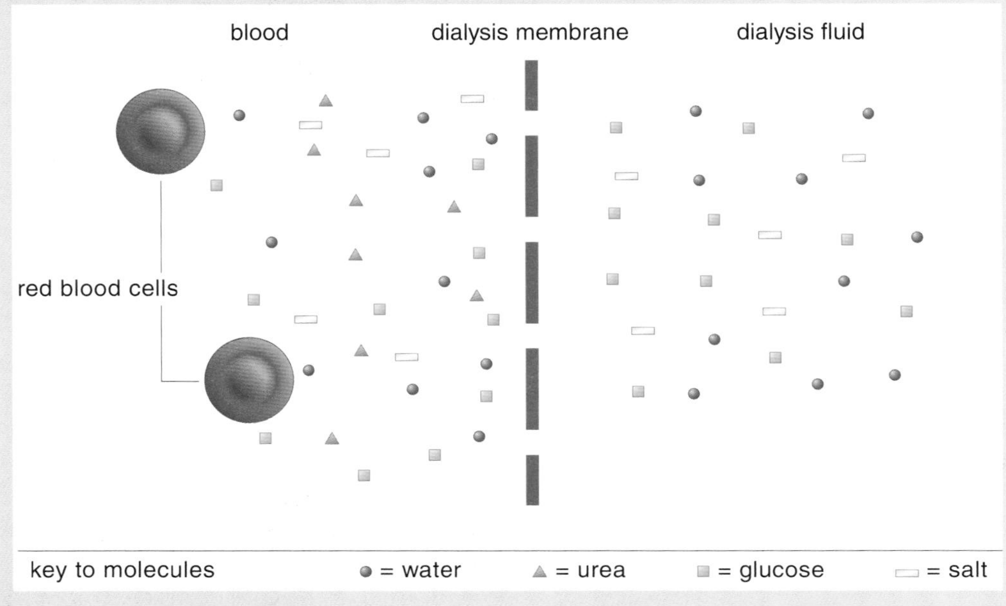

Figure 7 The start of dialysis

Websites

http://www.schoolscience.co.uk/content/4/biology/abpi/kidneys/kid4.html
Information about kidney problems.

http://www.howstuffworks.com
How the kidneys work.

Exam questions

1 The diagram shows part of the human urinary system.

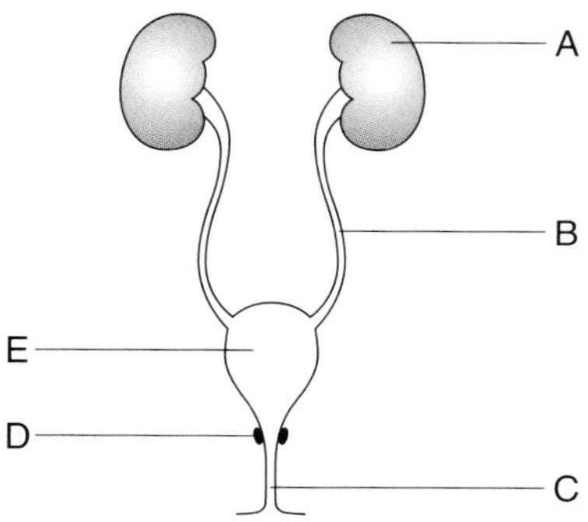

a) Name parts A, B and C. *(3 marks)*

b) Give the functions of D and E. *(2 marks)*

The urinary system helps control the amount of water in the body.

c) Name this process. *(1 mark)*

2 Urea is a toxic waste which must be removed from the body.

a) Name the organ which

(i) produces urea *(1 mark)*

(ii) removes urea from the blood *(1 mark)*

The diagram and the bar chart show what happens to blood passing through a dialysis machine.

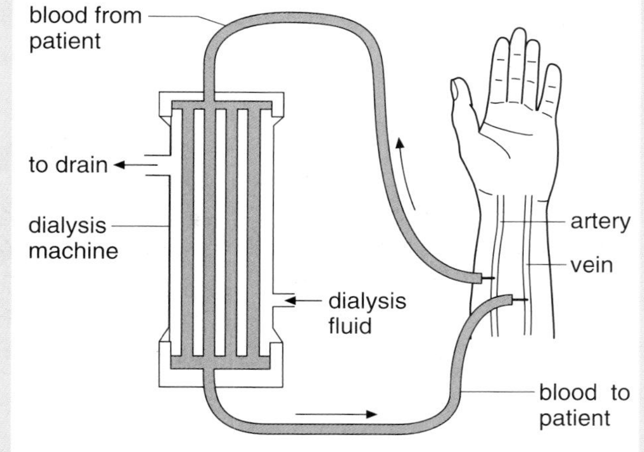

Bar chart to show the concentration of some blood components.

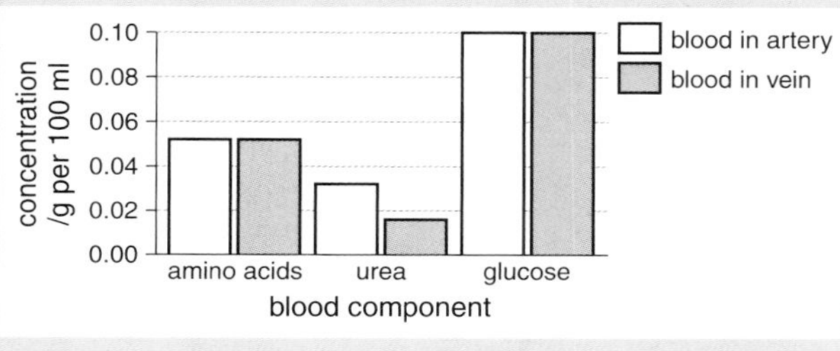

b) Give **one** similarity in the composition of the blood shown in the bar chart. *(1 mark)*

c) Describe and explain **one** difference in the composition of the blood shown in the bar chart. *(3 marks)*

Chapter 13

Sensitivity and Response in Plants

Learning objectives

By the end of this chapter you should know:

- Phototropism as a growth movement in response to light
- The commercial use of hormones in weed control, stimulation of flowering and fruit formation

Plants, like animals, respond to changes in the environment. However, they respond to fewer types of stimuli and in general the response is slower. Plants respond to the environmental stimuli that have the greatest effect on their growth. Most plants will respond to light, water and gravity. For example, roots will tend to grow towards water when a moisture gradient exists and shoots tend to grow away from the effects of gravity, i.e. they grow up. Reasons for these responses are fairly obvious as they ensure that the plants react in such a way that they receive the best conditions for growth.

The response of a plant shoot to light is called **phototropism** and this response has been investigated in detail to establish how it occurs.

Phototropism – responding to light

Most of you will have observed that plants grow in the direction of the light source. Plants left on a windowsill or against the wall of a house usually do not grow straight up, but bend towards the light source. You can probably also guess that this response ensures that the plant stem and leaves receive more light than they otherwise would do if there was no such response. This means that *more* photosynthesis takes place and there will be *more* growth.

Although it is easy to observe the effect of phototropism, what causes it to occur? Figure 1 shows the growth of young seedlings in unilateral light (light coming from one side or source only) and highlights some of the features of phototropism. Can you use the diagram to identify what part of the plant perceives (is sensitive to) the light source?

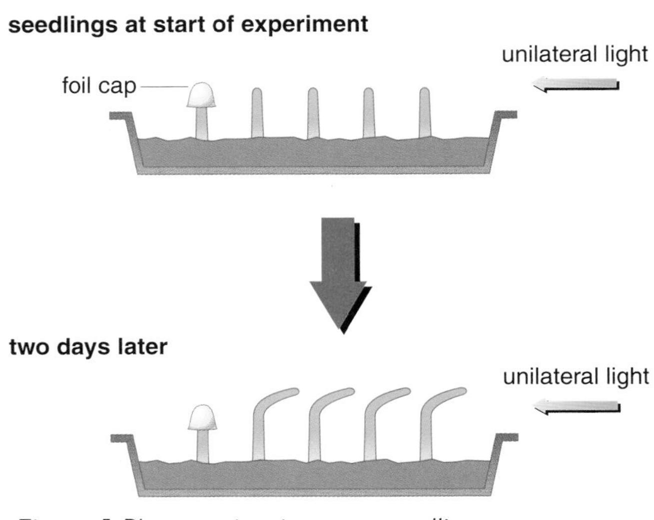

Figure 1 Phototropism in young seedlings

Figure 1 shows that it is the shoot tip that is sensitive to light, as when it is covered the phototropic response does not occur. Plant stems produce a hormone called **auxin** in the tip. When a stem is illuminated from one side this hormone tends to accumulate more on the non-illuminated side. As the effect of the hormone is to cause increased growth this leads to the non-illuminated side growing more rapidly than the side that is receiving most light. The differential growth that occurs when one side of the stem grows more than the other side leads to the stem bending in the direction of the light.

Questions

1 Using your knowledge of phototropism can you explain:

a) How it is possible to keep plants in unilateral light, for example a plant growing on a windowsill, growing straight?

b) Why plants that have their tips removed often stop growing?

The commercial use of plant hormones in weed control, flowering and fruit formation.

Auxin is only one of a range of plant hormones that have been identified. Many plant hormones are used by horticulturalists and gardeners for controlling weeds and in increasing flower and fruit production.

Hormones as weedkillers

It is often important to eliminate weeds as they can affect crop production by using the resources that the crops need. This competition for water, minerals, light and space between weeds and crops can severely limit the growth of crops.

A range of hormones can be used in weedkillers, but most contain synthetic (artificially produced) auxin that is similar in structure and effect to the naturally occurring auxins in plants. These weedkillers are particularly effective as they are selective. They are effective against broadleaved plants such as daisies and plantain, but do not have an effect on narrow leaved plants such as grasses and cereals. They work by causing the weeds to grow in such a rapid and uncontrolled way that they disintegrate.

Figure 2 A dock plant before (left) and after treatment with a weed killer

Questions

2 Why are gardeners advised not to spray weedkiller if heavy rain is expected?

The stimulation of flowering and fruit formation

Hormones can be sprayed onto commercially grown flowers, crop plants and fruit trees to ensure that flower production and/or fruit production is maximised.

Examples of this in action can be seen in fruit growing regions such as County Armagh. Normally when flowers are pollinated and fertilised these processes set in train a series of hormonal changes that leads naturally to fruit production. However, poor weather that damages flowers and decreases the number of insects available for pollination often leads to low pollination rates. If nature is left to run its course the fruit production would also be low. The use of hormones acts as a substitute for the pollination and fertilisation processes and ensures that the fruit production is not limited by poor pollination rates. The use of artificial hormones can also help make all the fruit develop and ripen at the same time. This can lead to greater efficiency at the time of harvesting.

There are many examples where hormones are used to produce a fruit that is more attractive to the consumer. Seedless grapes are becoming increasingly popular. Naturally an ovary in a vine will only develop into a grape if its ovules are fertilised to become seeds. The use of synthetic hormones can deliberately bypass and prevent the pollination and fertilisation process ensuring that the grapes develop without seeds.

Figure 3 These grapes are ready to eat. If they are seedless, hormones added by man will have been used in their development

Websites

http://www.bbc.co.uk/schools/gcsebitesize/biology/plants/planthormonsrev2.shtml
Information about plant hormones and phototropism.

Exam questions

1 The diagram shows an experiment in which oat seedlings were grown in a box. A hole was cut at one end of the box allowing light to enter.

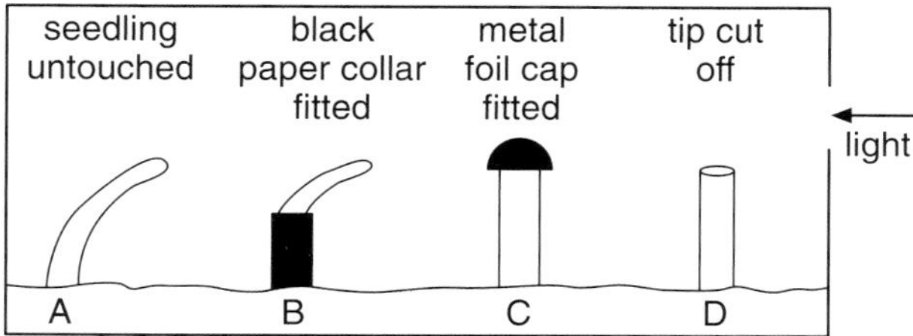

a) Which seedlings have grown towards the light?

(1 mark)

b) What name describes the response shown?

(1 mark)

c) Using the results of the experiment suggest which part of the seedling is sensitive to light.

(1 mark)

2 The diagram shows an investigation into the response of seedlings to light.

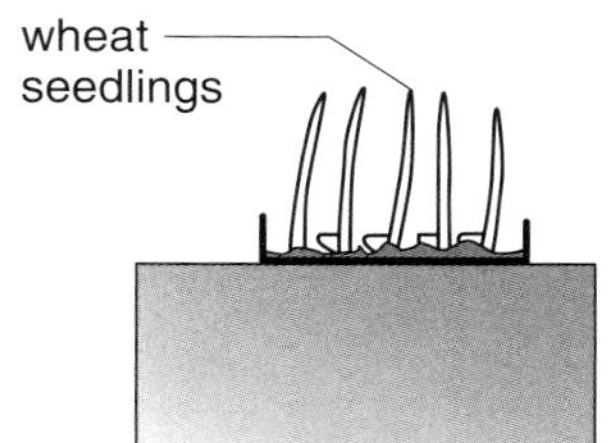

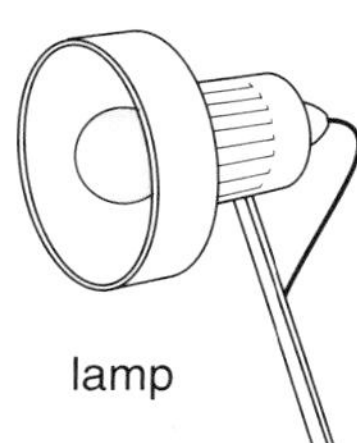

a) Describe **two** changes that will be visible in the seedlings after 48 hours.

(2 marks)

b) Name this response and the type of substance which controls it.

(2 marks)

c) Explain why this response is an advantage to the plant.

(2 marks)

3 The diagrams show the effect of spraying plant hormones on a field of wheat.

Before spraying

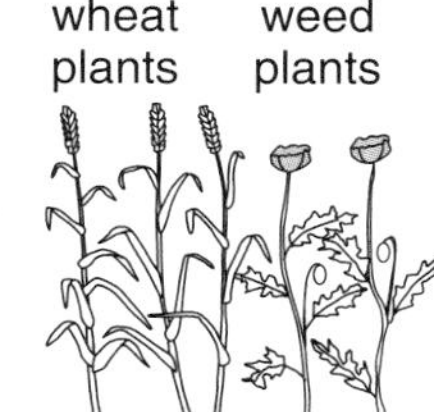

After spraying

a) Describe the effect of spraying the wheat field with plant hormone.

(2 marks)

b) Suggest how the hormone gets into the plants.

(1 mark)

c) Give two other uses of plant hormones.

(2 marks)

Chapter 14

Sensitivity and Response in Animals

Learning objectives

By the end of this chapter you should know:

- The role of receptors, coordinators and effectors
- The structure and function of the eye
- Reflexes and the reflex arc
- The action of the elbow joint
- The structure of the elbow joint
- The skin and its role in temperature regulation
- The action of insulin
- The action of adrenaline
- The action of sexual hormones, testosterone and oestrogen
- The effect of alcohol, drug and solvent abuse on the individual and on society

A major difference between plants and animals is that animals can respond to the environment in a more rapid and complex way. A change in the environment is called a **stimulus** and each stimulus often produces a specific **response**.

In animals each type of stimulus will be recognised by a **receptor** in the body. There are many types of receptors each capable of identifying a particular type of stimulus. For example, in our hand and fingers we have receptors sensitive to touch, pressure and temperature. If a receptor is stimulated it may cause an **effector** (muscle or a hormone producing gland) to produce a response.

This system of responding to the environment requires a co-ordinator to link between the receptor and the effector. The co-ordinator is usually the **brain** but can also be the **spinal cord**. Together these two structures make up the **Central Nervous System (CNS)**. The following table gives some examples of the link between stimulus and response.

Stimulus	Receptor	Co-ordinator	Effector	Response
Loud bang	Sound receptor in the ear	Brain	Muscle	Jump
Salty food	Taste receptor in the tongue	Brain	Muscle	Drink water
Scent of prey	Smell receptor in the nose	Brain	Muscle	Movement

Nerve cells or **neurones** link the receptors and effectors to the co-ordinator. A neurone carries information in the form of small electrical charges called **nerve impulses**. **Sensory neurones** connect receptors to the co-ordinator, and effector or **motor neurones** link the co-ordinator to the effectors. Figure 1 shows a motor neurone and the muscle (effector) that it stimulates.

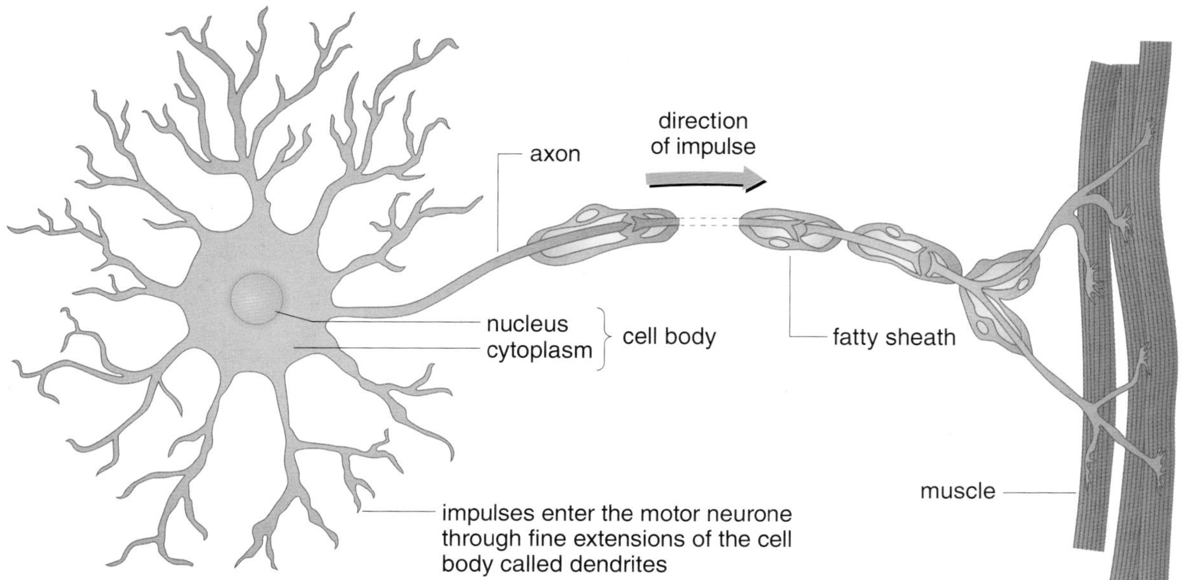

Figure 1 A motor neurone

Sensory and motor neurones do not make direct contact with each other in the brain or spinal cord. There are small gaps or junctions between neurones across which the impulses jump. These gaps are called **synapses**. This allows a lot of connections to be made (as in a telephone exchange). This is particularly important in the brain where millions of sensory and motor cells end and originate.

The co-ordinator can control whether or not a response should be made to a particular stimulus, and if so, what the response should be.

Neurones are often grouped together in large bundles called nerves. There are many nerves that leave the brain and the spinal cord to link with the rest of the body. In the next sections we shall see examples of receptors and effectors in the body.

The eye

The eye is a very complex sense organ that contains the receptors for sight. The receptors are found in a thin layer of cells at the back of the eye, the retina. Apart from the receptors the other parts of the eye are concerned with:

- protecting the eye against damage;
- focusing light rays on the receptors in the retina;
- controlling the intensity of light that enters the eye.

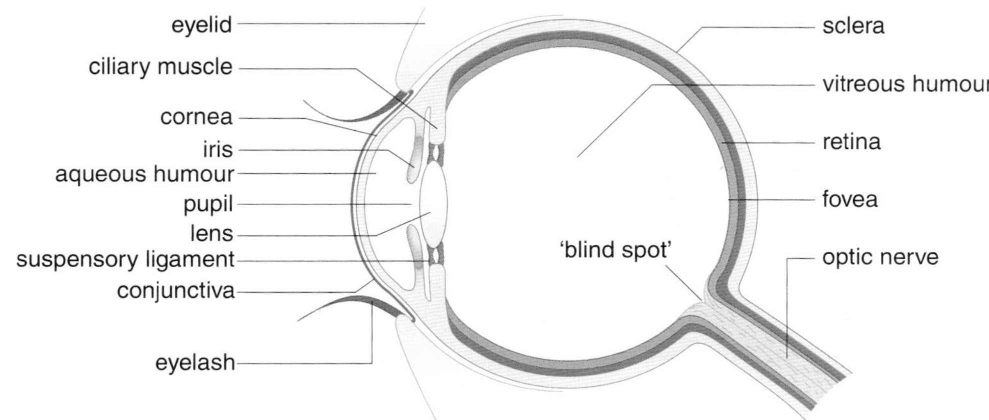

Figure 2 The human eye

The important features of the eye are summarised in the following table.

Part of eye	Function
Conjunctiva	A protective transparent covering that stops dust and dirt damaging the cornea. It also keeps the cornea moist
Cornea	Transparent part of the sclera that allows light to enter
Pupil	The opening in the middle of the iris through which light passes
Iris	Consists of muscles that contract and relax to control the size of the pupil
Lens	The lens bends (refracts) light and focuses the light rays on the retina
Retina	The retina contains the receptor cells that are sensitive to light. The central part of the retina (the fovea) contains a lot of light sensitive receptors and is particularly sensitive
Optic Nerve	Contains sensory neurones that link the retina to the brain. The optic nerve carries electrical impulses from the retina to the brain. The blind spot is the part of the retina where the optic nerve leaves. At this point there are no receptors and an image cannot be seen if it is focused on this part of the retina

The watery fluid, the aqueous humour, in the front part of the eye keeps this part of the eye at the right pressure, but it also allows the light rays to pass through. Similarly the jelly-like fluid, the vitreous humour, between the lens and the retina, also allows the light rays to pass through. Its main function is to keep the eye spherical, keeping the lens and retina the correct distance apart for focusing the light rays.

Controlling the amount of light that enters the eye

It is important that the correct intensity of light enters the eye and reaches the retina. Too little or too much light will prevent an image being produced. In addition, too much light can damage the sensitive cells in the retina. The muscles of the iris can contract or relax to change the size of the pupil. Dim light produces a large pupil to encourage as much light as possible to enter the eye. In bright light the pupil is reduced to a small size to reduce the amount of light entering.

Figure 3 The pupil gets larger in dim light

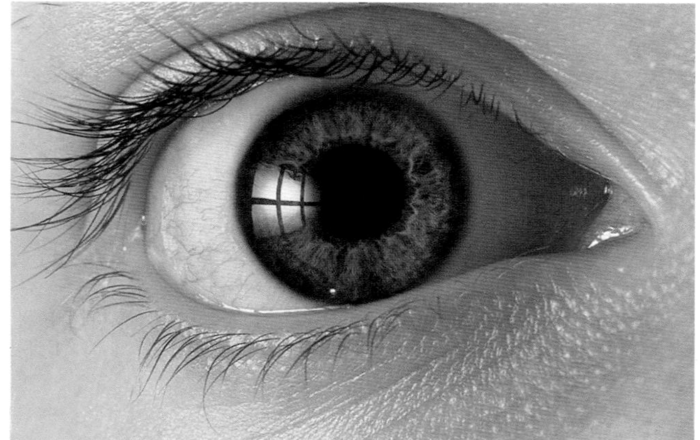

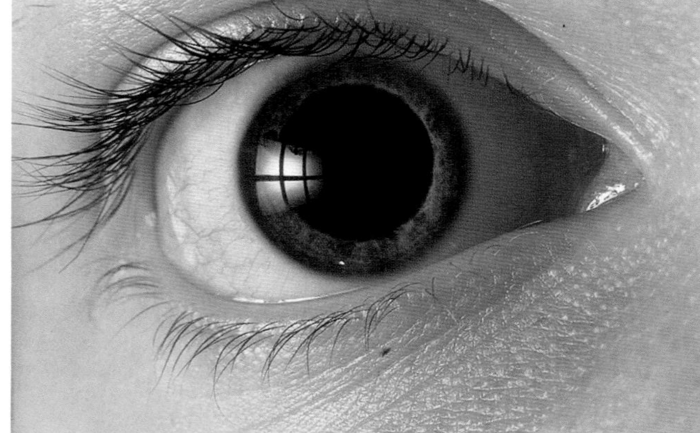

Focusing light rays on the receptors

When rays of light enter the eye they bend, or are refracted, as they pass through the cornea. The eye has no control over this refraction. The light rays are also refracted by the lens. However, the eye is able to change the shape of the lens and therefore how much refraction takes place at this point.

Why do we need to change the amount of refraction by the lens?

Light rays from close and distant objects arrive at the eye at different angles – see Figure 4. Rays from a distant object are parallel and need relatively little refraction before being focused on the retina. Rays from a close object need much more refraction if they are to be focused. Figure 4 shows that depending on how light rays enter the eye the lens is able to change shape and focus the light on the retina to form an image. The process of the lens changing shape to focus light on the retina is called **accommodation**.

a) eye focused on a **distant** object

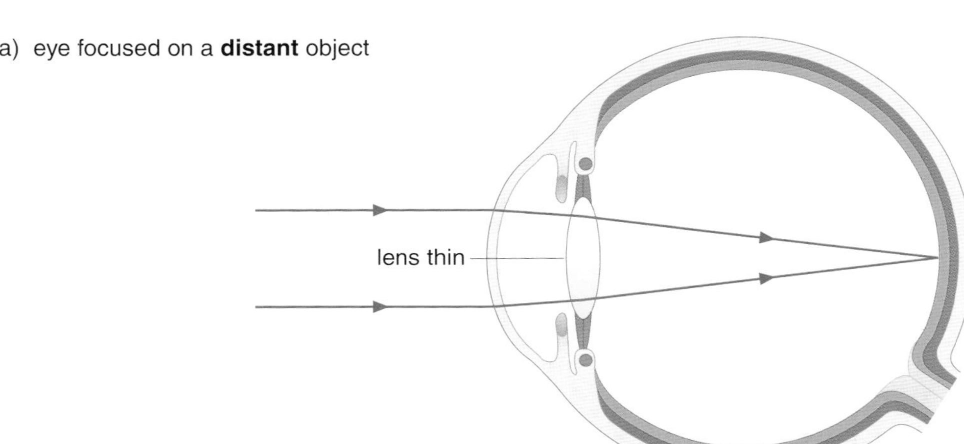

b) eye focused on a **near** object

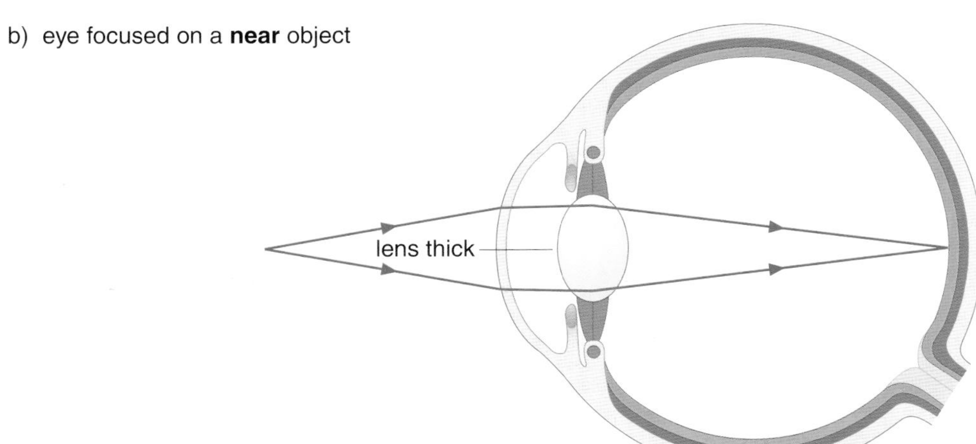

Figure 4 How an image is focused on the retina

How does the lens change shape?

The **ciliary muscle** (body) is a ring of muscle that surrounds the lens. The lens is attached to the ciliary muscle by **suspensory ligaments** that resemble small pieces of thread. If the ciliary muscle relaxes it springs out to give a bigger diameter. When this happens the suspensory ligaments pull the lens and it becomes thinner. The opposite happens when the lens gets fatter, the ciliary muscle contracts to form a tighter circle with a smaller diameter. The suspensory ligaments relax and with less pressure on the lens it is able to spring back to its original thicker shape.

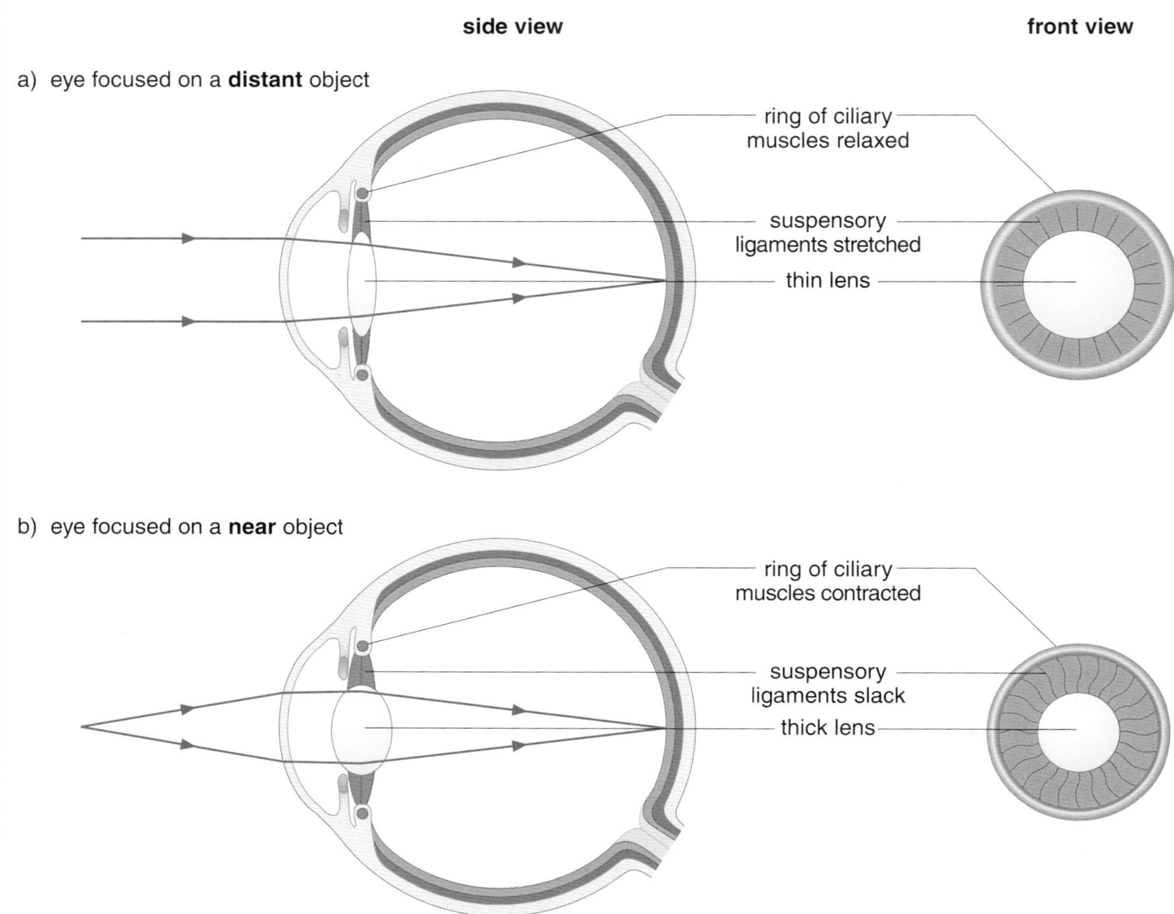

Figure 5 Changing the shape of the lens

The structure of the retina

The retina contains two different types of light sensitive receptors. The **rods** work in low light intensity but cannot distinguish between colours. The **cones** provide colour vision. The cones only work well in bright light but can provide greater precision (accuracy) than rods. The cones are concentrated in the centre of the retina around the fovea, and the rods are more numerous at the outer edges (periphery) of the eye.

Questions

1 Using this information can you suggest why:
   a) It is more difficult to judge distance at night compared to during the day.
   b) If an object suddenly enters your vision from one side you can identify its shape before you can identify its colour?

Protecting the eye

Apart from the conjunctiva the eye is protected by other structures. The eyelids and eyelashes trap dust and dirt and prevent these from reaching the eye. Tears are produced by a gland under the eyelids and are washed across the eye by blinking. Tears work by washing dust particles out of the eye. They also contain the enzyme lysozyme that has antiseptic properties and destroys bacteria on the surface of the eye. The eye is further protected by the blinking reflex and the ability of the iris to restrict the amount of bright light entering the eye. As many animals rely very heavily on sight it is important that the eyes are well protected.

Effectors in action – the elbow joint

The muscles that bend and straighten the lower arm at the elbow are a good example of effectors in action. The elbow is the pivot or fulcrum between the bone of the upper arm (the humerus) and the bones of the lower arm (the radius and ulna). The **biceps muscle** (the flexor) flexes or bends the arm. The **triceps muscle** (the extensor) straightens or extends the arm. It is necessary to have two muscles to bend and straighten the arm as muscles work by contracting and pulling. Muscles cannot push.

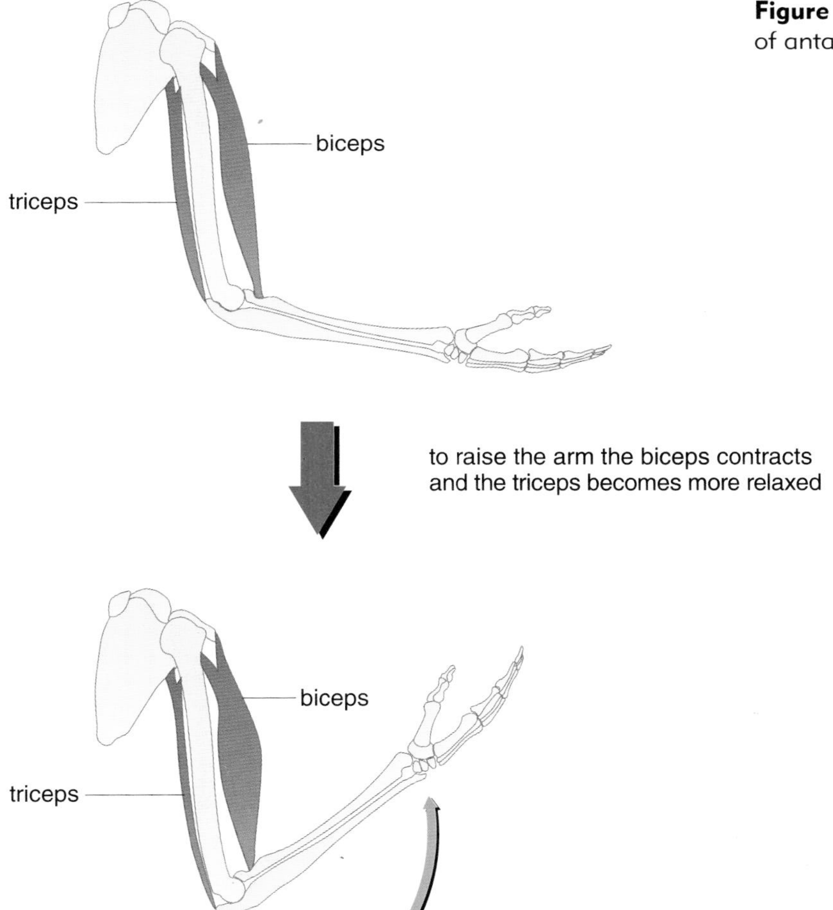

Figure 6 The elbow joint is an example of antagonistic muscles in action

Figure 6 shows how the biceps and the triceps muscles act as an antagonistic pair. **Antagonistic muscles** act in opposite ways to control the movement of the elbow joint.

In Figure 6 it is apparent that the biceps is contracting to raise the arm and at the same time the triceps is becoming more relaxed and more elongated.

Questions

2 Use Figure 6 to work out what the muscles must do to fully extend the arm (when fully extended the upper and lower arms will be in a straight line).

Figure 7 shows the elbow joint in greater detail, identifying some of the structures involved in keeping this hinge joint in good working order. The diagram identifies the roles of the **(fibrous) capsule**, the **synovial membrane**, the **synovial fluid** and the **(articular) cartilage**.

The **tendons** are structures that join the muscle to the bone and the **ligaments** hold the bones at a joint together. Both ligaments and tendons are tough but flexible. However, while ligaments are elastic and can stretch, tendons are not elastic and therefore they will not stretch.

Questions

3 Why is it important that ligaments can stretch to some extent but it is important that tendons do not?

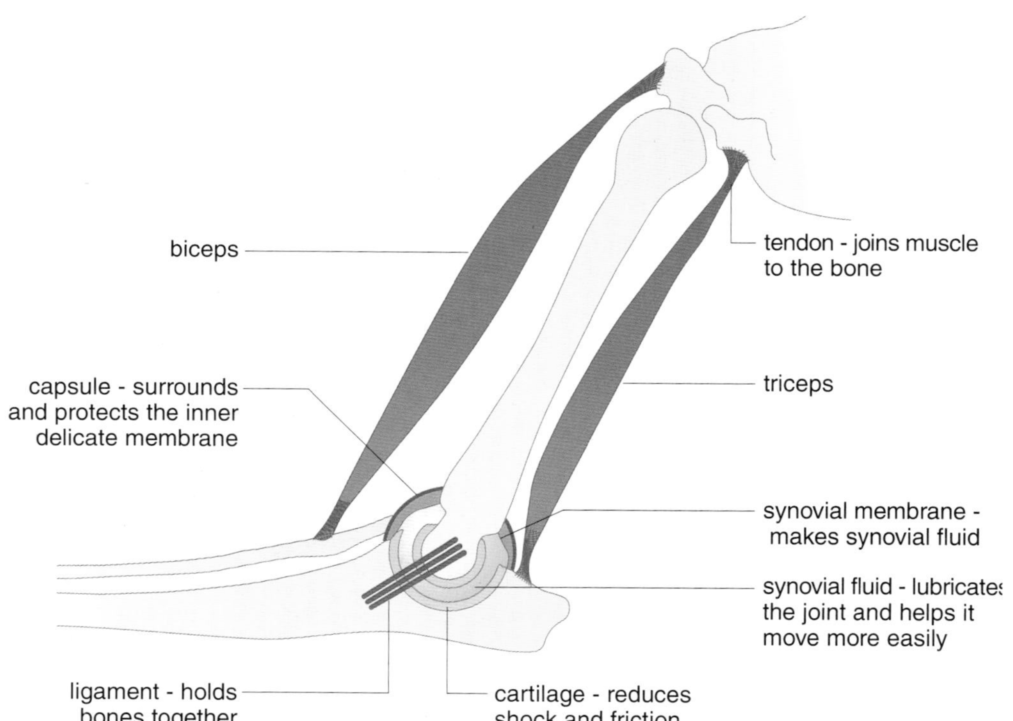

Figure 7 The elbow joint in detail

The movement of the lower arm is usually as a result of a voluntary action. This means we can consciously act and move our arm to carry out a response. Voluntary actions involve the brain as a co-ordinating and decision making centre. Occasionally we need to make very fast responses without involving active thought. This type of very rapid response is called a reflex action.

Reflex action

If we accidentally touch a very hot object we respond immediately by rapidly withdrawing our hand from the danger area. The advantage of this action is that we remove the hand before it can get burned too badly. This type of action does not involve any 'thinking' time as the time taken to consider a response would cause unnecessary damage to the body. All reflex actions have several characteristics in common:

- they occur very rapidly;
- they do not involve conscious thought;
- they are automatic and rigid in that they always occur in the same way.

What makes a reflex action so rapid? In a reflex pathway the total length of nerve pathway is kept as short as it possibly can be. In addition, there are relatively few synapses as these are the places where impulses travel relatively slowly. Figure 8 shows a photograph of a section through the human spinal cord. The photograph shows the dark central grey matter (coloured red) surrounded by the lighter white matter (coloured yellow). The spinal cord runs from the base of the brain to the lower back. At intervals along the spinal cord nerves leave the spinal cord and link with the rest of the body (Figure 9).

The spinal cord is an extremely important and delicate structure. To give it protection it is enclosed in the vertebral column (the backbone).

Figure 9 shows that where nerves leave the spinal cord the nerve has two entry or exit points on each side of the spinal cord. In the diagram the upper branch is called the dorsal root and the lower branch the ventral root. Different types of neurones are carried in these roots. Figure 10 shows the spinal cord at the position (base of the neck) where nerves travelling to the arm are entering and leaving.

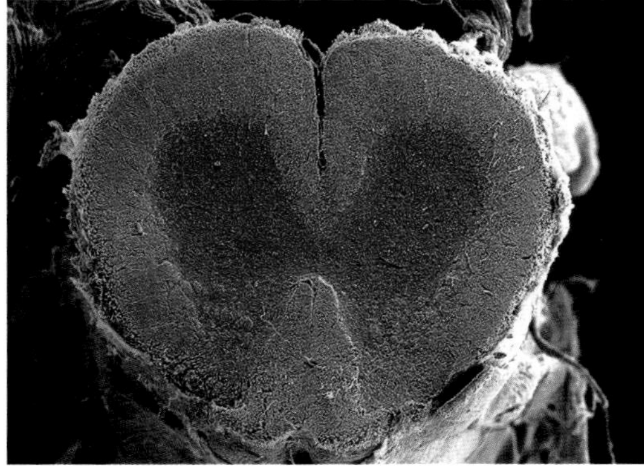

Figure 8 Cross-section through the spinal cord

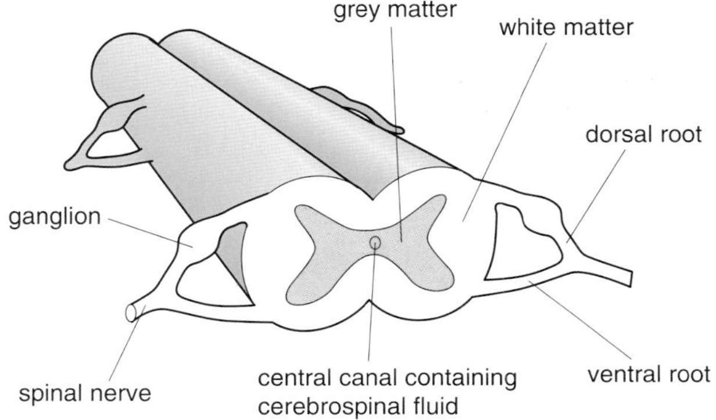

Figure 9 The structure of the spinal cord

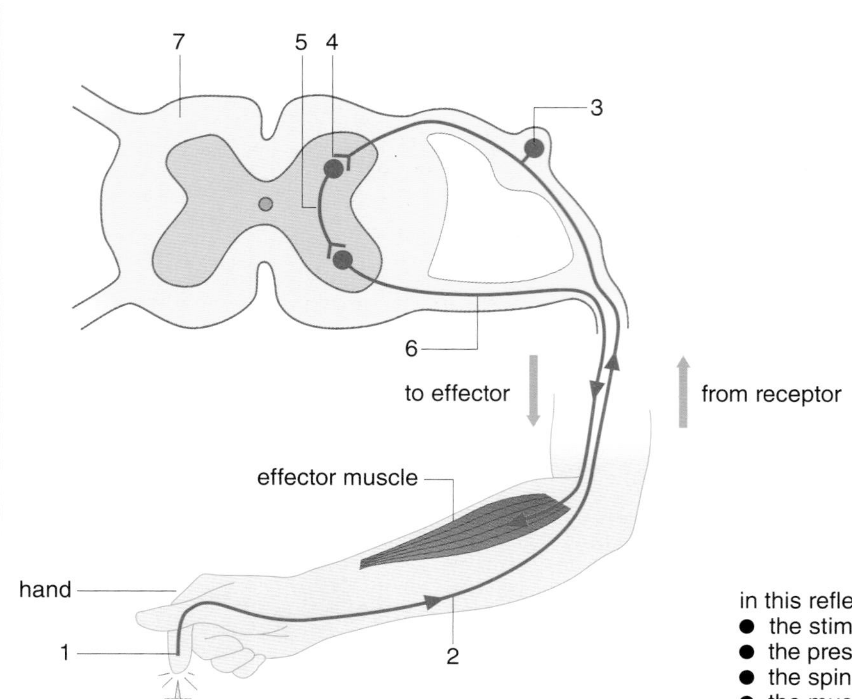

Figure 10 Section through the spinal cord showing a reflex arc to and from the hand

Figure 10 shows the nerve pathway involved when the hand touches a sharp object. There are three types of nerve cell involved in this response.

- *The sensory neurone* – this neurone carries the impulse from the receptors in the hand into the spinal cord. The cell body of the sensory neurone is on a short side branch in a swelling (ganglion) in the dorsal root.
- *The connector (association) neurone* – this neurone joins the sensory neurone to the motor neurone.
- *The motor (effector) neurone* – this neurone leaves the spinal cord via the ventral root and continues into the effector (muscle) in the arm.

The diagram shows that both the association and motor neurones begin with the cell body (unlike the sensory neurone). It is the large number of cell bodies that lie in the centre of the spinal cord that gives the grey matter its darker appearance. The white matter contains few cell bodies, but does contain the extended axons (cabling) of the neurones passing in and out (and up and down) the spinal cord. The diagram also shows that only two synapses are involved in this pathway. This system of structures that is involved in a reflex is called a **reflex arc**.

There are many other examples of reflex action in the body. Blinking and the dilation and constriction of the pupil are important in protecting the eye. Coughing and sneezing are other reflex actions. The knee jerk reflex is another example but it is unusual in two respects. This reflex does not have as obvious a protective role as the other examples given. It also does not have an association neurone. In the knee jerk reflex the sensory neurone is linked directly to the motor neurone.

The skin – a complex sense organ and its role in temperature regulation

The skin contains many receptors that are sensitive to touch or pressure. Other receptors are sensitive to changes in temperature. As well as operating as a sense organ the skin itself plays a major part in temperature regulation. It is important to keep our body temperature as close to the optimum of 37°C as possible. If the temperature increases much above this value the body's enzymes will become denatured. If the temperature falls too much the enzymes will not work as efficiently.

But how does the skin keep the body temperature constant? Figure 11 shows the skin in both hot and cold conditions.

a) the skin in hot conditions

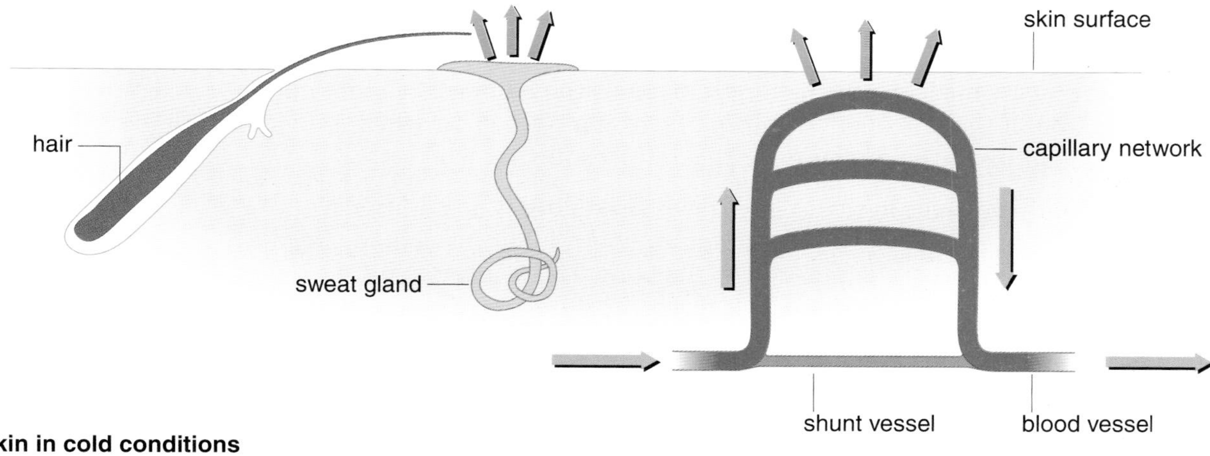

b) the skin in cold conditions

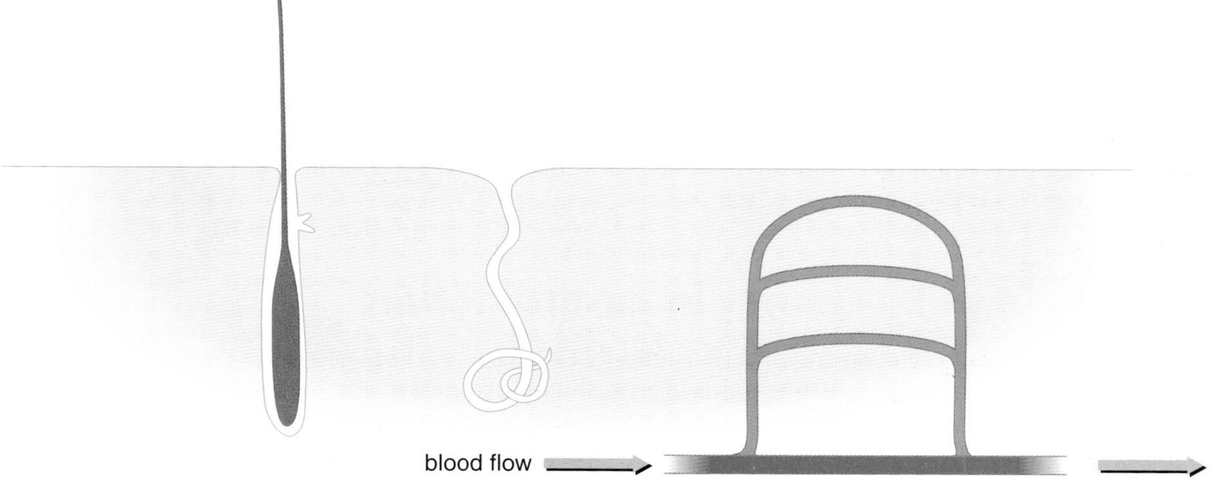

Figure 11 The skin and its role in temperature regulation

As can be seen in Figure 11 if the body begins to get *too hot* the following changes occur:

- More blood flows through the capillaries in the skin surface. Shunt vessels in the skin close and this restricts the amount of blood that can flow through them. Therefore more blood is forced into and through the skin capillaries. Heat carried by the blood can then escape through the skin surface by the process of radiation. This process where more blood than normal is directed through the surface of the skin is called **vasodilation**.
- **Sweating.** The sweat glands in the skin produce sweat which is released onto the surface of the skin. The evaporation of this sweat uses heat energy from the body and this helps cool the body down.
- The erector muscles that control the hair on the skin's surface relax and this causes the hairs to lie flat against the surface. The effect of this is that there will not be an insulating layer of air trapped between the hair and the skin.

If the body gets *too cold* the following changes occur:

- The shunt vessel opens and allows more blood to flow through. Less blood now flows through the skin capillaries and as less blood is near the surface of the skin less heat is lost by radiation. This condition is known as **vasoconstriction**.
- The sweat glands stop producing sweat.
- The erector muscles contract and this pulls the hairs into a more upright position. If there is enough hair on the skin a layer of air which provides excellent insulation is trapped. This reduces further heat loss.

In addition to changes in the skin surface, **shivering** is an additional mechanism that is involved in temperature control. Shivering is the involuntary contraction of some of the muscles in the body. This contraction uses energy produced in respiration. Some of the energy released in respiration is produced as heat and this helps to warm the body up. Therefore shivering is an important response when we get too cold. Some heat may also be produced due to friction between individual muscles. To conserve heat most mammals also have an insulating layer of fat underneath the skin. This layer can be particularly thick in mammals that live in cold habitats.

Questions

4 Using the information above can you explain one major difference between how a hairy mammal such as a dog or cat reduces heat loss from the body compared to a human.

The role of hormones in co-ordination

Hormones are chemicals produced by the body that have an important effect on control or co-ordination. Hormones are produced by special glands, called endocrine glands, that release the hormones they produce directly into the blood. Hormones affect many aspects of our development including growth and reproductive development. Two very important human hormones are insulin and adrenaline. The roles of each of these hormones will be discussed in turn.

Insulin

Insulin is the hormone that prevents blood glucose (sugar) levels from becoming too high. Glucose is constantly needed by all cells for respiration and therefore must always be present in sufficient concentration. However, if there is too much glucose in the blood this will cause osmotic and other problems to the cells of the body.

Insulin is produced by special cells in the **pancreas** in response to increasing or high blood glucose levels. This will usually occur after a meal, especially if the meal is rich in carbohydrates. The insulin will act to *reduce* blood sugar levels by:

- *converting* glucose to **glycogen** which can be stored in the **liver**;
- *increasing* the rate of respiration by the body's cells;
- *increasing* the uptake of glucose from the blood into the cells.

When blood glucose levels are low less insulin is produced and the above processes (which would decrease levels even further) do not take place.

Figure 12 highlights the relationship between blood glucose levels and insulin.

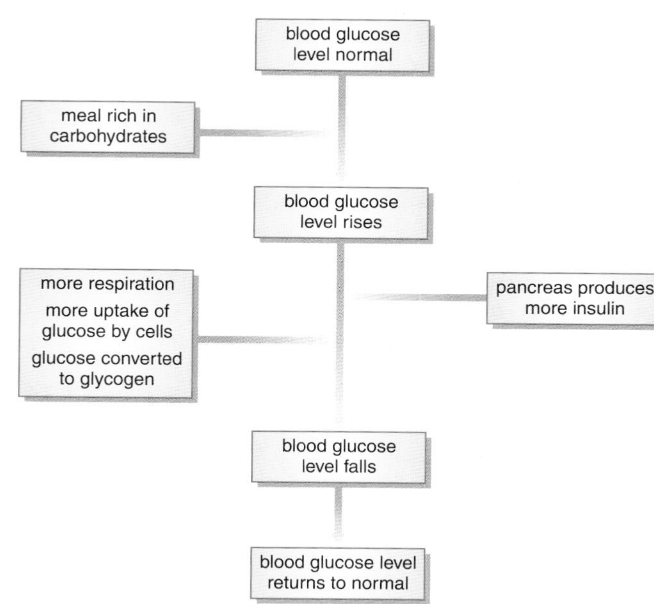

Figure 12 The effect of insulin on blood glucose levels

Negative feedback

Figure 12 shows that as the blood glucose level increases the rate of insulin production increases in order to reduce blood glucose levels. Similarly it is the fall in blood glucose level that causes the release of insulin to slow down or stop. This is an example of feedback where the level of insulin released is reduced by the falling levels of glucose in the blood. Feedback mechanisms are an important feature of most hormones. Feedback processes are vital in hormonal control as it is just as important to prevent the glucose level from falling too much as it is to prevent it from becoming too high.

Questions

5 Use Figure 12 to describe and explain the relationship between blood glucose concentration and the volume of insulin released by the pancreas. Your answer should include a sketch that shows the interaction between blood glucose concentration and insulin production.

Diabetes

This is a condition where the body does not produce enough insulin to keep blood glucose levels at a controlled level. Individuals that develop diabetes are unable to control their blood glucose levels without treatment and the following symptoms are often present:

- There is sugar in the urine. This happens because blood glucose levels are so high that some sugar is excreted through the kidneys.
- Affected individuals are often thirsty. The high blood glucose levels draw water out of the cells by osmosis and the cells become dehydrated.
- There are frequent visits to the toilet to eliminate the water that is drawn into the blood by osmosis.
- Irritability and confusion may result.
- If diagnosis and treatment is delayed for too long a coma can result.

Diabetes is a fairly common condition (and increasing in occurrence) in young people. It is usually treated by the injection of insulin and a carefully controlled diet where the intake of carbohydrate is accurately monitored.

Figure 13 shows a young child injecting herself with insulin.

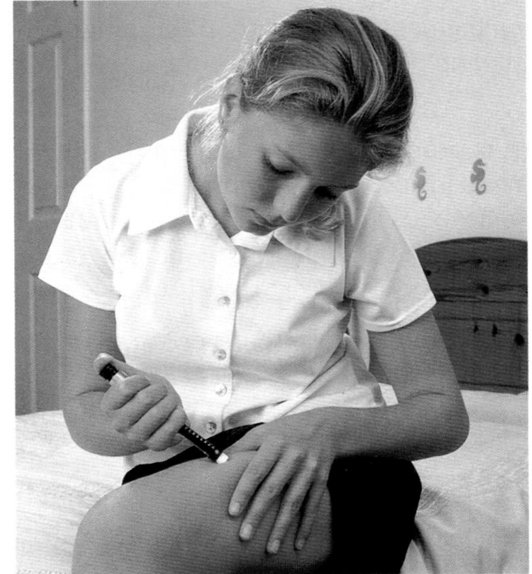

Figure 13

Even with the use of insulin injections and a carefully controlled diet it is difficult for people with diabetes to control blood sugar levels very accurately. Problems may arise if either too much insulin is taken or if not enough food is eaten at regular intervals. If the blood sugar level drops too far a hypoglycaemic attack (a hypo) may occur and unconsciousness will result. If blood glucose levels remain too high for a long period of time complications such as eye damage can result.

Questions

6 Why does insulin have to be injected as opposed to taken in tablet form? Clue: Insulin, like all hormones, is a protein.

7 Why do people with diabetes often take extra glucose (a biscuit or a glucose drink) before they take part in vigorous exercise?

8 As part of their regular routine people with diabetes check their blood glucose levels regularly. What should they do if their blood glucose level is too high when tested?

The type of diabetes normally developed in childhood is referred to as Type 1 diabetes. The diabetes that usually only develops in older people (Type 2 diabetes) has a slightly different cause in that insulin is produced but it ceases to work effectively. Many people with Type 2 diabetes are able to regulate their blood sugar levels by diet alone without the need for insulin injections.

Adrenaline

Adrenaline is produced by the adrenal glands, small structures that lie above the kidneys. Adrenaline is known as the 'fight or flight' hormone in that it prepares the body for action in an emergency situation. Adrenaline can also be produced when a person is excited such as when they are about to take part in an important race or attend an interview.

Adrenaline produces many changes in the body, all of which are designed to decrease response time or increase awareness. These changes include:

Response produced by adrenaline	Effect of response
Glycogen converted to glucose in liver	More glucose available for respiration
Heart beats faster	More glucose and oxygen pumped to the muscles for more respiration, therefore more energy produced
Bronchioles dilate	More air is drawn into the lungs and therefore more oxygen is available for respiration
Breathing rate increases	More oxygen available for respiration
Pupils dilate	More light enters the eye
Blood is diverted away from the skin and gut to the muscles	More glucose and oxygen available where needed in emergency situation (muscles) as opposed to gut where the processes of digestion and absorption can be suspended for a period of time. These changes give the 'butterflies in the stomach' feeling that is experienced at times of rapid adrenaline production

As a result of these changes that take place in the body we are more equipped to respond to danger or to other stimuli. We can run faster and for longer and we are generally more aware of surrounding environmental stimuli.

Both adrenaline and insulin act fairly rapidly in producing responses. Most hormones act slowly and produce their effects over a long time scale. Examples of hormones acting in this way are the sex hormones, testosterone and oestrogen.

Testosterone and oestrogen and the development of secondary sexual characteristics

Testosterone, produced by the testes in males, and oestrogen, produced by the ovaries in females, are important hormones in overall sexual development. One effect they have is the development of the secondary sexual characteristics that are a feature of puberty. The changes that occur in males and females are different but in both sexes they serve to prepare the bodies for reproduction, both physically and by increasing sexual awareness and drive. Some of the secondary sexual characteristics produced by testosterone and oestrogen are summarised in the table below.

Males	Females
Body hair and pubic hair develops	Hair grows in pubic regions and in the armpits
The sexual organs (genitals) enlarge	The sexual organs enlarge and the breasts develop
The body becomes more muscular	The pelvis and hips widen
The voice deepens	Menstruation begins
Sexual awareness and drive increases	Sexual awareness and drive increases

Hormones are not the only chemicals that affect our bodies. Co-ordination of the body is affected by alcohol and drugs. The effect of alcohol and drugs on the body is discussed in the next section.

The effect of alcohol, drug and solvent abuse on the individual and society

Drugs are chemicals that alter the physical or mental state of the individual who takes them. Alcohol has been an accepted part of the culture of many societies for centuries. However, the abuse of alcohol, other drugs and solvents, that alter your physical or mental state can cause very serious problems for the individuals concerned and for society in general. Some drugs such as caffeine are legal and socially acceptable. Alcohol is legal in many, but not all countries. In most countries drugs such as cannabis, ecstasy and other similar drugs are banned. The position for some drugs such as cannabis is subject to ongoing debate. The main features of some of these substances in highlighted below.

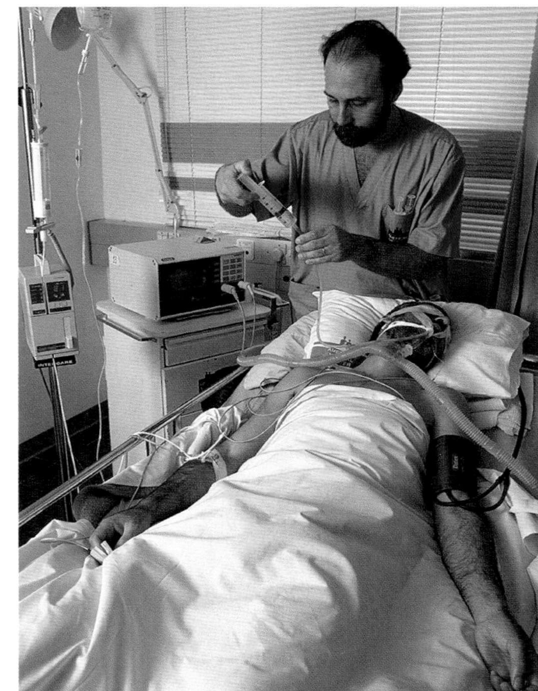

Figure 14 A heroin addict being treated for an overdose

- **Alcohol** – alcohol causes impaired judgment, blurred vision and lack of control or inhibition. Long term use can lead to addiction and liver damage.
- **Stimulants** – caffeine is a stimulant found in coffee, tea and some soft drinks. The effect is to increase the heartbeat and generally raise awareness. Other stimulants include amphetamines (uppers, speed) and cocaine. These also increase the heartbeat and raise awareness but can also cause impairment of vision and judgment. They can also lead to feelings of anxiety. Addiction can result from using some stimulants.
- **Depressants** – these include tranquillisers (sleeping pills) and barbiturates (downers). They cause drowsiness and can lead to psychological dependence. Alcohol can also be classified as a depressant as it slows down nervous actions and also has a sedative effect.

- **Hallucinogens** – drugs like ecstasy and LSD cause hallucinations or mind-altered states. Hallucinogens can cause 'bad trips' or 'flashbacks'. These drugs can cause damage to the nervous system and brain. There are occasional examples of ecstasy causing death.
- **Solvents** – includes glue, lighter fuel and industrial chemicals. When inhaled they can cause loss of control, blurred vision and nausea. Permanent damage to the brain and other organs can result.

Other drugs normally associated with medicinal purposes can cause problems when abused. Painkillers such as paracetamol can cause serious harm if the recommended dose is exceeded. Some painkillers can also lead to dependence or addiction. The overuse of antibiotics can lead to antibiotic resistance in bacteria. They can also cause side effects and destroy useful bacteria that live in the gut.

Alcohol, drug and solvent abuse can have serious short term and long term effects on the body. The abuse of these substances can also cause many problems for society. These problems include increased medical costs. They may also cause or contribute to family and marriage problems, violence and vandalism and work-related problems.

Websites

http:web.ukonline.co.uk/webwise/spinneret/
Excellent information on the eye, the reflex arc and drugs.

http://www.learn.co.uk/
More information on the eye and the nervous system in general.

Exam questions

1 The diagram shows a section through an eye.

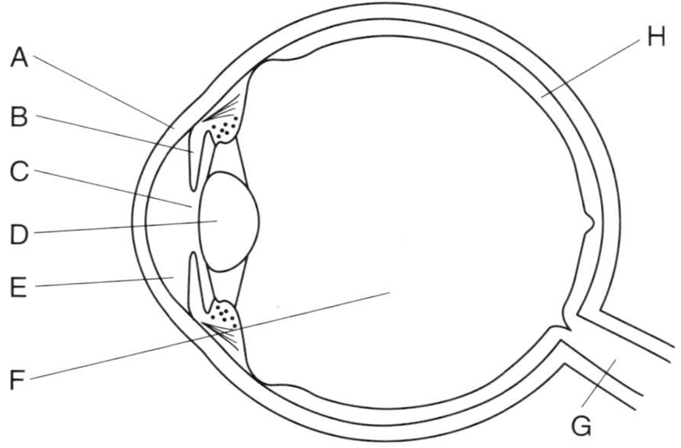

For each sentence give the correct letter from the diagram to complete the sentence.

a) The light enters the eye through the conjunctiva and the ___.

(1 mark)

b) The ___ focuses the light on the retina.

(1 mark)

c) An image is now formed on the light sensitive cells and the ___ sends a message to the brain.

(1 mark)

d) (i) What happens to the size of the pupil when the light intensity decreases?

(1 mark)

(ii) What is the importance of this change?

(1 mark)

2 a) The diagram shows the bones of the human arm with two of the attached muscles.

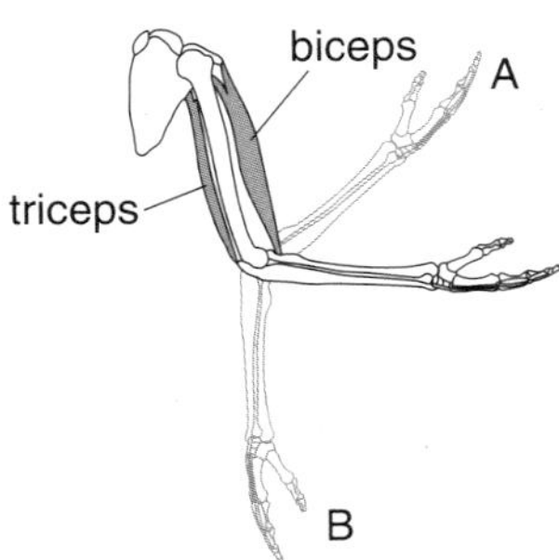

Use the diagram to copy and complete the table.

	Name of muscle	Action
Arm at position A		Relaxed
		Contracted
Arm at position B	Triceps	
	Biceps	

(2 marks)

b) What name is given to muscles, like the biceps and triceps, which have opposite effects?

(1 mark)

3 The diagram shows part of an elbow joint.

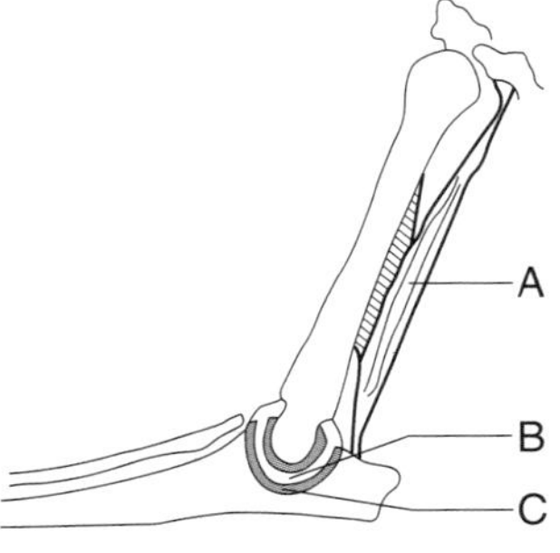

a) Name parts A, B and C.

(3 marks)

b) What effect does contraction of muscle A have on the arm?

(1 mark)

4 The diagram shows a reflex arc.

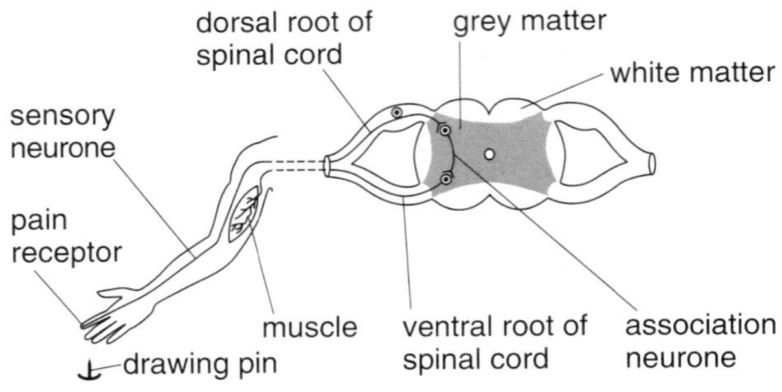

a) Use the diagram to help describe the pathway of an impulse from the stimulus to the association neurone.

(4 marks)

b) Describe the response when this impulse reaches the effector.

(2 marks)

5 The diagram shows some of the structures present in the skin that are involved in temperature regulation.

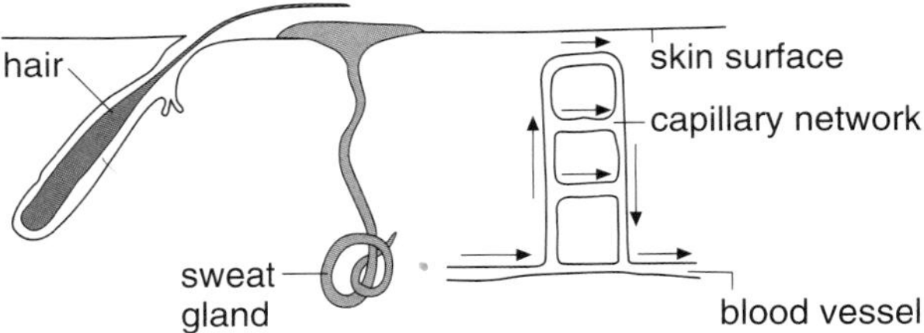

Using the diagram describe and explain **two** ways in which the skin is attempting to lose heat.

(4 marks)

6 The diagram shows blood vessels near the surface of the skin in different conditions.

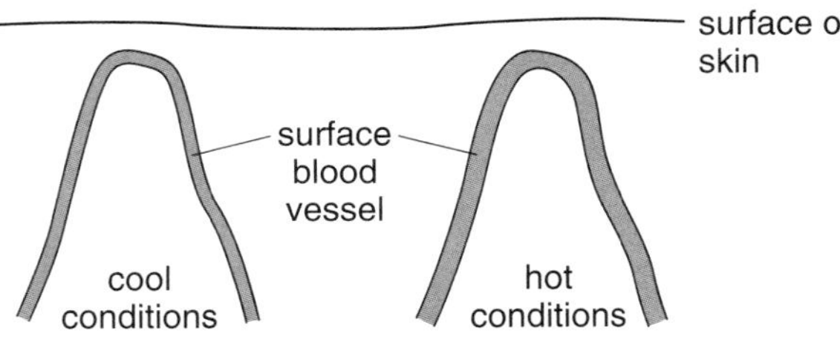

Describe and explain how changes in the surface blood vessel leads to cooling of the body in hot conditions.

(3 marks)

7 The diagram shows how high blood glucose levels are controlled by insulin.

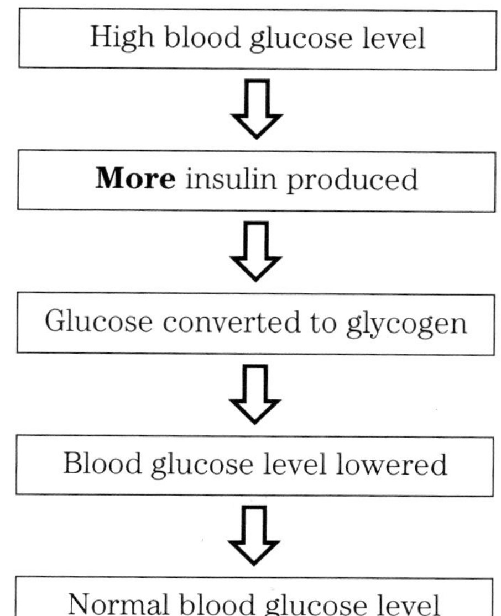

a) Which organ converts glucose to glycogen?

(1 mark)

b) Shauna is a diabetic who does not produce her own insulin.

She gave herself an insulin injection at 8 am.

She left for school without having any breakfast.

By break-time, Shauna was feeling very unwell.

The school nurse gave her a glucose drink and she quickly felt better.

Use the diagram to help explain what happened to Shauna's blood glucose level throughout the morning.

(4 marks)

8 One effect of adrenaline is to rapidly divert blood away from the skin, making the individual appear pale.

a) Explain the benefit of this reaction in preparing the body for an emergency.

(2 marks)

b) If the emergency involves strenuous physical activity, suggest the advantage of the skin eventually changing from a pale to a flushed appearance.

(2 marks)

c) State **one** other effect (not already mentioned in your answer to a)) that adrenaline has on the body.

(1 mark)

9 The average blood alcohol level (mg/100 cm³ of blood) for women of two different sizes after taking different amounts of alcohol is shown in the graph.

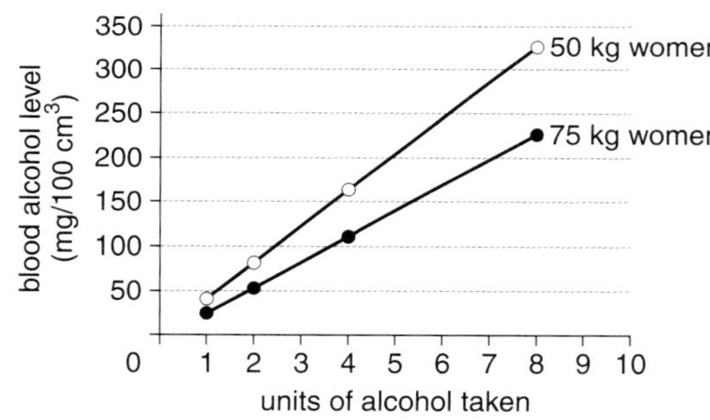

a) Give **two** trends shown by these graphs.

(2 marks)

b) Why is it recommended that drivers do not drink at all before driving?

(1 mark)

c) State **one** harmful effect that drinking too much alcohol over a long period can have on the body.

(1 mark)

Chapter 15

Habitats and Sampling

Learning objectives

By the end of this chapter you should:

- Be able to state how to take samples from a habitat
- Be able to state the factors that can affect organisms in a habitat including temperature, light, water and the extent of cultivation
- Be able to interpret results from a habitat investigation if given information about the living organisms and factors that affect them

Habitats

Ecology is the study of organisms and the environment they live in. The place an organism lives is its **habitat**. You will study one example of a habitat possibly woodland, seashore, pond, or river. Some examples are shown in Figure 1.

All these habitats have animals and plants living in them. The distribution of both animals and plants depends on physical factors, as well as the other living organisms in that habitat. Life on Earth depends on energy from the Sun which plants use in photosynthesis to produce sugars and oxygen. In most habitats, therefore, the first organisms are plants, but in the case of ponds or marine environments the simple organisms that trap the light are called **plankton**.

Living organisms are affected by **physical factors** in their environment and the way these factors vary. These include the temperature of their surroundings, the amount of sunlight and the amount of water. In some cases the amount of cultivation of the habitat that has taken place is also important.

Figure 1

Habitat study and sampling

When studying a habitat one of these factors is often measured and studied to see if it relates to the distribution of animals or plants in the habitat.

Plant distribution

In woodland the levels of light can vary depending on the shade produced by the larger trees or shrubs. To measure light levels a simple light meter can be used and the distribution of plants measured to see whether there is any link between the light levels and the number or types of plants present. To record the plants present a sample is usually taken since it is impossible to count every plant in an area.

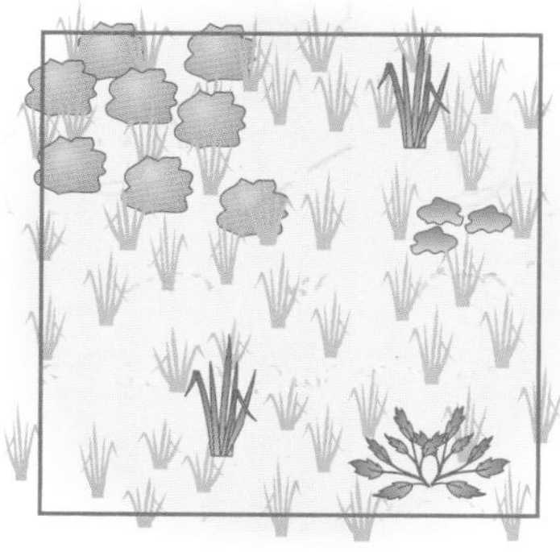

Counting organisms is impossible here so a rough estimate of percentage cover is taken, that need not add up to 100%.

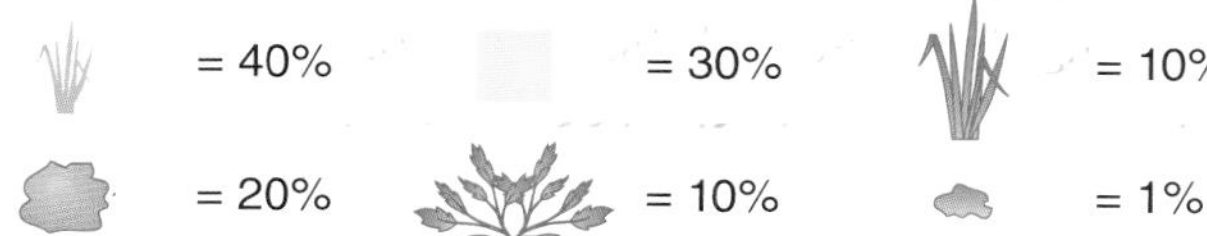

Figure 2

This is usually done by using **quadrats** and estimating the percentage cover of each type of plant in that area. The quadrat can be used in one of two ways. In random sampling the quadrat is thrown several times in the area under investigation and the percentage cover of plants recorded wherever the quadrat lands. A grid of the area can be drawn up and random numbers generated to indicate which parts of the area should be studied. Alternatively a line can be laid across the area under investigation with the quadrats laid along this line and the percentage cover of plants in each quadrat recorded. The line is called a **belt transect**.

The abundance of organisms within quadrats placed at regular points along a line is recorded **Figure 3**

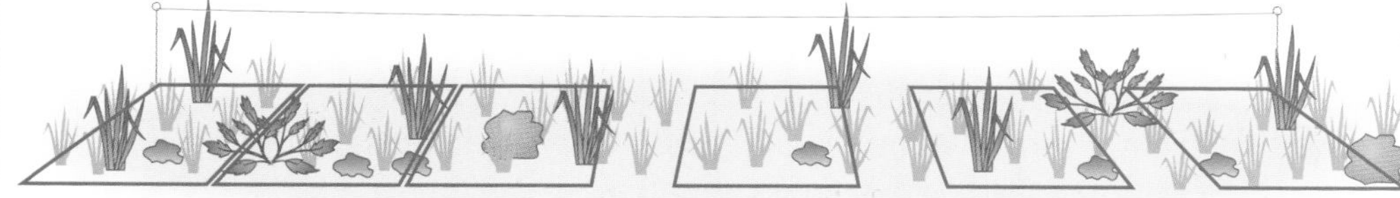

Animal sampling

To investigate the types and relative numbers of small animals, for example insects that don't fly in woodland or other habitats, a **pit fall trap** can be used. The location of these traps must be marked so that if they are left they can be easily found again.

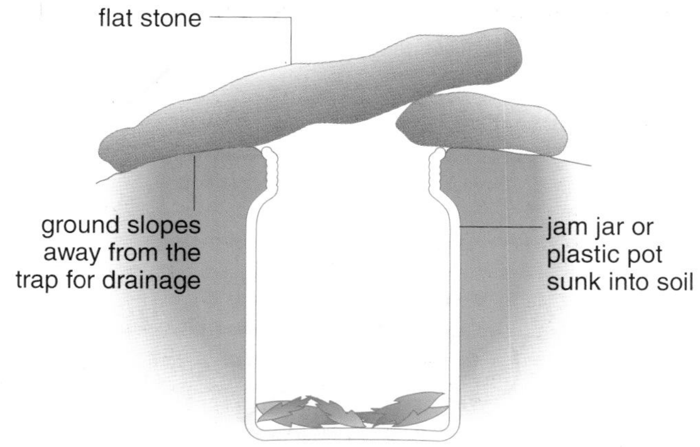

Figure 4 A pitfall trap

Another device that can be used to collect small insects is a **pooter**, which is used to suck them up.

Alternatively samples of insect life can be collected from bushes by using a **sweep net**, pulling it through the vegetation and then emptying it out onto a tray. When studying a pond or stream a different type of net can be used to gather the animals present in the habitat.

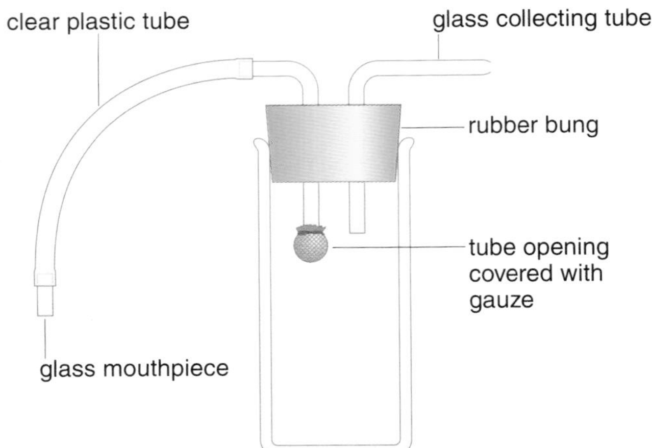

Figure 5 A pooter

Figure 6 Using a sweep net to sample a grassland

Figure 7 A net can also be used to sample a pond or stream

Other factors that can be measured

Other physical factors such as temperature can be important in habitats and it may be possible to measure these using probes, which can store this information until you return to the laboratory. Temperature is important to all living organisms since they all have reactions that are controlled by enzymes which are temperature dependent. Particular environments may have factors that are important only in that habitat, for example on the seashore the types of seaweeds vary with the region of the shore, the tides and for how long the seaweeds are covered by water. This is because some seaweeds can withstand drying out better than other varieties.

Water is a very important physical factor because it is essential for all living organisms, since cells are largely composed of water. Oxygen is essential for animal respiration and plants need adequate levels of carbon dioxide for photosynthesis. In addition plants need a mineral supply from the soil or water in which they live.

Questions

1 In the habitat you studied what physical factors affected the animals and plants you were investigating?

2 What sampling methods did you use in your habitat investigation?

Websites

http://www.offwell.free-online.co.uk/biol_sampl_cont.htm
Useful information on sampling methods.

Exam questions

1 Copy and complete the table by selecting, from the list, an appropriate sampling method for each organism.

Methods of sampling

quadrats **pooters** **pitfall traps** **nets**

Sampling method	Organism
	Large ground beetles
	Dandelion

(2 marks)

2 The microscopic green plant *Pleurococcus* lives on tree trunks. A group of students carried out field work on the distribution of this plant.

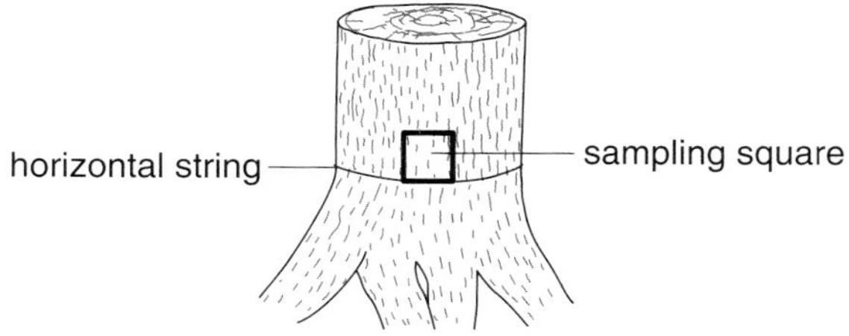

- They investigated the relationship between density of *Pleurococcus* and the direction faced by *Pleurococcus*.
- The density of the *Pleurococcus* in each sampling square was given a density score of between 1 and 6 where 6 was the most dense.
- The direction in which the plant colonies faced was determined using a compass.

The table shows the results obtained.

Direction faced by *Pleurococcus*	Density score of *Pleurococcus*/ relative density
South	1
South west	1
West	3
North west	5
North	6
North east	4
East	2
South east	1

a) The diagram shows the density score at each compass point. Copy and complete the diagram by shading the correct number of sections.

West is done for you. *(2 marks)*

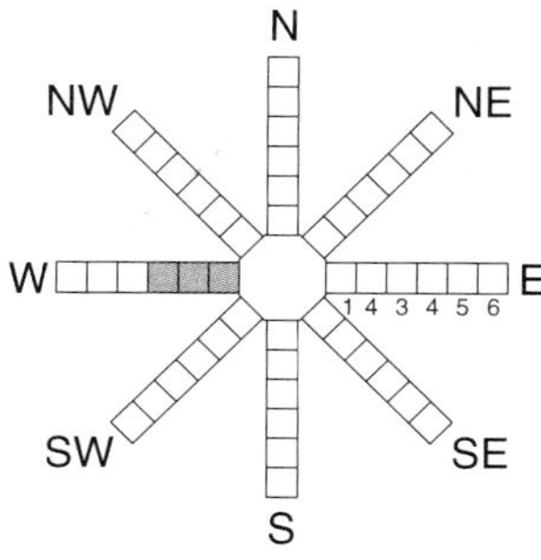

b) Describe the trend shown in the diagram. *(1 mark)*

c) Suggest **two** physical factors which may affect the distribution of *Pleurococcus*. *(1 mark)*

d) Suggest how the group of students could obtain more reliable results. *(1 mark)*

Chapter 16

The Transfer of Energy and Nutrients

Learning objectives

By the end of this chapter you should know:

- The components of food chains and webs and energy flow
- Pyramids of numbers and biomass
- Energy losses between trophic levels
- The carbon cycle
- The nitrogen cycle
- Fertilisers
- The role of microbes in sewage treatment and in compost heaps

An **ecosystem** is a community of organisms that are interdependent on each other and the environment in which they live. Examples of ecosystems include grasslands, woodlands and lakes. If ecosystems are able to remain stable for long periods of time there must be some way in which energy continually enters the system to replace the energy that is lost through respiration and the many energy-requiring activities that occur. Where does this energy come from?

The energy comes from the Sun and is trapped by green plants in the process of photosynthesis. Plants that can photosynthesise are known as **producers** as they produce their own food and they in turn provide food and energy for other organisms. The herbivores (plant eating animals) that feed on plants are known as **primary consumers** and the carnivores (animals that eat other animals) that feed on primary consumers are known as **secondary consumers**. Animals that feed on secondary consumers are **tertiary consumers** and so on.

This sequence of producers trapping the Sun's energy and this energy then passing into other organisms as they feed, is known as **energy flow**.

The different stages in the feeding sequence can also be referred to as **trophic levels**. Producers occur in trophic level 1 and primary consumers are trophic level 2 etc.

Food chains and food webs

Figure 1 shows a sequence or chain of living organisms through which energy passes. It is an example of a **food chain**. Food chains show the feeding relationships and energy transfer between a number of organisms. Examples of some other food chains are shown in Figure 2.

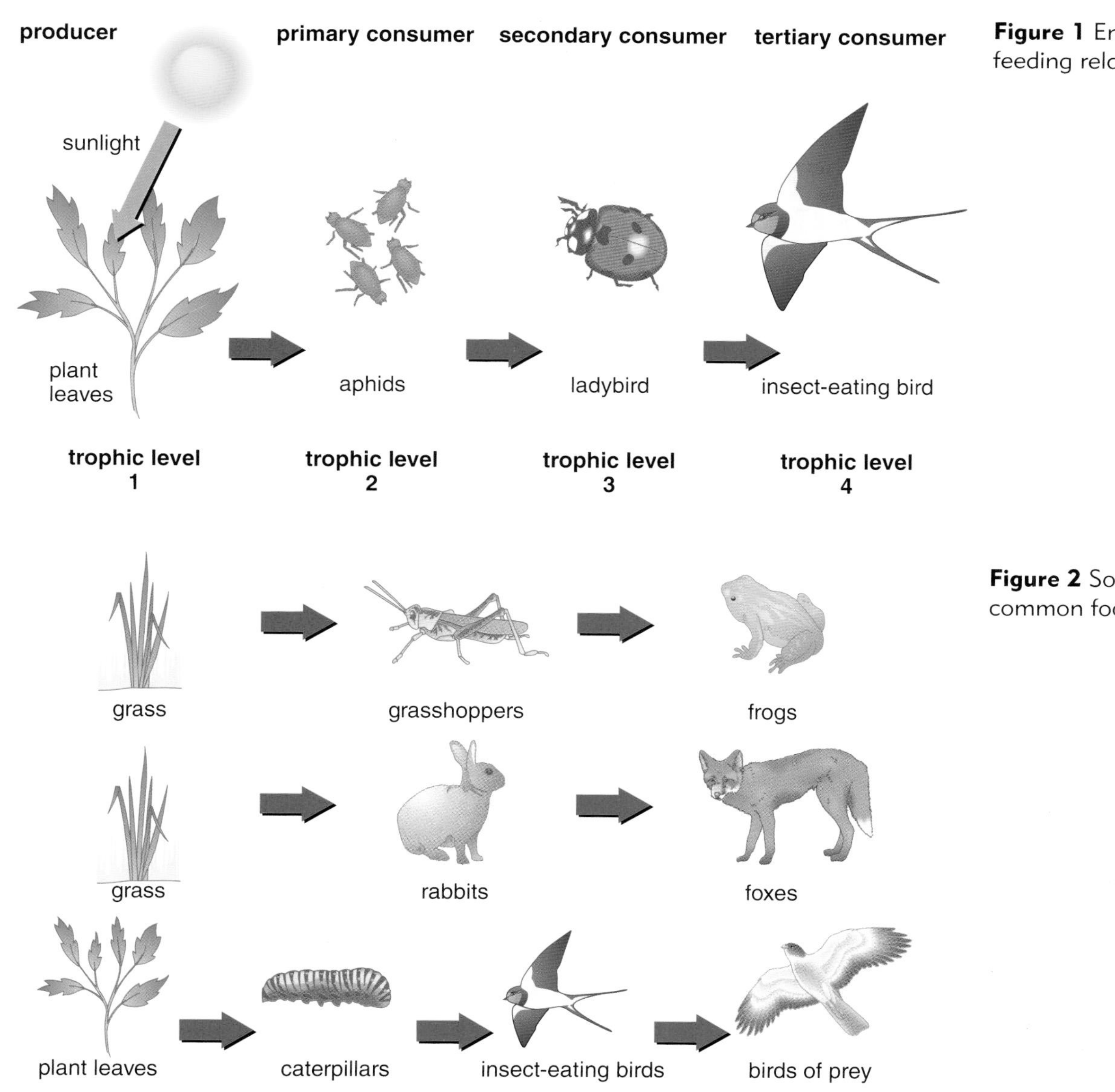

Figure 1 Energy and feeding relationships

Figure 2 Some common food chains

These examples show that in all food chains the first organism is the producer and they provide food and energy for primary consumers and so on. Of course, food chains are very simplistic in that they do not show the complex interactions that usually exist. In reality very few animals have only one food source.

Questions

1 Why is it risky for animals to have only one food source?

Food webs show how a number of food chains are interlinked and they give a much more realistic picture. Figure 3 shows how the food chains shown above are built up into a food web. The food web shown is only part of the story as there will be many more links and organisms involved than those listed.

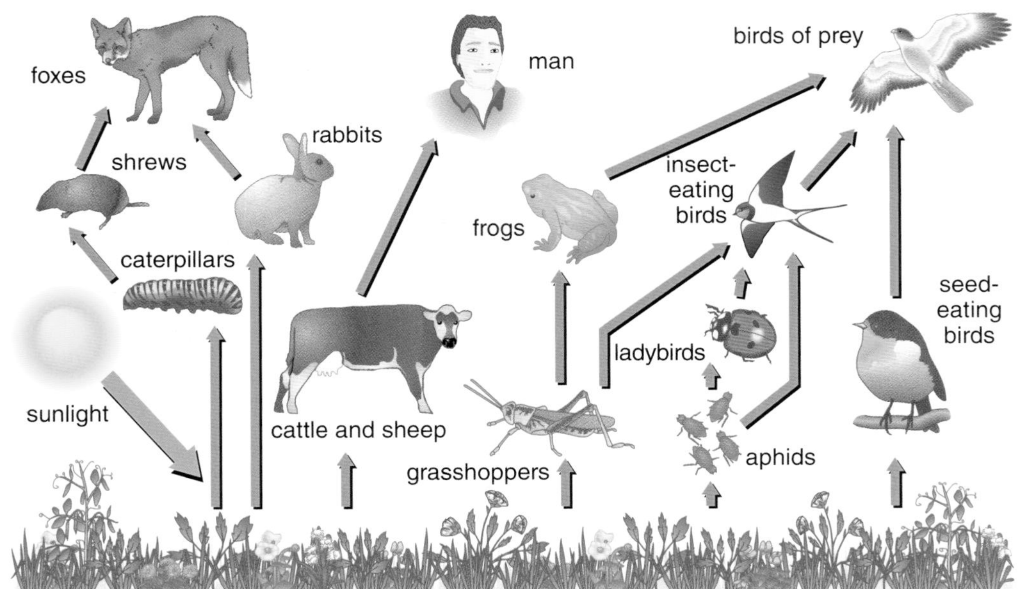

Figure 3 A grassland food web

Pyramids of numbers and biomass

For a food web to be sustainable there must be enough food for all the organisms involved. There will usually be more producers than there are primary consumers and more primary consumers that there are secondary consumers. The number of organisms at each stage of a food chain can be represented in a **pyramid of numbers**. Figure 4 shows a typical pyramid of numbers. The term pyramid is used as the shape will usually resemble a pyramid.

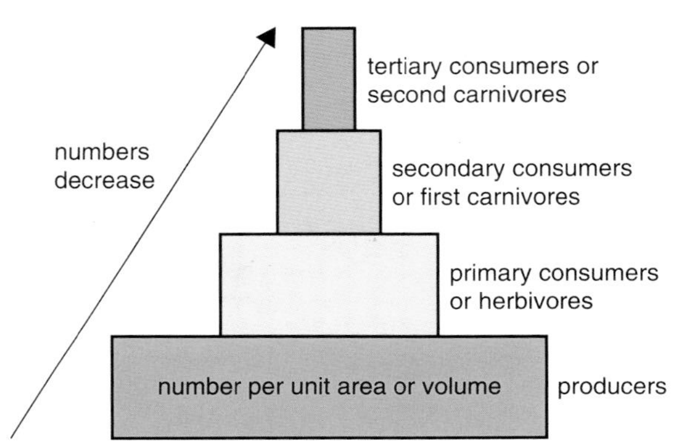

Figure 4 Pyramid of numbers

Pyramids of numbers can sometimes be misleading as they do not take into account the size of the organisms involved. The pyramid of numbers in Figure 5 highlights this problem. In the second example, each tree (the producer), may sustain many primary consumers therefore giving an atypical shape or inverted appearance.

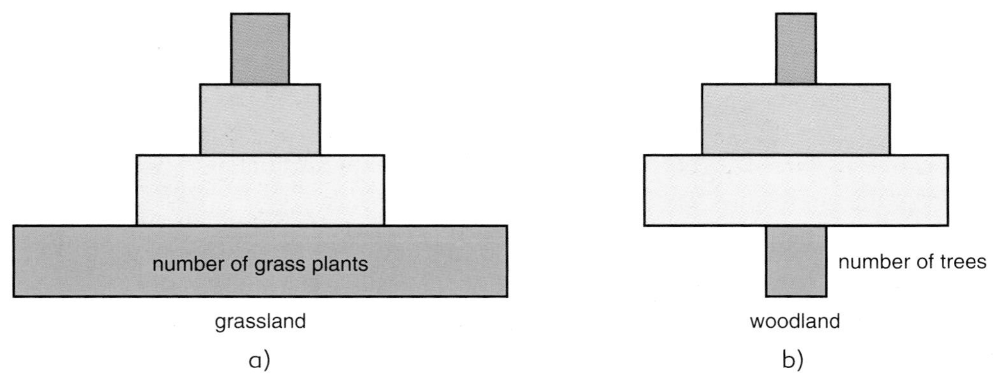

Figure 5 Pyramid of numbers for a) a grassland community and b) a woodland community

You can see this for yourself if you examine the leaves of a tree carefully. You will find many small insects feeding on, and occasionally inside, the leaves of one tree.

When looking at energy flow through a food chain it is sometimes more accurate to use a **pyramid of biomass**. These diagrams represent the mass of living tissue in the organisms concerned. Figure 6 shows that if we use a pyramid of biomass for the woodland pyramid in Figure 5 it is no longer inverted and it now has the typical pyramid shape.

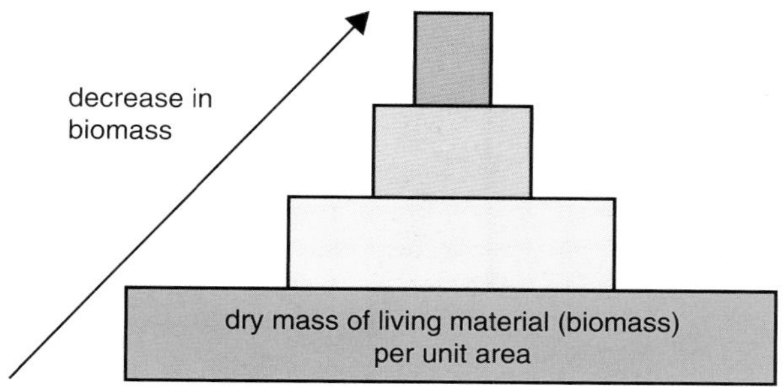

Figure 6 Pyramid of biomass for a woodland community

Trophic levels revisited

All the food chains in Figure 2 are relatively short, containing no more than four organisms. This is because energy is lost at each stage of energy transfer.

Even the absorption of light energy by plants is not particularly efficient (usually much less than 10% of the light energy hitting the leaves is converted into starch during photosynthesis). Energy is lost as light passes through leaves, or is reflected, or is used up in chemical reactions and for many other reasons. However, this loss of energy is not significant for most plants as there is no shortage of light energy coming from the Sun!

The transfer of energy between plants and animals and between animals of different trophic levels, following feeding, is usually between 10 and 20%. This means that for every 100 g of plant material available, only between 10 and 20 g is built up as tissue in the herbivores body. The same principle applies when carnivores eat herbivores. This loss of energy is due to three main reasons. These are:

- Not all the available food is eaten. Most carnivores do not eat the skeleton or the hair or fur of their victim.
- Not all the food can be digested.
- A lot of energy is lost in respiration. Respiration provides the energy for movement, growth, reproduction etc. In birds and mammals a lot of energy is used in maintaining a constant body temperature. The energy that is lost in respiration cannot be passed on to the next link in the chain.

Figure 7 shows why food chains are relatively short and it also helps explain why pyramids of biomass are the shape they are. So much energy is lost at each trophic level that a long food chain would not be sustainable. Now that we are aware of this energy loss it is interesting to examine some food chains that involve humans.

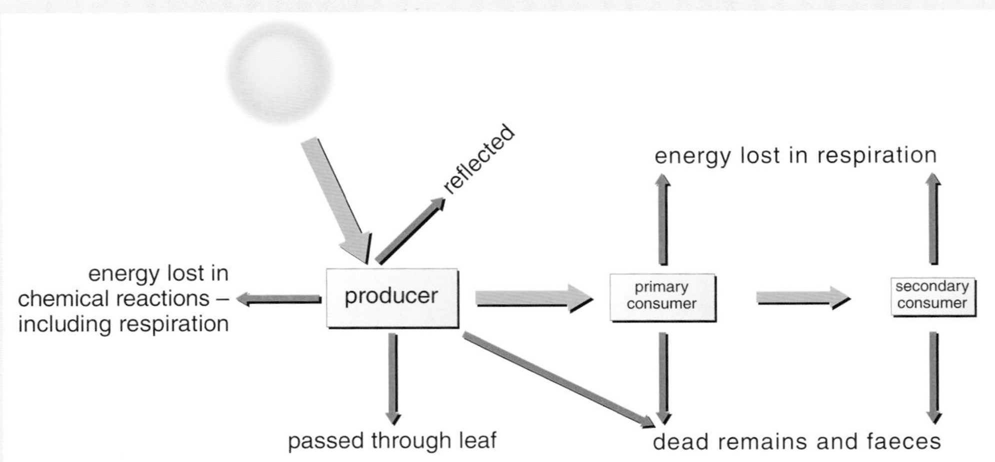

Figure 7 Energy flow and energy loss

Food chains in the feeding of man

A commonly used example of a food chain involving man is

grass ⟶ cow ⟶ man

A diet involving meat products is sustainable in countries where there is enough land to produce the grass and crops necessary to feed the cattle or other animals. Due to the combination of the energy loss between the producers and the domestic animals and then between the animals and man much more land is required than would be necessary if people fed directly on the producers, where there is only one stage involving energy loss.

As a result of this energy loss very short food chains are common in densely populated countries, largely due to their greater efficiency in energy transfer. The use of rice as the staple diet in much of Asia is an example.

Nutrient cycles

We have already noted that energy flows through food webs and that this usually happens as part of the feeding process. Figure 7 shows that energy must continually enter the system from sunlight as it is lost from all living organisms during the process of respiration. This is why we use the term energy flow.

If we now look at the flow of **nutrients** in more detail we will see that it differs from the flow of energy in important respects. In a stable ecosystem the gain or loss of nutrients from the system will be small and, unlike energy, the nutrients can be recycled as part of a **nutrient cycle**.

Nutrient cycling involves the processes of decay and decomposition. For recycling to occur dead organisms must be broken down during the decay process. Many organisms are involved in this process and they include earthworms, woodlice and many types of insects. **Fungi** and **bacteria** are the **decomposers** that complete the process by breaking down the organic compounds into their simplest components such as nitrates and other mineral ions.

Questions

2 Why do decay and decomposition take place much faster in warm conditions?

Two very important nutrient cycles are the **carbon cycle** and **nitrogen cycle**.

The carbon cycle

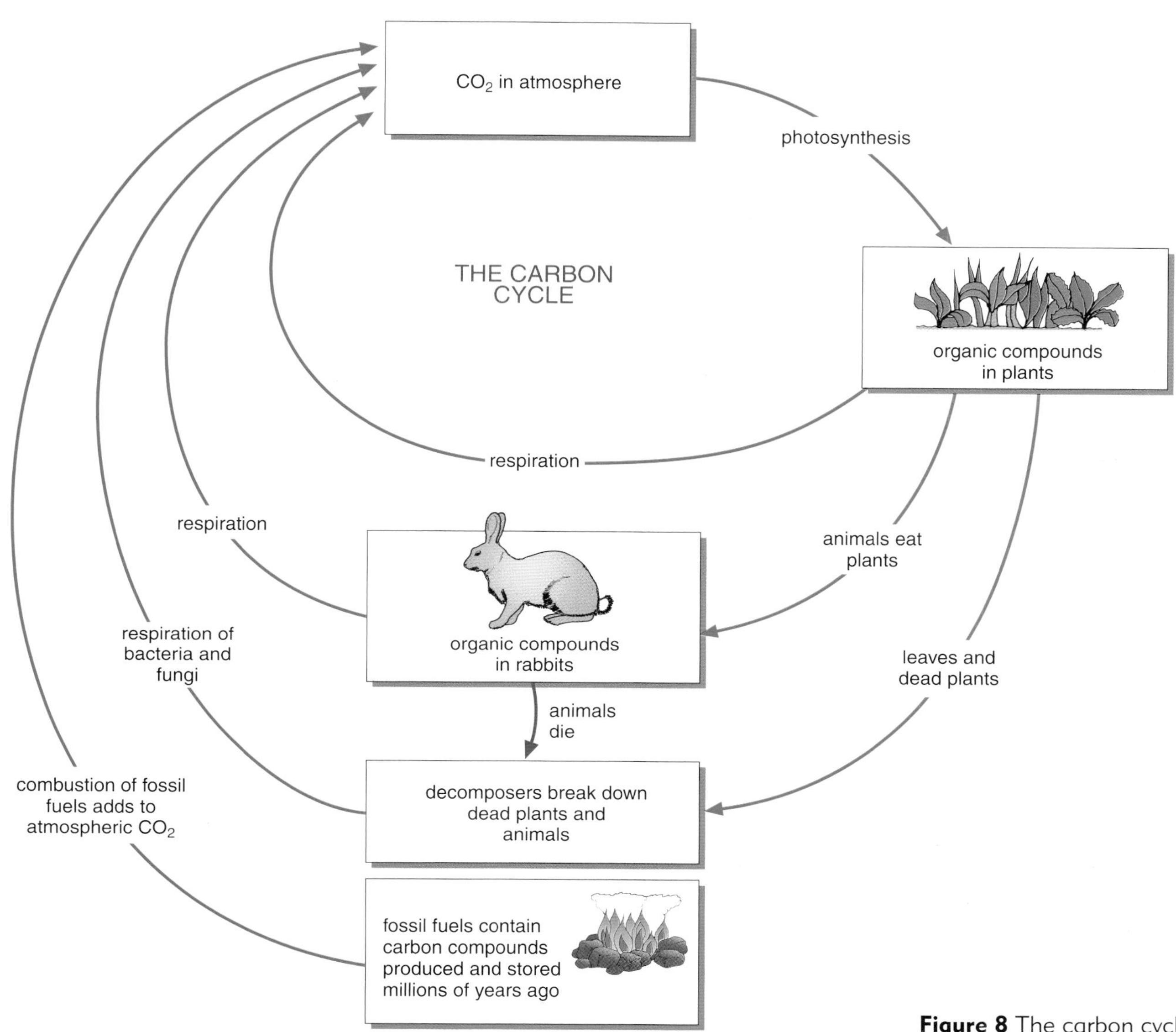

Figure 8 The carbon cycle

Carbon is an essential element in every living organism. For example, proteins, carbohydrates and fats all contain carbon. The carbon cycle is the exchange of carbon between living organisms, but also includes transfer between these organisms and the carbon dioxide in the atmosphere. There is a vast reserve of carbon in the atmosphere in the form of carbon dioxide – there is also a lot dissolved in the seas and oceans. The main processes in the carbon cycle are:

- **Photosynthesis** – during photosynthesis carbon dioxide is taken in by plants and built up into sugar and starch and other organic compounds.
- **Feeding** – animals eat the plants (or other animals) and the carbon is built up into organic compounds which can be transferred further along the food chain.
- **Respiration** – when plants, animals and decomposers respire they return carbon compounds to the atmosphere as carbon dioxide.

- **Combustion** – as carbon rich reserves of coal, oil and gas are burnt the carbon is returned to the atmosphere as carbon dioxide. These and other fossil fuels were formed millions of years ago when the plants (and animals) did not decay but were preserved due to the particular geological conditions of the time.

For many years there has been some concern that the carbon cycle is not balanced. There is considerable evidence to show that atmospheric carbon dioxide levels are rising. This is probably due to both the increased burning of fossil fuels and the deforestation that has taken place throughout the world. The increase in combustion and the decrease in photosynthesis that has resulted has increased carbon dioxide levels.

The resulting **greenhouse effect** has led to **global warming**, causing melting icecaps, rising sea levels and climate change. To reduce the effect of global warming, a reduction in forest clearance, the planting of more forests and the reduced use of fossil fuels are encouraged. The effect of global warming is discussed in more detail in Chapter 17.

The nitrogen cycle

Most of the nitrogen in plants and animals is in the form of amino acids and protein. This is a more complex cycle than the carbon cycle and in understanding the cycle it is worthwhile splitting it into three phases. These three phases are:

- *The build up of nitrogen into amino acids and protein in plants and animals and the eventual breakdown of these compounds into nitrates.* Plants absorb nitrogen as nitrates and use them to make protein. As plants (and animals) are eaten the proteins are eaten, digested and then built up into other proteins in sequence. Eventually the nitrogen is returned to the ground as urine or faeces or through the process of death and decay. **Decay or putrefying bacteria** and **fungi** break down the proteins to release ammonia. A second very important group of bacteria, **nitrifying bacteria**, break the ammonia or ammonium compounds down into nitrates and the cycle can continue.
- **Nitrogen-fixing bacteria** *are a special group of bacteria that can convert nitrogen gas into nitrates.* These bacteria can be found in the soil or frequently in small swellings (root nodules) in the roots of a particular group of plants called legumes. Legumes include peas, beans and clover. The relationship between the legumes and the bacteria is complex, but an important one in which both benefit. The bacteria gain carbohydrates from the legumes and they in turn provide a ready source of nitrates for the benefit of the plants. The process of converting nitrogen from the atmosphere into nitrates is called **nitrogen fixation**.
- **Denitrifying bacteria** *convert nitrates into atmospheric nitrogen.* This is a wasteful and undesirable process. Denitrifying bacteria are anaerobic and are most commonly found in waterlogged soils. Their effect in well-drained soils is much reduced. The process of converting nitrates into nitrogen is called **denitrification**.

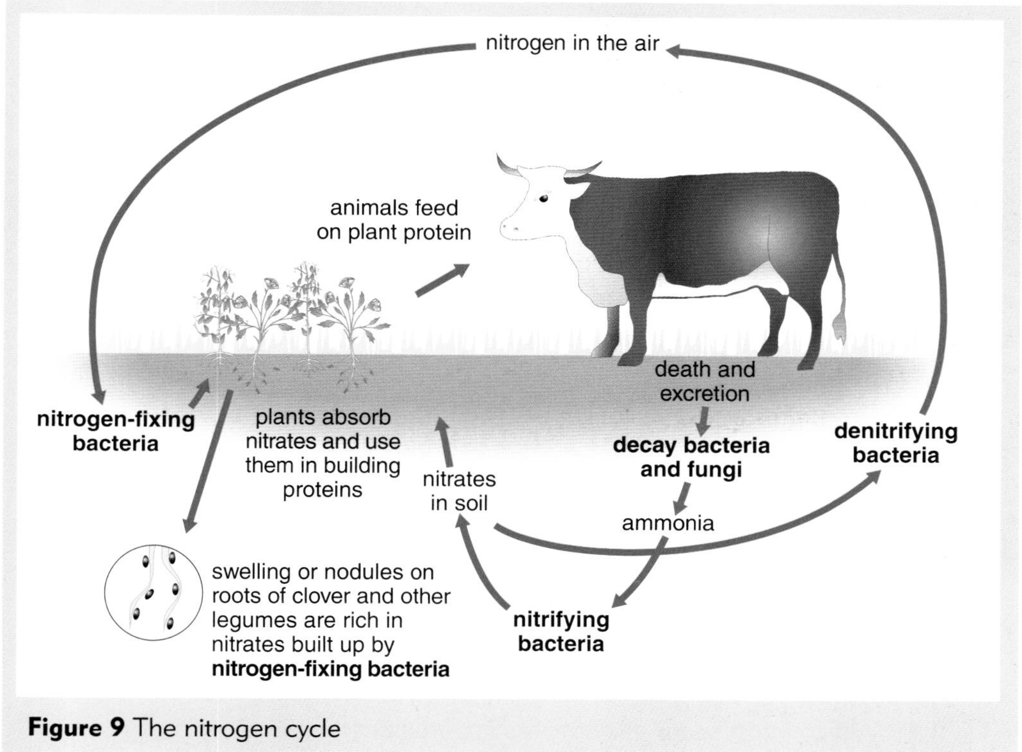

Figure 9 The nitrogen cycle

Questions

2 When crops are harvested the normal recycling of nitrogen is disrupted. How can the soil nitrogen levels be maintained?

3 Explain the benefit of planting clover as part of a grass mix on land being grazed by cattle.

Replacing lost nitrogen – the use of fertilisers

The growing and harvesting of crops inevitably leads to a reduction in soil nitrogen levels (and those of other important elements). Fertilisers can replace the lost nutrients. Fertilisers can be natural (farmyard manure and compost) or artificially produced. Artificial fertilisers are usually rich in N (nitrogen), P (phosphorus) and K (potassium). There are advantages and disadvantages with both types of fertiliser.

- **Manure and compost** is difficult to store and spread. It is difficult to know or control the balance of the different minerals in natural fertiliser. However, it is less soluble than artificial fertiliser and less will be lost by leaching and run-off into waterways. Natural fertiliser also helps improve general soil quality as it adds to the humus content of the soil.
- **Artificial fertiliser** is soluble and can easily be washed away possibly creating pollution problems. It can lead to osmotic problems in plants if allowed to build up in high concentrations in the soil. On the plus side it is much easier to store and apply artificial fertiliser in a controlled manner.

An additional disadvantage with artificial fertiliser is that it is expensive and this can be a significant factor in the cost of crops or animal products. The advised use of manure or compost where possible highlights the value of recycling for both economic and environmental reasons.

Recycling paper

The recycling of paper is another example that highlights the economic importance of recycling. While only a small volume of the paper we use is recycled, the percentage is increasing. This is partially due to greater public awareness of the importance of recycling and the increasing number of collection points.

The recycling of paper makes good economic sense as it reduces the harvesting of wood and saves energy in the paper making process. In addition it decreases the level of paper waste produced. Unfortunately it is difficult to make high quality paper during recycling. Recycled paper can also be more expensive to produce and the process of recycling can cause environmental damage.

The role of microbes in sewage disposal and composting

In both sewage disposal and in the use of compost heaps microbes are important in the decay process.

Microbes and sewage

Sewage plants are systems that are designed to break down sewage in such a way that the products can be released into rivers or the sea without causing high levels of pollution. Following the screening or filtering of waste to remove material, usually man made, that cannot be digested, settling tanks separate the waste into liquid and solid (sludge) components. The suspended solids settle to the bottom of the tank due to the effect of gravity. Two different groups of microbes are used to deal with the liquid and solid components.

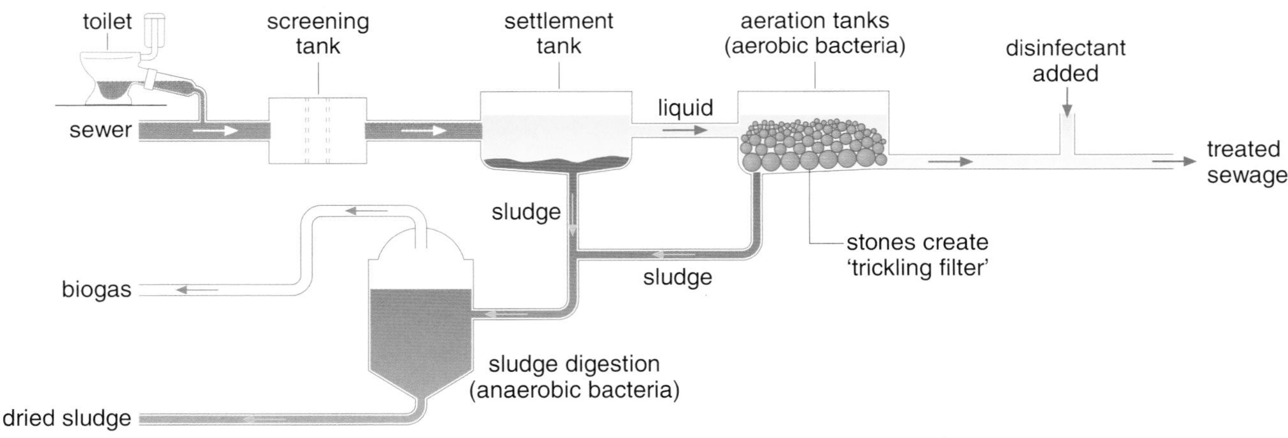

Figure 10 The treatment of sewage

- **Aerobic bacteria** (and some microscopic algae) digest the liquid waste in special aeration tanks that help maintain aerobic (oxygen rich) conditions. The liquid sewage trickles over the stones in the aeration tank. As it does so bacteria covering the stones digest much of the remaining sewage in the liquid. The use of stones in the tank helps increase the surface area over which the bacteria can digest the sewage. Following this stage, chlorine or another suitable disinfectant, is added to destroy harmful microbes in the liquid before it is released into the sea or other waterway.

- Solids from the settlement tanks and a smaller volume that has settled in the aeration tanks enters the sludge digester. In this tank **anaerobic bacteria** digest the sludge that has formed from the solids to form biogas and the solid residue. The residue can be used as fertiliser and the biogas can be used as fuel.

Sewage works provide an example of microbes at work in a large-scale industrial setting. Some isolated houses may not be connected to a sewage system but have a septic tank at the end of the garden instead. A septic tank is a much simpler version of a sewage works and it also involves bacteria digesting organic waste.

The compost heap is another example of microbes at work in the garden.

The compost heap

Compost heaps are formed of grass cuttings, fallen leaves, potato and other vegetable peelings and many other household and garden products that are **biodegradable**. Microbes decompose these remains to form compost that is rich in minerals and makes an excellent natural fertiliser. The microbial activity can be so intense that the inside of a heap can become very warm as a result of heat produced during respiration. As the decomposition takes a very long time to complete gardeners can speed up the process by cutting holes in the sides of the compost bin or use more open plan structures to increase oxygen flow. It is also possible to add 'starter packs' of microbes to start the decay process. Lime is also sometimes added to stop the decomposing material becoming too acidic as this will reduce the efficiency of the microbes.

Compost heaps often contain large numbers of earthworms and other small **detritivores** such as beetles which help with the decay process. The earthworms help the process in exactly the same way they help decay and decomposition in soil.

- Earthworms feed on the waste that is added to the compost heaps and pass most of this (about 80 %) through their bodies to form worm casts. The fungi and bacteria can decompose the waste easier when it is in this partially digested form.
- Earthworms create burrows that allow oxygen to penetrate deep into the heap and also help with drainage.

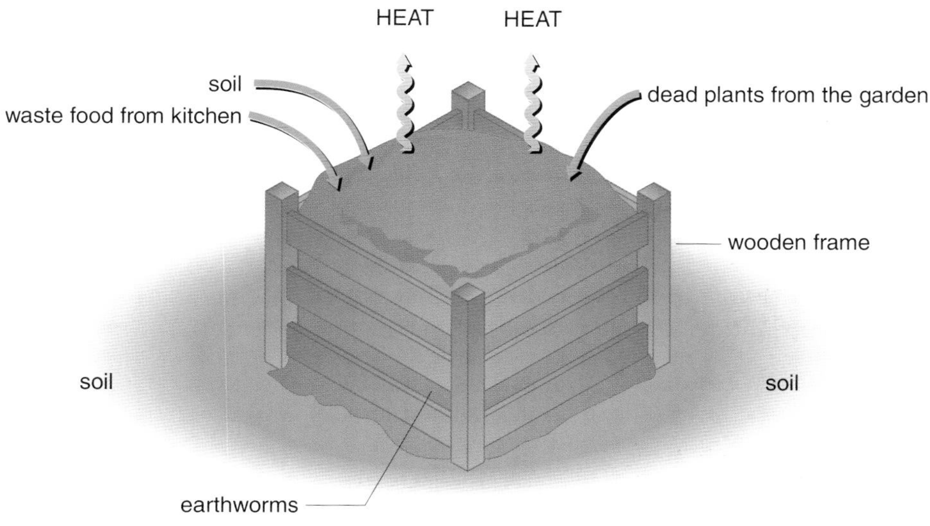

Figure 11 A compost heap and the materials used to make it

Much of this chapter has involved the cycling of nutrients and energy flow. Figure 12 highlights some of the most important points.

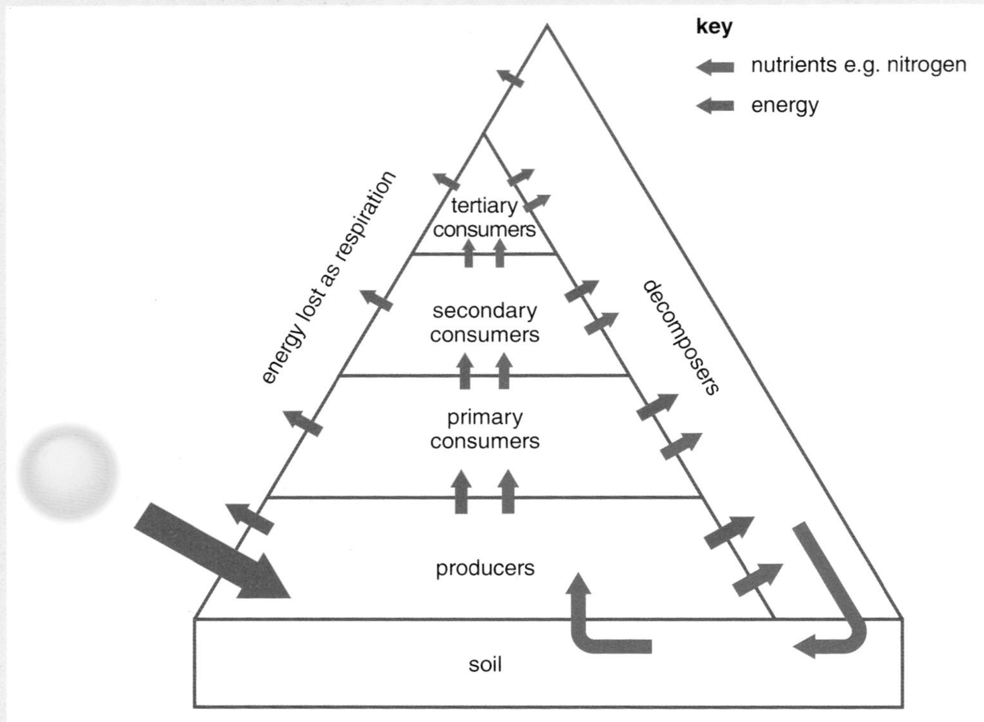

Figure 12 Nutrient cycling and energy flow

Questions

5 Use Figure 12 and your knowledge to explain:

a) Why the terms nutrient cycle and energy flow are used.

b) Why the size of the producer section in the diagram is larger than the tertiary consumer section.

c) What would happen to nutrient cycling and energy flow if there was no sunlight.

d) What would happen if there were no decomposers.

Websites

http://www.purchon.com/ecology/carbon.htm
Interactive carbon cycles and other useful information.

http://www.bbc.co.uk/schools/gcsebitesize/biology/ecology/index.shtml
Contains interactive worksheets on nutrient cycles and energy flow.

http://www.alienexplorer.com/ecology/e36.html
Includes good examples of food chains, webs, pyramids of numbers and biomass.

Try your own searches. Good examples are ‘food chains’ and ‘composting + conditions’.

Exam questions

1 The diagram shows the flow of energy through a food chain. Energy values are given in kJ per m^2 per year.

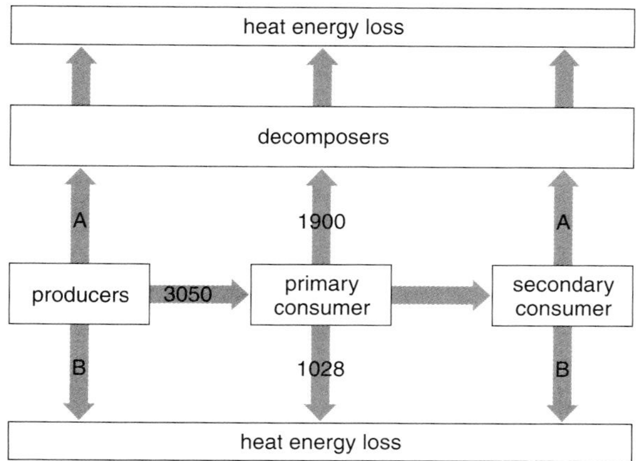

a) What is the original source of energy for the producers? *(1 mark)*

b) Name the processes indicated by arrows A and B. *(2 marks)*

c) Calculate what percentage of the energy available to the primary consumer is converted into a form which could be passed to the secondary consumer. Show your working. *(3 marks)*

d) How would the amount of energy available to the secondary consumer compare to that available to the primary consumer? *(1 mark)*

2 The diagram shows what happened to the energy contained in 1 m^2 of grass.

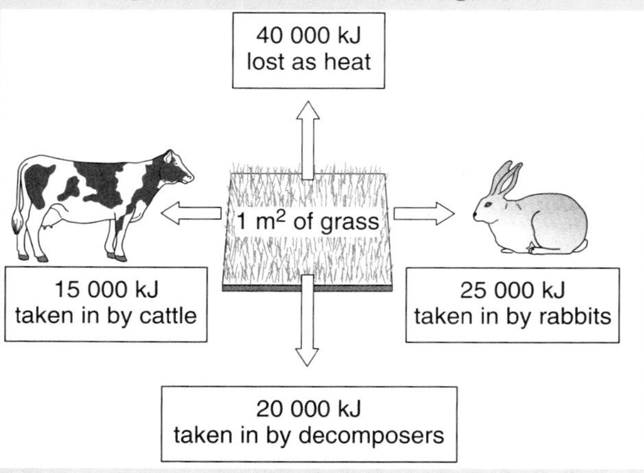

a) Calculate the amount of energy which was present in 1 m^2 of grass. *(1 mark)*

b) What was the source of energy for the grass? *(1 mark)*

c) Explain the benefit to the farmer of removing the rabbits from his field. *(2 marks)*

3 The pie charts show the materials used to make paper in the UK, in 1988 and 1998.

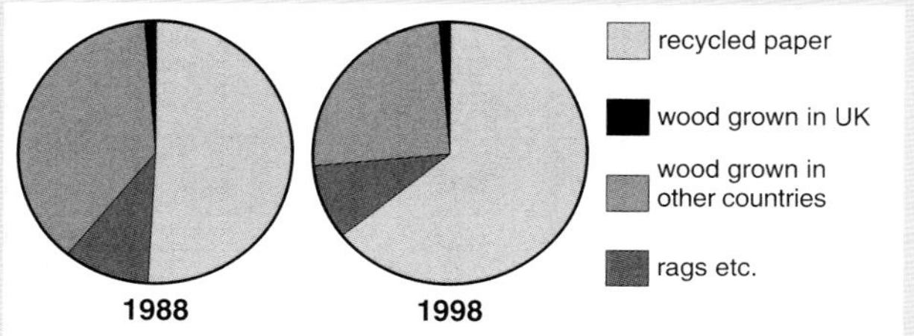

a) Describe **two** differences in the materials used in 1988 and 1998. *(2 marks)*

b) Give **two** advantages, to the environment, of recycling paper. *(2 marks)*

c) Give **one** disadvantage of recycled paper. *(1 mark)*

4 a) The diagram shows part of the nitrogen cycle.

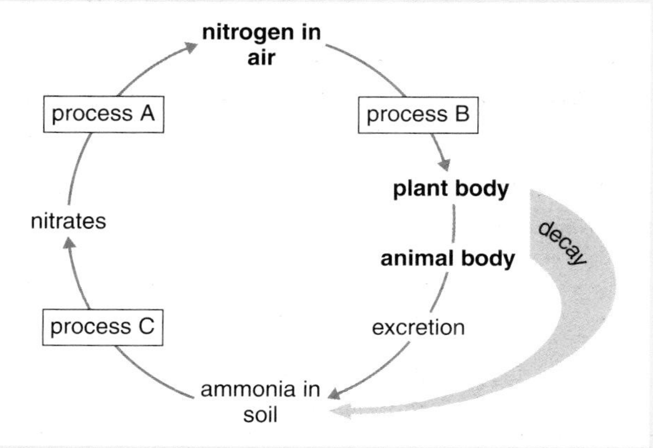

(i) Name processes A, B and C. *(3 marks)*

(ii) What type of micro-organism is responsible for processes A, B and C? *(1 mark)*

(iii) Explain why a farmer does not want process A occurring in his soil. *(2 marks)*

b) The table shows the average yearly yield of six plots of wheat after different fertiliser treatments.

Plot	Treatment	Yield of grain/ tonnes per km^2
1	none	95
2	nitrogen only	155
3	nitrogen, phosphorus	165
4	nitrogen, phosphorus, potassium	210
5	farmyard manure	245
6	complete artificial fertiliser (nitrogen, phosphorus, potassium, sodium, magnesium)	250

(i) Plot a bar chart of the treatment against yield. *(5 marks)*

(ii) Describe how nitrogen is absorbed by plants. *(2 marks)*

(iii) Give two advantages of using complete artificial fertiliser rather than farmyard manure. *(2 marks)*

(iv) Give two disadvantages to the environment of using artificial fertilisers. *(2 marks)*

5 a) The diagram shows part of a food web.

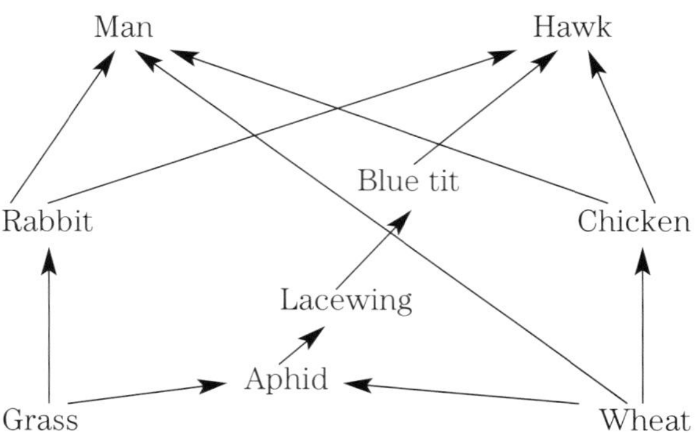

(i) Copy and complete the food chain from the web.

Grass				

(3 marks)

(ii) On which trophic level is the rabbit found? *(1 mark)*

The diagram shows the passage of energy through a rabbit.

(iii) Explain how the energy in the rabbit originated from the Sun. *(2 marks)*

(iv) Calculate the percentage of the energy eaten by the rabbit which would be available for Man to eat. Show your working. *(2 marks)*

(v) Give **two** uses of energy, produced during respiration, by the rabbit. *(2 marks)*

(vi) Describe how the energy in urine and faeces is released. *(2 marks)*

(vii) Explain why, in terms of energy, it would be better for Man to eat wheat rather than chicken fed on wheat. *(3 marks)*

b) The government has set a target for 25% of household waste to be recycled.

(i) Give two ecological advantages of recycling paper.
(2 marks)

(ii) Give one disadvantage of recycling paper.
(1 mark)

(iii) Suggest two reasons why recycling is sometimes uneconomic.
(2 marks)

(vi) Why do farmers sow fertiliser on their fields?
(1 mark)

(vii) Give two advantages, to the farmer, of using artificial fertiliser rather than farmyard manure.
(2 marks)

(viii) Suggest two reasons why farmers sow less artificial fertiliser in the autumn.
(2 marks)

6 a) The diagram shows part of the nitrogen cycle.

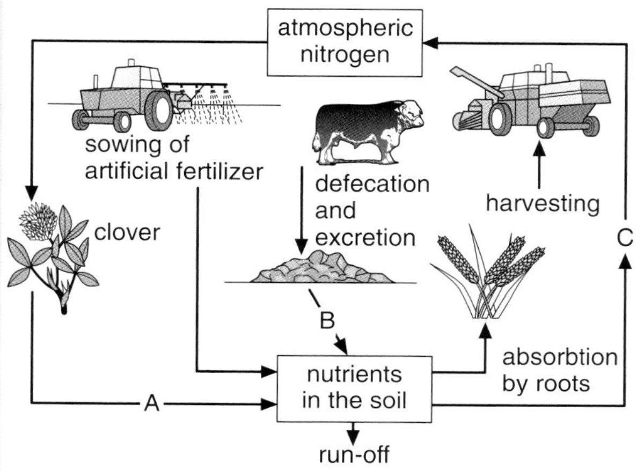

(i) Name the processes A, B and C.
(3 marks)

(ii) Name **two** types of micro-organism which carry out process B.
(2 marks)

(iii) Suggest how ploughing encourages process A.
(2 marks)

(iv) In what form is nitrogen absorbed by plants?
(1 mark)

(v) What effect does harvesting have on the level of nutrients in the soil?
(1 mark)

b) The diagram shows some of the stages in the treatment of sewage.

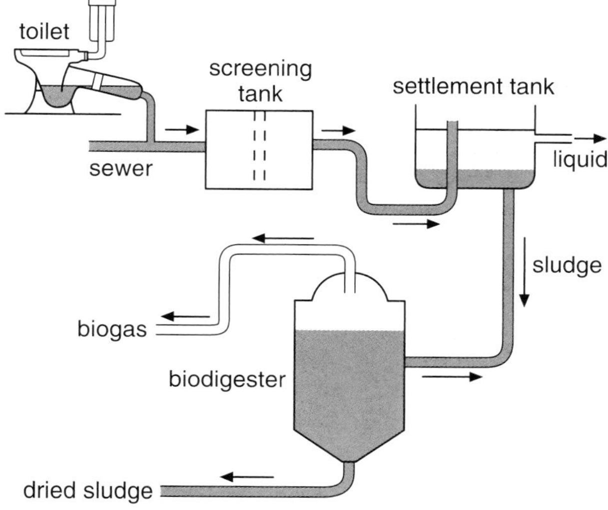

(i) Why is dried sludge used as a fertiliser on farmland?
(1 mark)

(ii) Explain why the untreated sewage should not be put directly on to farmland.
(1 mark)

(iii) Give **one** use for the biogas produced in the biodigester.
(1 mark)

(iv) Explain what must happen to the liquid containing suspended solids before it can be discharged into a river.
(2 marks)

Chapter 17

Pollution

Learning objectives

By the end of this chapter you should:

- Be able to explain the sources of air pollutants such as soot and sulphur dioxide – their effects on living organisms and some methods of reducing these sources of pollution
- Be able to explain the sources of air pollutants, carbon monoxide and lead – their effects on living organisms and some methods of reducing these sources of pollution
- Be able to give the sources of water pollution, the process of eutrophication and some measures that would reduce water pollution
- Be able to explain the use of landfill sites and measures to reduce rubbish production
- Be able to explain the use of incinerators to burn rubbish and some of the problems with this method of dealing with rubbish
- **Be able to explain the sources and consequences of acid rain, the greenhouse effect and the ozone layer along with some possible remedies**

Humans have inhabited the Earth for millions of years. However in the last few hundred years they have started to have a major impact on the ecosystem of the Earth as their numbers and influence have increased. Many developments have led to improvements in the living conditions and survival of humans, especially in developed countries. However this has often been produced by overexploitation of natural resources and without consideration of the long-term effects on the environment.

Pollutants

Pollutants are substances that cause damage to the environment. There are three main areas in the environment in which they cause damage. These will be considered in turn.

Air pollution

Most air pollution is caused by the burning of fossil fuels either in power stations, industries, homes, or in the engines of cars. The effects of air or water pollution may be local, but sometimes depending on the weather or water currents the pollutants can travel hundreds of miles from their source and cause damage in another country. This is one reason why many governments are now trying to co-ordinate and set targets to reduce pollution of all kinds, for example in 2002 a World Summit in Johannesburg, South Africa took place and agreed on some targets for reducing pollution.

The main pollutants

1 **Soot** – this is produced when most fossil fuels burn and produce solid particles. The soot can cause damage to the lungs in humans and it can also cover the leaves of plants and reduce their ability to photosynthesise.

2 Coal and oil and other fossil fuels contain sulphur. When they are burnt the sulphur is converted into sulphur dioxide gas. Large industrial burning and power stations produce the majority of sulphur dioxide. The problems occur when this gas dissolves in the water in the atmosphere and then falls as **acid rain**. Other chemicals in car exhausts also form acids in this way. Acid rain causes the pH of the soil to change and because of this certain minerals do not remain in the soil at their normal levels. This change in composition of soil minerals can lead to the death of trees over a period of time. The acid rain also affects the pH of ponds, rivers and lakes causing the death of the plants and animals within them.

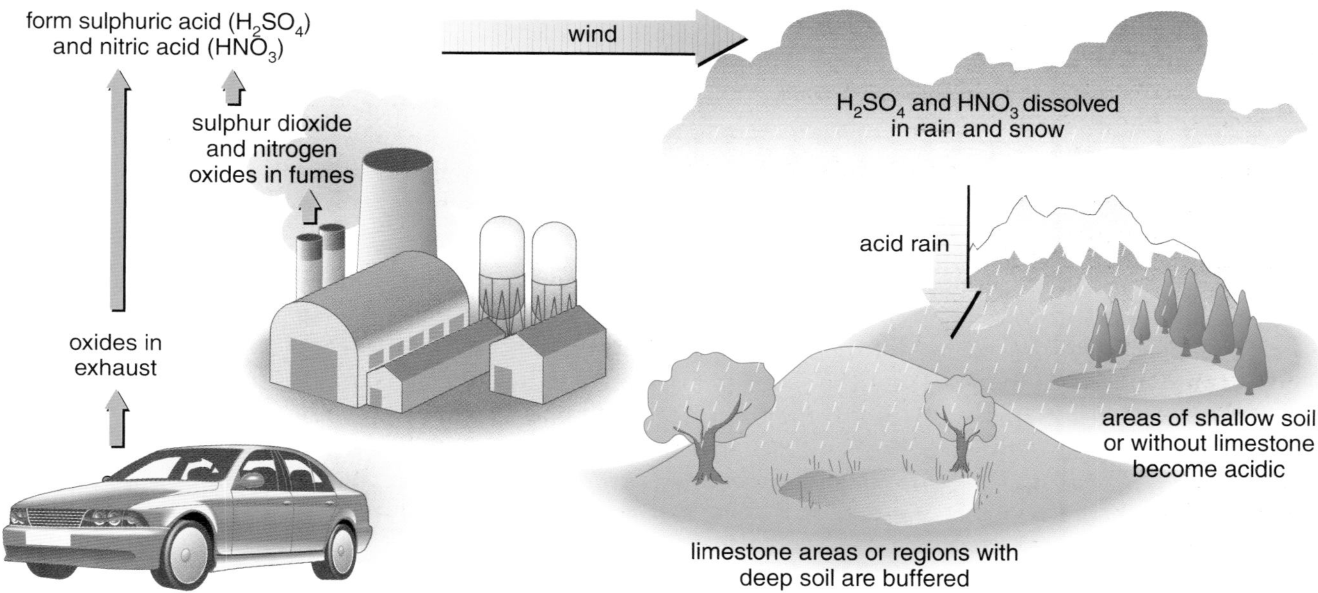

Figure 1 Acid rain can have devastating effects hundreds of miles from where the sulphur dioxide gas was formed

3 Carbon dioxide is always produced when fossil fuels burn, but if there is not enough oxygen then **carbon monoxide** is produced. It is present in car exhaust fumes and causes problems because it combines permanently with haemoglobin in the red blood cells and prevents them from combining with oxygen. In high levels it can cause suffocation.

4 **Lead** – this is present in some car fuels to help them to burn efficiently, but it can cause brain damage in humans.

To try to reduce these pollutants smokeless fuels that produce fewer particles can replace some existing fuels. Developments in fuel production means that more and more fuel is lead free. In addition more efficient designs of power stations and treatment of the wastes produced can reduce the levels of air pollutants.

Figure 2 Fossil fuel power stations release many pollutants

Alternative fuels such as biogas or alcohol may also offer some alternatives to energy production and transportation with less polluting consequences. Less wasteful use of energy and alternative methods of energy production could also contribute to reducing pollution levels.

Acid rain

The acid rain formed from sulphur and nitrogen oxides is thought to be responsible for the loss of considerable numbers of trees in Europe. It causes the release of aluminium from compounds in the soil and this then interferes with the ability of plants to take up calcium ions from the soil. As well as this the increased acidity of the soil may affect soil microbes and therefore the break down and release of minerals into the soil. The effect is to reduce the availability of minerals to the plants and trees, so the trees start to lose their leaves or needles (defoliation), their root growth is then affected and they are more prone to disease and damaging weather conditions such as drought or frost.

In rivers and lakes the increased acidity slows decomposition since it affects bacterial activity. Algae may grow, but other species may suffer. In addition fish may die due to aluminium poisoning which is released from nearby soils because of the increased acidity of the rain. Adding lime to the water can help, since it increases the pH and causes the aluminium to precipitate.

The greenhouse effect

The Earth receives radiation from the Sun and this heats the Earth. The Earth absorbs some of the radiation from the Sun, but some is also reflected back up into the Earth's atmosphere. There are several gases in the Earth's atmosphere that absorb this radiation and prevent it escaping from the atmosphere. The most important gases are carbon dioxide, methane and water. They form a 'blanket' around the Earth and keep the air and Earth warm.

However the amounts of these gases in the air are increasing, particularly the amount of carbon dioxide. This is thought to be due to our increased use of fossil fuels and perhaps also due to deforestation. This has led to a rise in the Earth's temperature called global warming. There is a lot of controversy about some of the figures and possible effects of global warming but a few are outlined below.

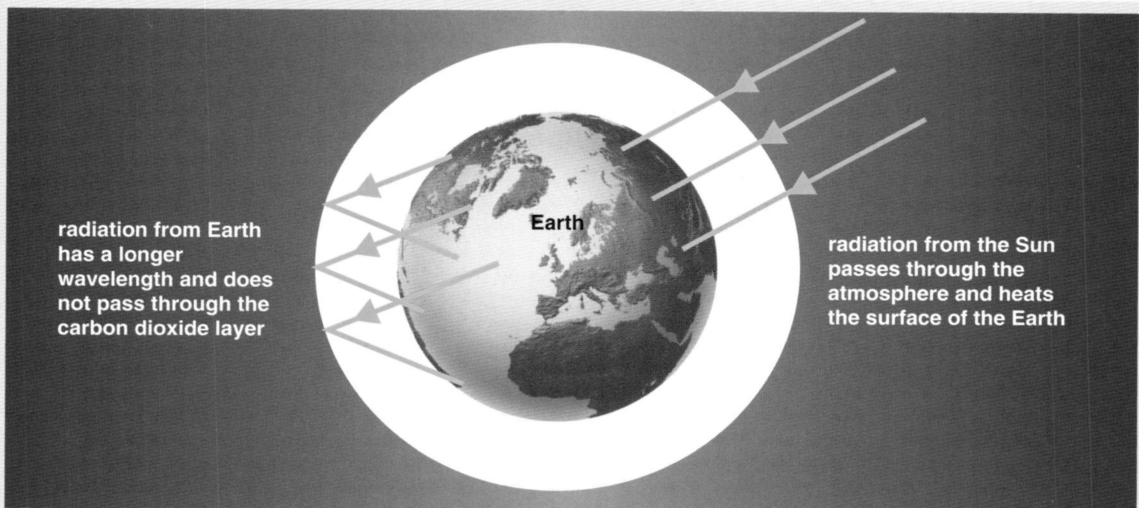
radiation from Earth has a longer wavelength and does not pass through the carbon dioxide layer
Earth
radiation from the Sun passes through the atmosphere and heats the surface of the Earth

Figure 3 The greenhouse effect

- Melting of the polar ice caps causing a rise in sea levels.
- Changes in weather patterns with more storms, more prolonged periods of drought and changes in the Gulf Stream, which gives Western Europe its mild climate.
- Changes in the patterns of vegetation growth due to climate change.
- Changes in animal and plant numbers as habitats change.

The ozone layer and its destruction

Ozone (O_3) is a gas that is found in the upper atmosphere. It is important because it absorbs ultraviolet light from the Sun and prevents too much of it from reaching the Earth. High currents carry ozone from the equator regions of the Earth towards the polar regions. Ozone is formed when ultraviolet light splits oxygen molecules (O_2) and then joins one of these atoms to another oxygen molecule.

In the 1970s satellite measurement of the levels of ozone in the atmosphere began. It was soon realised that the levels of ozone in the atmosphere above the Antarctic were dropping and more recently levels above the Arctic have also dropped. It is thought that the main cause of the decreasing levels is the level of CFCs (chlorofluorocarbons) in the atmosphere. These chemicals were used in aerosols and refrigerators. The chlorine in the CFCs reacts with and depletes the ozone. Many countries have tried to reduce levels of use of CFCs and have developed some substitute substances. However because CFCs are very long lasting, those already in the atmosphere will have an effect for many years to come.

Lower levels of ozone in the atmosphere, and therefore increased levels of UV light penetrating the atmosphere, lead to problems such as higher levels of skin cancers, and immune deficiencies in humans. In addition there is concern that some types of plants could be effected and be unable to photosynthesise. This could have consequences for food chains including the production of food crops and also add to global warming if the amount of plant life was reduced.

Water pollution

Figure 4 Sewage being discharged into the sea in Morocco

Water is polluted from a variety of sources and has various effects.

- Some power stations use water as a coolant when they are generating electricity. The water is then returned to the river or sea. However this hot water from power stations can damage the aquatic habitat, because hot water contains less dissolved oxygen. This can lead to the death of animals and plants even though there may be no damaging chemicals present in the water.
- Metals and other chemicals disposed of into a river or stream can kill animals including fish.
- Most pollution of water courses in this country is as a result of organic waste or fertiliser run-off from fields. Organic waste may be slurry from cattle or other animals, or untreated sewage.
- The extra minerals in the water from these organic wastes cause extra growth in small plants called algae. Due to their small size but relatively large surface area, they are able to quickly absorb these minerals and this leads to a very rapid increase in their numbers. These plants may then cover the waters surface, preventing oxygen from the air dissolving in the water, and thereby reducing the levels of oxygen in the water. The algae do not live for long and when they start to die they are decomposed by microbes (mainly microbes). These microbes use up oxygen from the water and so the level of oxygen drops even further. If the process continues then animals in the water, from insects to fish may die. This process is called **eutrophication**.

More careful use of fertilisers, and other methods of disposal of slurry can reduce the problem of water pollution. In addition proper treatment of sewage, where it is aerated and passed through filter beds containing microbes that break it down, and then chemically treated, results in a large reduction in the pollution from this source.

Land pollution

Figure 5 Curently 80% of the UKs rubbish is dumped in landfill

In the developed world we are very wasteful of natural resources, in Britain alone we throw away 20 million tonnes of waste in dustbins every year. Some of this could be recycled, reused, or composted. Currently most of our rubbish ends up being buried in landfill sites, but there is a limited amount of land suitable for this process. The alternative is to dispose of the rubbish by burning it in an incineration plant. These are expensive to build and when they burn the rubbish the fumes they produce are toxic and can pollute the atmosphere. It is possible to use some types of incineration plants to generate power as they burn the rubbish. There is not a straightforward solution to the problem of rubbish disposal. It will be an increasing problem until we start to reduce production of rubbish and become less wasteful in our use of the resources in the world around us.

Questions

1 Draw a table and complete it as a summary of one of the main pollutants. Include the following categories: name of pollutant, source of pollutant, effect of pollutant, possible measures to reduce pollutant.

Websites

http://www.greanpeace.org.uk/
Information about various aspects of pollution with topical information.

http://www.worldwildlife.org/
Information about endangered species, forests and climate change.

http://www.johannesburgsummit.org
About the earth summit in 2002.

Exam questions

1 Farmers sometimes add fertiliser to fields but excess nitrates from the fertiliser can run off into nearby rivers causing pollution.

a) What substance will the water plants make using these nitrates?

(1 mark)

b) What effect will this have on the water plants?

(1 mark)

c) Explain how an increase in water plants can lead to the death of fish in the river.

(4 marks)

d) Name one other source of water pollution.

(1 mark)

2 Copy and complete the table.

Environment	Polluting substance	Effect
Air	Soot	
Water		Eutrophication
	Household rubbish	Litter

(3 marks)

3 Copy and complete the table.

Pollutant	Source	Effect
Sulphur dioxide	Car exhausts, burning coal and oil.	Lung diseases, reduced photosynthesis and gas exchange in plants.
Lead	Car exhausts, old piping and paint.	

(4 marks)

4 The diagrams show the greenhouse effect in 1900 and that predicted in 2030.

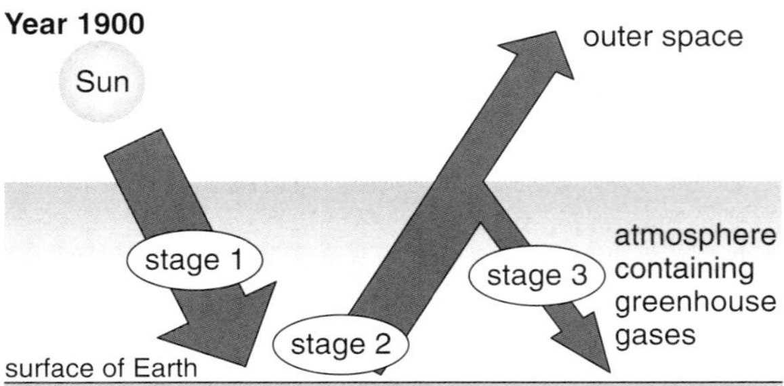

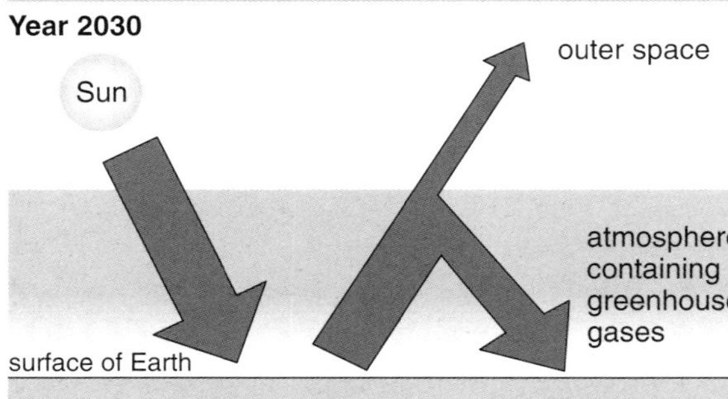

Use the information in the diagrams to help answer the following questions.

a) Describe stages 1–3 shown in the diagram for the year 1900.

(3 marks)

b) What effect does stage 3 have on the Earth's surface?

(1 mark)

c) Use the diagrams to give **two** changes predicted in the greenhouse effect.

(2 marks)

d) Suggest **two** other environmental changes which may be caused by the greenhouse effect in 2030.

(2 marks)

e) Name **two** greenhouse gases and give a source for each.

(4 marks)

f) Explain how deforestation could contribute to changes in the amounts of greenhouse gases.

(3 marks)

g) Give **two** other environmental effects of deforestation.

(2 marks)

The tissues of trees contain carbon which is recycled in forests.

h) Describe how the carbon is recycled when the trees die.

(3 marks)

Chapter 18

Conservation and Populations

Learning objectives

By the end of this chapter you should:

- Be able to explain what conservation is and why it is important
- Be able to explain the consequences of deforestation and the necessity for reafforestation and afforestation
- Be able to explain the measures taken to manage fish stocks and prevent overfishing
- Be able to state what pesticides are used for and how they can accumulate in the food chain
- Be able to explain the necessity for international action on pollution and conservation and consider some of the problems with implementation of strategies for conservation
- Be able to name and explain the various factors that affect population growth rate and decline
- Be able to give the factors that affect the size of the human population and methods that are used to control it

Conservation

Conservation is the management of the Earth's natural resources so that they are sustained and present for this generation and future generations. The aim of conservation is to preserve habitats and the variety of organisms that live within them, to minimise the destruction of these environments and to promote sustainable use of the Earth's resources.

Humans are the dominant species on the planet and due to their increasing numbers and use of resources there is a need to make a co-ordinated effort to try to ensure the long-term survival of the different habitats. What happens in one area of the world may have consequences elsewhere, for example use of resources in one country may lead to climate change elsewhere, or may affect animals that move from one area to another during their life-time. There is a need to try to preserve the **biodiversity** of the planet, i.e. all the plant and animal species that exist. Species that we do not even know about may well provide valuable sources of raw materials or produce chemicals that are useful in the treatment of disease. If such species became extinct then the habitat may suffer and along with it our knowledge of processes or materials that could be useful.

Conservation requires the co-ordination and co-operation of different bodies within or between countries. In 1991 Europe adopted a habitat directive with the aim of preserving natural habitats including woodland, chalk grassland, bogs and wetlands with funds available to help protect these habitats. However there are always competing considerations which mean that the process of conservation of such habitats is not without controversy. Housing and transport needs are often at odds with the need to conserve areas which may also provide necessary raw materials. This is not only true in our own country but on a worldwide basis. Rainforest destruction in South America continues to occur with logging of huge areas of the forests, suppling hardwood to developed countries. The removal of areas of forest is called **deforestation**.

Total global forest cover has declined from 3.21 billion hectares in 1990 to 3.12 billion hectares in 2000. In Brazil the rate of loss of rainforest was 1.2 million hectares per year in 1992 but in the last ten years this has accelerated to 2 million hectares a year. The Asia Pacific region has lost 30% of its forests in the past 40 years.

To combat this problem we need to try to develop programmes of reafforestation or afforestation. This involves either replenishing former forests or planting new ones that can be used in a sustainable way. These programmes allow some of the older trees to be felled to provide wood, employment and income, but these are then replaced. This process has to take place over quite a long time scale since it may take 30 years or more for the replacement trees to grow.

Deforestation has both local and worldwide consequences. It can lead to the loss of stability in the soil and soil erosion. Tree and plant roots help maintain the structure of the soil, without these roots there may be mud slides or an increase in flooding, as well as deterioration in the fertility of the soil. The populations of South American countries are increasing and their need for foreign currency to pay for goods, fuels the continued destruction of the forests.

Farmers in these countries also continue to clear the land to grow crops and in many cases the diversity of the forest is replaced by the growing of one crop such as maize or sugar cane. This is called **monoculture**. This method of growing crops is often accompanied by the over use of fertilisers and pesticides. If one species is grown exclusively then it tends to attract the pests and diseases of that crop and there may be no natural predators in that environment, so more chemicals need to be used to ensure a good crop. The soil also has no chance to renew its fertility so more fertiliser must be added.

a)

b)

Figure 1 a) This rainforest in Malaysia has been cleared for agricultural purposes. b) A monoculture in South Africa

The loss of vast areas of forest also has consequences for the rest of the Earth, with fewer trees there is less photosynthesis and so less absorbance of carbon dioxide and reduced production of oxygen. This loss of carbon dioxide absorbance may also contribute to the greenhouse effect.

In many areas of the world there are species that are declining in numbers which may become extinct if measures are not taken to halt their decline. Corncrakes are a species of bird that is found in Scotland, Northern Ireland and the west coast of Ireland. They spend most of their time hidden in tall vegetation. Once common, their numbers have declined and they have been put on the **Red List** of threatened species, which is a register of those species that are most endangered. Corncrakes nest in barley oats or hay fields. These crops are now cut much earlier in the year, so there is less food available for the birds and some can even die in the harvesting process. In some areas schemes have been introduced to leave margins at the edge of fields for corncrakes to shelter in. Farmers are encouraged to start mowing from the centre of a field which allows corncrakes time to escape. Farmers are also encouraged to delay mowing until August when all corncrake chicks will have hatched and grown large enough to escape the mowers.

There are many other species that are endangered, these include orang-utans, white rhinos, great white sharks, snow leopards, marine turtles, barn owls, cornflowers and many British species of butterfly.

Conservation of these species needs to involve local people and they often need to have incentives, such as gaining income from ecotourism. The number of critically endangered mammals, i.e. those on the brink of extinction rose from 169 in 1996 when the first accurate figures were available to 181 in 2002.

Habitats are comprised of a wide variety of animal and plant life, which are **interdependent**. Once the natural balance is disturbed not just one species of organism is affected, but the whole habitat is unbalanced and this disruption can have global consequences.

The introduction of new species to habitats where they are not normally found can cause great disruption. The introduction of rabbits into Australia had devastating consequences. These new species often out-compete the species found naturally in the habitat. These alien species disrupt the normal balance by either damaging the habitat or causing a decrease in the numbers of a particular species naturally found there. In addition the alien species may not have any natural predators in the new habitat and so their numbers may grow unchecked.

The case of the decline of the red squirrels shows that the processes involved may not be obvious at first. Grey squirrels were introduced to Britain from America. These grey squirrels out-competed the native red squirrels, causing their numbers to plummet. It was thought that the grey squirrels being larger had edged out the red ones in direct competition for food. More recently a different explanation has been put forward. Grey squirrels can digest chemicals in acorns that red squirrels cannot. Both species feed on hazelnuts, but grey squirrels also eat acorns. Therefore grey squirrels can find more food and store more as fat which gives them a greater chance of survival in the winter. Linked with this they also have a much higher reproductive rate.

Pesticides

Pesticides are substances used to kill pests, with herbicides being used to kill weeds – they are usually used to kill plants that are competing with food crops. Growing crops in monoculture allows for large amounts to be grown and harvested together, often weeds are treated with herbicides since they are relatively easy to apply and this allows continued growth of the crop.

Insect pests are treated with insecticides, which are another form of pesticide. The most well know of these is DDT, the use of which is now banned in the developed world. DDT was first introduced as a pesticide in the 1950s and 1960s. Subsequently it was noticed that many bird populations, especially those of predatory birds such as sparrow hawks had declined. Investigations showed that as well as having high levels of DDT in their tissues the eggs these birds were producing had very thin shells and so the young often didn't survive. DDT is not broken down in the body of animals and so remains there. Animals at the top of the food chain were therefore accumulating high levels of this poison as they ate their food. In developing countries this chemical is still used, particularly in spraying to kill mosquitoes that carry malaria, since this spraying is relatively simple and in some areas is effective in malaria prevention.

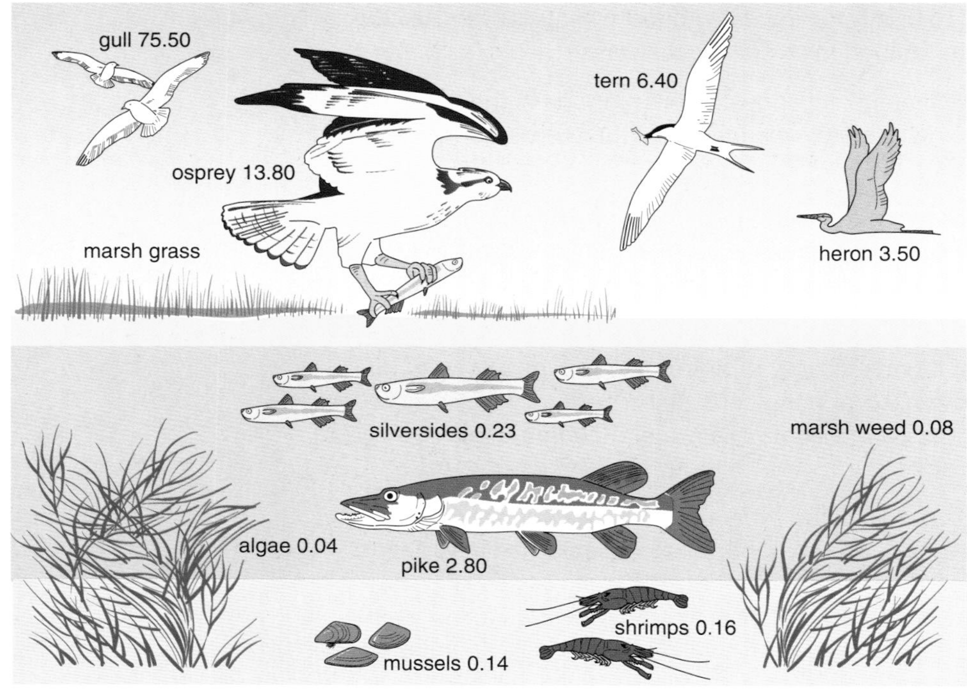

Figure 2 DDT is absorbed into the tissues of organisms at each level of the food chain, with those higher up the chain accumulating higher levels of the poison. Figures are in parts per million of DDT

Conservation of fish stocks

Fish stocks have been dwindling world wide mainly due to the use of much larger fishing trawlers, often equipped with technology that enables them to track shoals of fish. This has resulted in **overfishing**. Canada's cod population off its east coast crashed in 1992 and fishing had to be stopped in the hope that the small remaining population would survive and repopulate the waters. A similar pattern has been seen in the North Sea where the cod population has fallen by 60 % in 20 years. There are now calls for all cod fishing in Europe to be banned to prevent the cod from becoming extinct. Herring stocks in the North Sea have also declined. Certain measures need to be taken to try to manage the fish stocks, so that the fish are not removed at a faster rate than the rate at which they can be replaced by reproduction. These measures include:

1 Research and knowledge of the fish, their life cycle, feeding grounds and breeding grounds. This enables reliable estimates of the numbers of adults that can be taken without damaging the fish population, to be drawn up.
2 **Quotas** – i.e. laws on how many fish can be caught in terms of size and also at what time of the year the fishing can take place. This means not fishing during the breeding season to allow the numbers of fish to increase.
3 Using larger **mesh sizes** of nets so that the younger fish can escape and breed and increase the population.
4 Making it an offence to catch smaller fish. However one of the problems with this is that some smaller fish can end up in nets with the larger ones; even if the smaller ones are returned to the sea they often have been damaged and do not survive.
5 Setting up **sanctuaries** or areas where fishing is prohibited for example the spawning or nursery areas.
6 **Decommissioning** of boats to reduce the numbers of trawlers catching fish and compensating fishermen for their decommissioned boats.

The European Union has a Common Fisheries Policy to deal with overfishing. However there is always dispute over the figures for sustainable fish stocks and different countries do not always agree on the division of the quotas, since this may effect their fishing industries and economies.

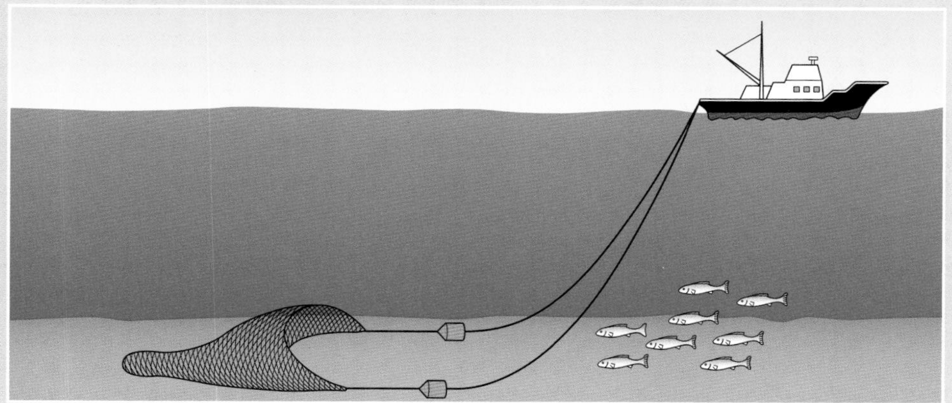

Figure 3 To avoid overfishing, nets with larger mesh sizes should be used

International action on pollution and conservation

The world we live in is made up of many different environments that are interdependent. Activities such as development and pollution in one country may have effects on other habitats and environments elsewhere. Air pollution and water pollution can be driven by wind or water currents hundreds of miles from their sources and have major effects on other habitats, wildlife and humans.

In 2002 an international conference on pollution was held in Johannesburg. Delegates from 190 countries attended and limited agreement was reached on some policies including the following:

- countries would try to stop the loss of biodiversity
- More countries agreed to try to reduce CO_2 emissions (USA was a notable exception,
- countries would try to reduce the number of people in the world without basic sanitation to half the current number by 2015 (current number 2.4 billion)
- countries would try to provide clean drinking water to more people

Many facts associated with pollution and conservation are disputed and remain controversial. Different countries have various priorities that make it difficult to achieve universal agreement on the issues involved. In most cases the issues are complex and do not have straightforward solutions, but in developed countries we could do more to reuse, recycle and conserve raw materials and protect habitats, as well as assisting less affluent nations in their attempts to provide for their people whilst still preserving habitats and resources. At the conference in Johannesburg it was recognised that richer countries need to increase their aid to poorer countries. They were encouraged to increase their aid to give 0.7 % of their national income to enable better living standards for those in poorer countries and to help with the development of habitat conservation.

Populations

The **population** of a species is its total number in that area. This depends on the birth rate and the death rate for that species.

The **birth rate** is the average number of births for every 1000 individuals in a population each year.

The **death rate** is the average number of individuals who die each year for every 1000 in a population.

Populations tend to follow a pattern of development called a **population growth curve**. This shows the numbers in the population over a period of time. It follows the same pattern for most species, but the time scale may vary considerably depending on the species, for example in bacteria or simple organisms the time scale may be a few days, whereas in the case of the human population the time scale is thousands of years.

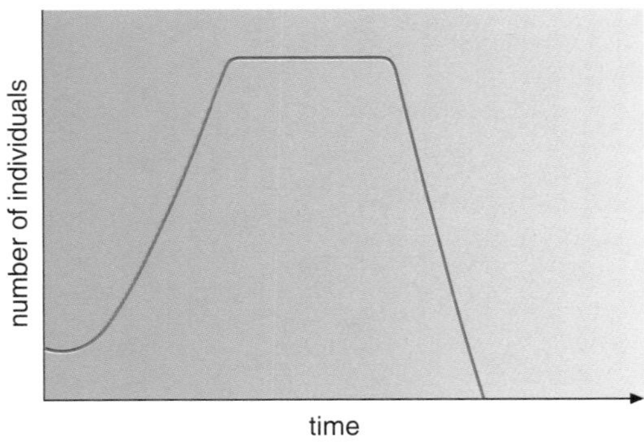

Figure 4 Population growth curve

The growth pattern is divided into four stages: the lag, rapid growth stage, plateau and death or decline phase. During the **lag phase** there is slow growth in numbers followed by a **rapid growth phase**, since if the organisms have a ready food source, space and other necessary requirements their numbers will increase dramatically. Generally after a period of time this is followed by a stage where there is stability in numbers when the birth rate is exactly equalled by the death rate – this is called the **plateau phase**. Finally the organisms may run out of space, food or may accumulate waste or may become subject to predation by other organisms and so the numbers start to decline – the **decline phase**. Other factors that can influence populations are immigration of new members into the population or emigration to other areas.

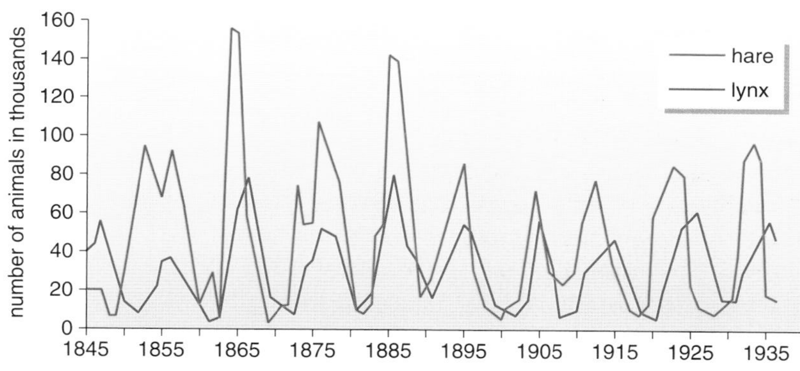

Figure 5

Some studies have shown cycles where an organism increases in numbers followed by an increase in numbers of its predator. This then leads to a reduction in the numbers of prey followed by a reduction in the numbers of predators at a later stage. However care needs to be taken when interpreting some of these figures, since other factors such as change in the diet of the prey may also be influencing figures. This is true of the most often quoted example of the lynx and hare populations in the 1800s and early 1900s. It is now thought that a cyclic change in the growth of vegetation that formed the hares diet may have been the main reason for the changing population of hares, rather than the number of lynx.

Questions

1. Give three steps that could be used to conserve one particular animal or plant.
2. Why is it difficult to get agreement on what measures should be taken to conserve animals and plants.

The human population

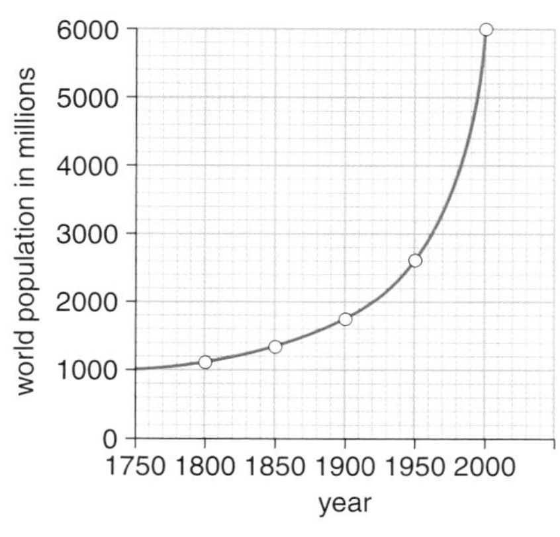

Figure 6 Growth curve of the human population since 1750

The human population has shown dramatic increases in the last few hundred years. This has been due to a combination of factors including:

1. Improvements in agriculture and machinery.
2. Improved diet.
3. Improved hygiene especially the efficient disposal of sewage and the purification of water.

4 Improvements in medical care. These include vaccination, better methods of treating diseases including the development of antibiotics and better surgical techniques, as well as greater knowledge of the prevention of illness.

As the rate of growth continues it puts increased pressure on the world's resources. However people in developed countries use a disproportionate amount of the Earth's resources. In these countries the population numbers are in rapid decline with the use of contraceptives and many people deciding not to have children, or to have only a small number. In other areas of the world, especially the developing world, the rate of population growth is still increasing. Some countries, such as China, have a government policy to limit the number of children to one per family in an effort to reduce their population and the demands on natural resources. In other developing countries increasing numbers of people cause problems since they are competing for food and shelter in areas that struggle to produce enough food for the existing population.

Websites

http://www.greenpeace.org.uk/
Information about various aspects of pollution with topical information.

http://www.worldwildlife.org/
Information about endangered species, forests and climate change.

http://www.johannesburgsummit.org
About the Earth Summit in 2002.

Exam questions

1 The population of mice in a woodland area was found to be 1000. During the next month the following information was collected.

- Number of births = 207
- Number of deaths = 242
- Number of immigrants = 10
- Number of emigrants = 21

a) Calculate the number of mice in the population at the end of the month. *(2 marks)*

b) Give **one** reason for each of the following.

(i) Mice dying *(1 mark)*

(ii) Mice emigrating *(1 mark)*

2 The graph shows changes in the population of algae in a pond.

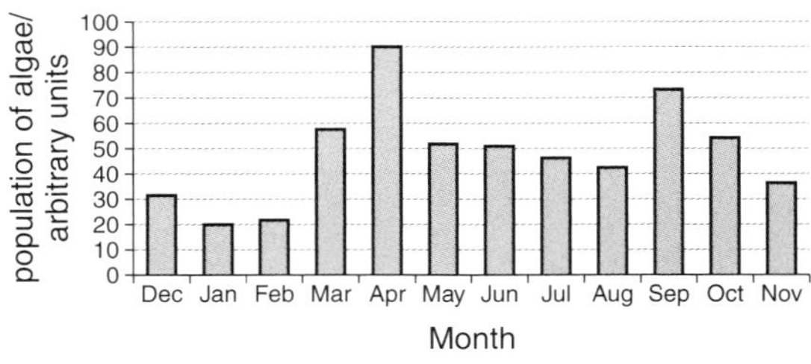

a) Describe the change in the population of algae from April to October. *(2 marks)*

b) Suggest **two** factors which may have caused the changes in the population of algae from January to April. *(2 marks)*

3 Over-fishing has reduced the population of some types of fish in the North Sea.

a) Why does over-fishing affect population numbers?

(1 mark)

b) Explain how over-fishing may be prevented by:

(i) having a closed season.

(1 mark)

(ii) increasing the size of mesh used in fishing nets.

(2 marks)

c) Give **two** other methods used to manage the stocks of fish in the North Sea.

(2 marks)

4 Humans have damaged the environment by deforestation.

a) Explain what is meant by the term deforestation.

(1 mark)

b) Suggest how deforestation affects the number of species living in the area.

(1 mark)

c) Give one way the atmosphere is changed by deforestation.

(1 mark)

5 The graph shows changes in the number of yeast cells in a sugar solution.

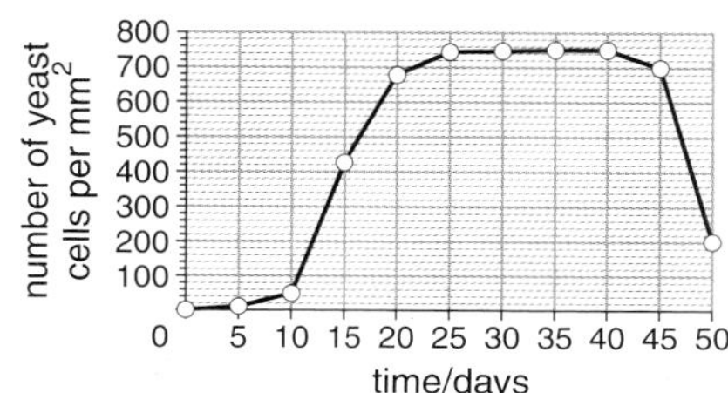

a) Describe the change in the number of yeast cells between 10 and 20 days.

(1 mark)

b) Explain this change in terms of birth and death rate.

(2 marks)

c) Suggest one reason for the change in the number of cells between 40 and 50 days.

(1 mark)

Chapter 19

Human Reproduction

Learning objectives

By the end of this chapter you should:

- Be able to identify the parts of the male and female reproductive systems and state their functions
- Be able to state that fertilisation takes place in the oviducts and explain the development of the embryo on its way to the uterus
- Be able to identify the placenta, umbilical cord amnion and amniotic fluid
- Be able to state the main events of birth
- Be able to explain the functions of the umbilical cord, amnion, amniotic fluid and how they are adapted for their functions
- Be able to explain the steps necessary to maintain health during pregnancy and promote the healthy development of young children
- Be able to state the physical and emotional changes that take place in boys and girls in adolescence
- Be able to describe and explain the events of the menstrual cycle
- Be able to explain the importance of responsible attitudes to sexual behaviour, how STDs are caused, how they can be prevented and the principles of contraception
- Be able to explain the causes of infertility and how hormones can be used to help in ova production
- Be able to explain the major steps of in vitro fertilisation
- Be able to explain the applications of artificial insemination and embryo transfer in animals

All species need to be able to reproduce to ensure the continuation of the species.

Humans and mammals carry out **sexual reproduction**, which involves the joining of two **gametes** – the egg (ovum) and the sperm. The advantage of sexual reproduction is that it produces variety in the offspring. In addition, particularly in the case of humans, the offspring are protected inside the body of the mother during their initial development and then spend considerable time under the care of their parents.

Figure 1 shows the human male and female reproductive systems.

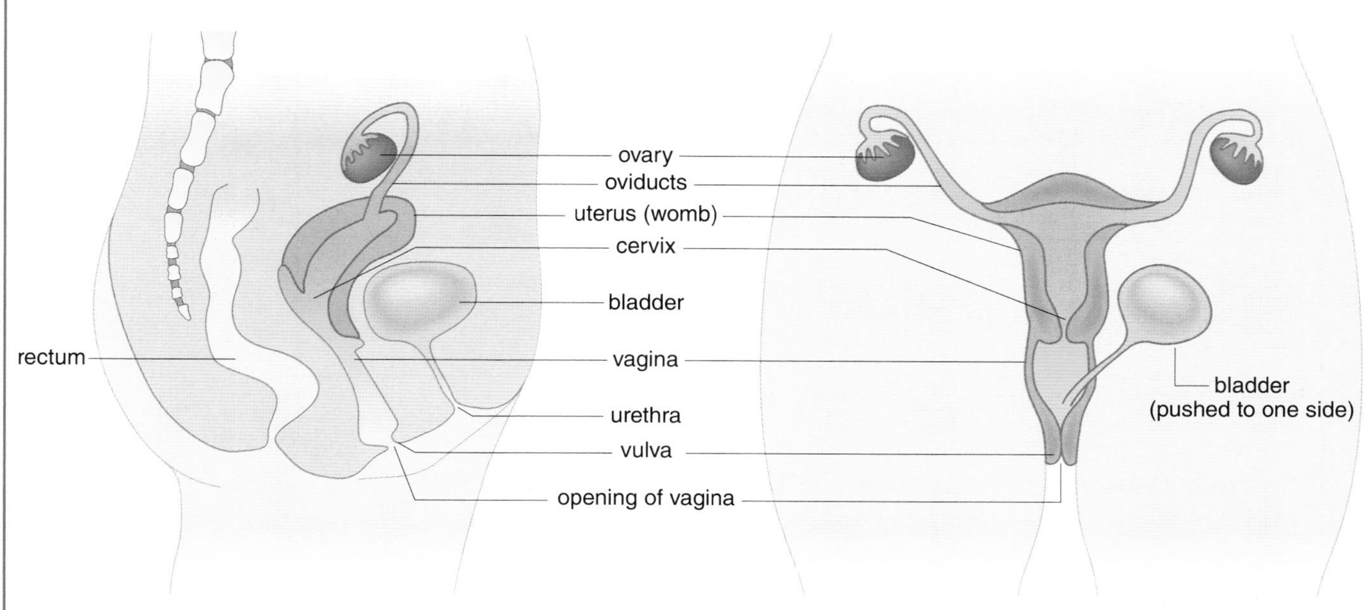
ovary
oviducts
uterus (womb)
cervix
bladder
rectum
vagina
urethra
vulva
opening of vagina
bladder
(pushed to one side)

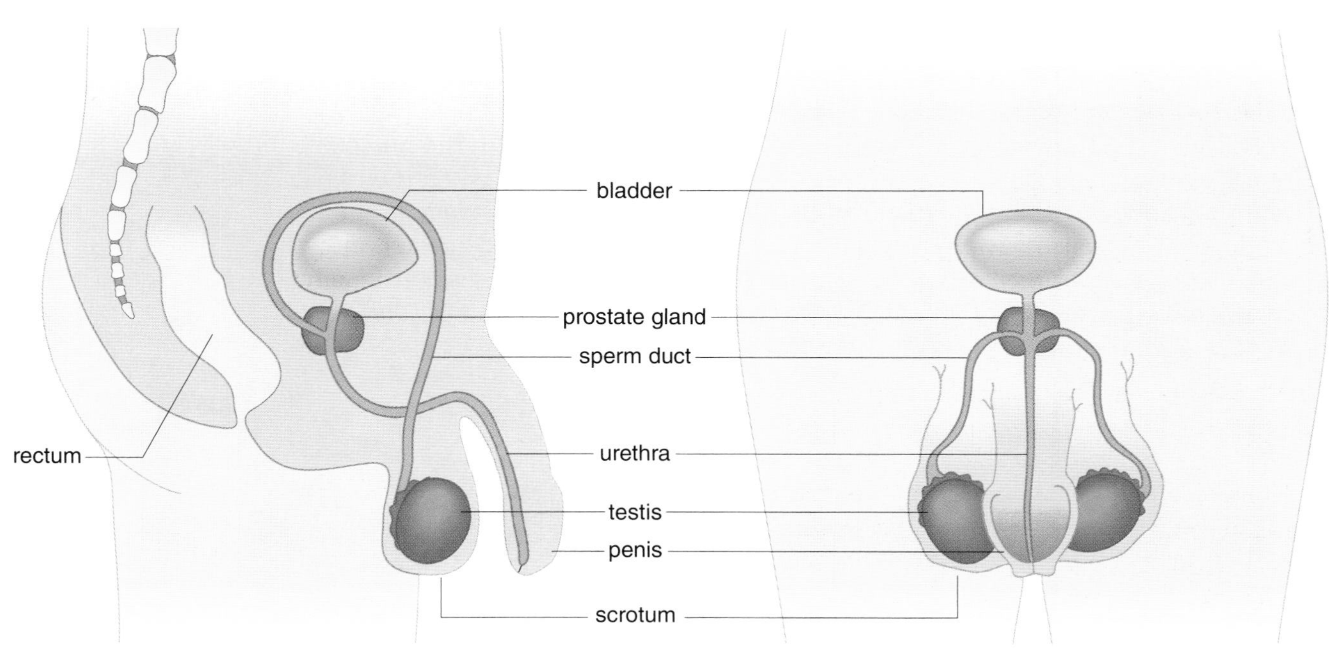
bladder
prostate gland
sperm duct
rectum
urethra
testis
penis
scrotum

Figure 1

The functions of the male and female reproductive systems are given below.

Male reproductive system

Structure	Function
Testes	Production and development of sperm
Scrotum	Sac to protect the testes
Sperm ducts	Carries sperm to the urethra
Prostate gland	Produces secretions which carry the sperm
Urethra	Carries urine, or fluid containing sperm down through the penis
Penis	Organ that carries the sperm to the vagina

Female reproductive system

Structure	Function
Ovaries	Produce eggs (ova)
Oviducts	The site of fertilisation. Carry the ova fertilised or unfertilised to the uterus
Uterus	Allows the development of the fertilised ovum and produces structures to help its growth
Cervix	To restrict the opening of the uterus
Vagina	To allow entry of the penis for fertilisation
Vulva	Protection of the vagina and produces lubricant to allow sexual intercourse to take place

Fertilisation and early development of the embryo

Fertilisation takes place when the nucleus of the ovum fuses with the nucleus of the sperm. Each gamete carries with it 23 chromosomes and when the two join they form one cell with 46 chromosomes. Fertilisation takes place in the oviducts. The sperm have to travel up the vagina, through the uterus and into the oviducts. After fertilisation the **zygote** (fertilised ovum) divides continually by **mitosis** (a type of cell division) to produce a ball of identical cells. The **zygote** then continues to travel down the oviducts to the uterus.

Figure 2

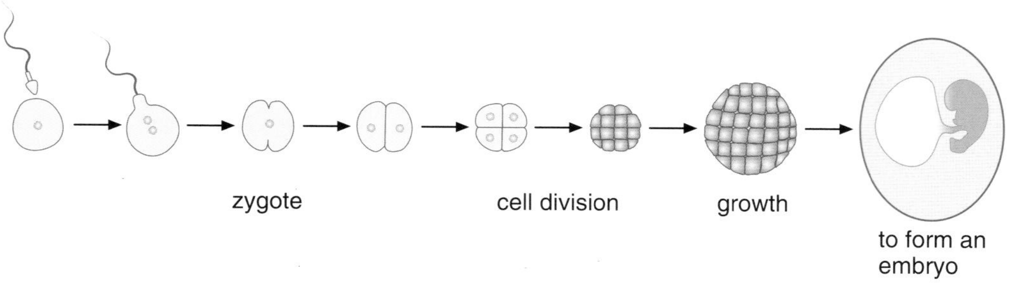

When it arrives in the uterus the zygote fuses with the lining of the uterus (**implantation**). Gradually, at the point where the zygote has joined the lining of the uterus, the **placenta** and **umbilical cord** form. The cells in the zygote continue to divide, but now start to develop into specialised cells. To help protect and cushion the zygote – now called the embryo – a membrane called the **amnion** develops around it. The cavity between the amnion and the embryo fills with fluid called the **amniotic fluid**.

Birth

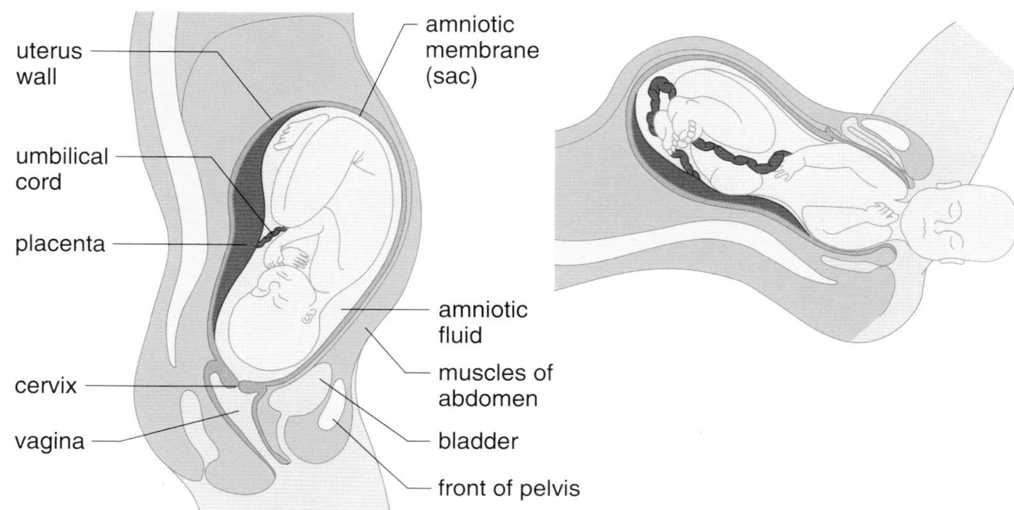

Figure 3 Birth

The embryo continues to develop inside the uterus for nine months. After about four weeks the baby is called a **foetus**. Gradually, during the first months all the organs are formed and in the later part of the pregnancy the foetus starts to become much larger. Towards the end of the nine months the baby will usually turn so that it is upside down inside the uterus, ready to be born. The first sign that the process of birth is about to start is usually when the mother begins to feel pain caused by contractions of the muscles of the uterus. These pains gradually become more powerful and more frequent. The cervix starts to widen and the amniotic membrane ruptures. This is called the 'breaking of the waters'.

Gradually the uterine contractions push the baby down through the cervix and vagina. After the baby is born the umbilical cord is cut. The contractions continue for a while until the placenta is pushed out. This is called the **after-birth**.

Specialised structures developed during pregnancy

The amnion and amniotic fluid enclose the developing foetus to cushion and protect it. Inside this amniotic sac the foetus is linked to its mother's blood supply via two structures, the umbilical cord and the placenta. The umbilical

Figure 4

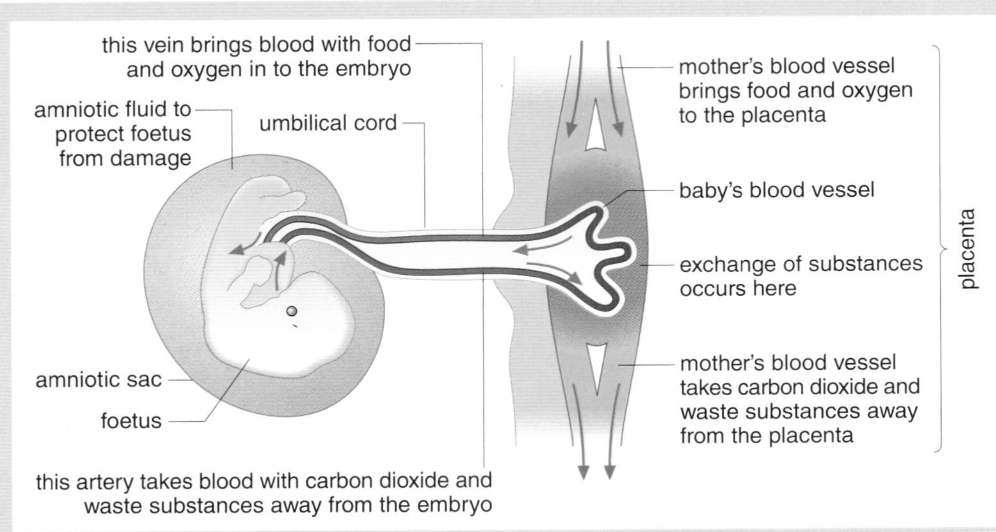
this vein brings blood with food and oxygen in to the embryo
amniotic fluid to protect foetus from damage
umbilical cord
mother's blood vessel brings food and oxygen to the placenta
baby's blood vessel
exchange of substances occurs here
placenta
amniotic sac
foetus
mother's blood vessel takes carbon dioxide and waste substances away from the placenta
this artery takes blood with carbon dioxide and waste substances away from the embryo

cord carries blood vessels linking the placenta and the foetus. These blood vessels, called the **umbilical artery** and **vein**, carry nutrients and oxygen to the foetus and waste such as urea from the foetus to its mother. These blood vessels are unusual because the umbilical artery carries the waste products whereas the umbilical vein carries the nutrients and oxygen. These blood vessels are linked to the placenta. The placenta has a large surface area for the exchange of gases such as oxygen and carbon dioxide and the movement of nutrients and waste products. The membranes of the blood vessels are thin to allow for diffusion to take place, but the mother's and foetus' blood do not mix in the placenta. The foetus may have a different blood group from its mother, if the two bloods were to mix they would clump and this could cause death.

Pregnancy and the needs of the young child

During pregnancy the foetus gains all its nutrients from its mothers blood. It is important that the mother eats a balanced diet to ensure that the developing foetus is supplied with all the nutrients it requires to grow. The mothers blood is usually monitored during pregnancy to check if there are any problems and in recent years it has been recommended that women ensure they have sufficient folic acid in their diets to ensure good development of the foetus (particularly of its nervous system).

Since the placenta has permeable membranes to allow substances to pass across into the foetal blood, it also allows small molecules other than food and gases to pass across. This includes substances such as alcohol and drugs, including heroin and amphetamines. If the mother is a drug addict the baby will also be one when it is born. It has to be weaned off the drug and may have suffered damage during its development. Alcohol consumption during pregnancy seems to result in increased chances of miscarriage and underdevelopment in the baby. Smoking during pregnancy is linked with babies of lower birth weight. The carbon monoxide in cigarette smoke is thought to be the cause since it results in less oxygen being carried in the blood. If there is less oxygen in the mother's blood the foetus will receive less oxygen. Vaccination against rubella is usually carried out in schools to try to ensure that there is less likelihood of a women contracting rubella when she is pregnant, since this can also cause damage to the foetus.

After birth the baby requires a lot of care to ensure that it develops and thrives. At first the baby lives by drinking milk. Breast milk produced by the mother has some advantages over bottled milk since it contains antibodies produced by the mother. These antibodies help to protect the baby from infections straight after birth. Breast milk also contains the correct proportions of nutrients to meet the child's needs. However in some cases it is not possible to breast-feed the baby and bottle formulas of milk have been developed.

Figure 5 Children need a stimulating environment

It takes a while for the baby's digestive system to develop before it can start to eat more solid food, but after some months it is necessary to start to change the babies diet since the one substance not contained in milk is iron. The baby has sufficient supplies of this mineral to last for several months, but eventually a more varied diet is needed. Iron is needed for the production of haemoglobin for red blood cells.

Babies are totally reliant on their parents. They need a loving and caring environment with stimulation to ensure good mental and physical development.

Puberty

This is a period of development during which large physical and emotional changes take place in an individual. The physical changes are detailed below, but along with these are emotional changes. Individuals want to be more independent and they also become more sexually aware. This can lead to confusion and arguments with parents or other adults. Gradually individuals learn to adjust to the physical and emotional changes, as do those around them, as they develop into adults.

In girls the major physical changes during puberty are an increase in height, development of breasts, growth of hair in the armpits and pubic region. Along with this menstruation begins.

In boys the physical changes are also an increase in height, the development of hair in the armpits and pubic region, together with facial hair, deepening of the voice and growth of the testes and penis.

These changes in boys and girls are known as **secondary sexual characteristics**.

Menstruation

This process starts at puberty in girls and continues usually once a month until the **menopause** when the process stops.

About every month one ovum is developed so that it is mature enough to be fertilised. This ovum undergoes changes in the ovary over a period of approximately 14 days. At the same time hormones ensure that a thick lining is developing in the uterus ready for the ovum if it is fertilised. After about 12 days the ovum is released from the ovary, this is called **ovulation**, and the ovum starts to travel along the oviduct. If it is fertilised the ovum will remain in the uterus and develop into a foetus. If the ovum is unfertilised it travels on down into the vagina together with the lining of the uterus which comes away with some blood. This is called **menstruation** or a period. The first day of the

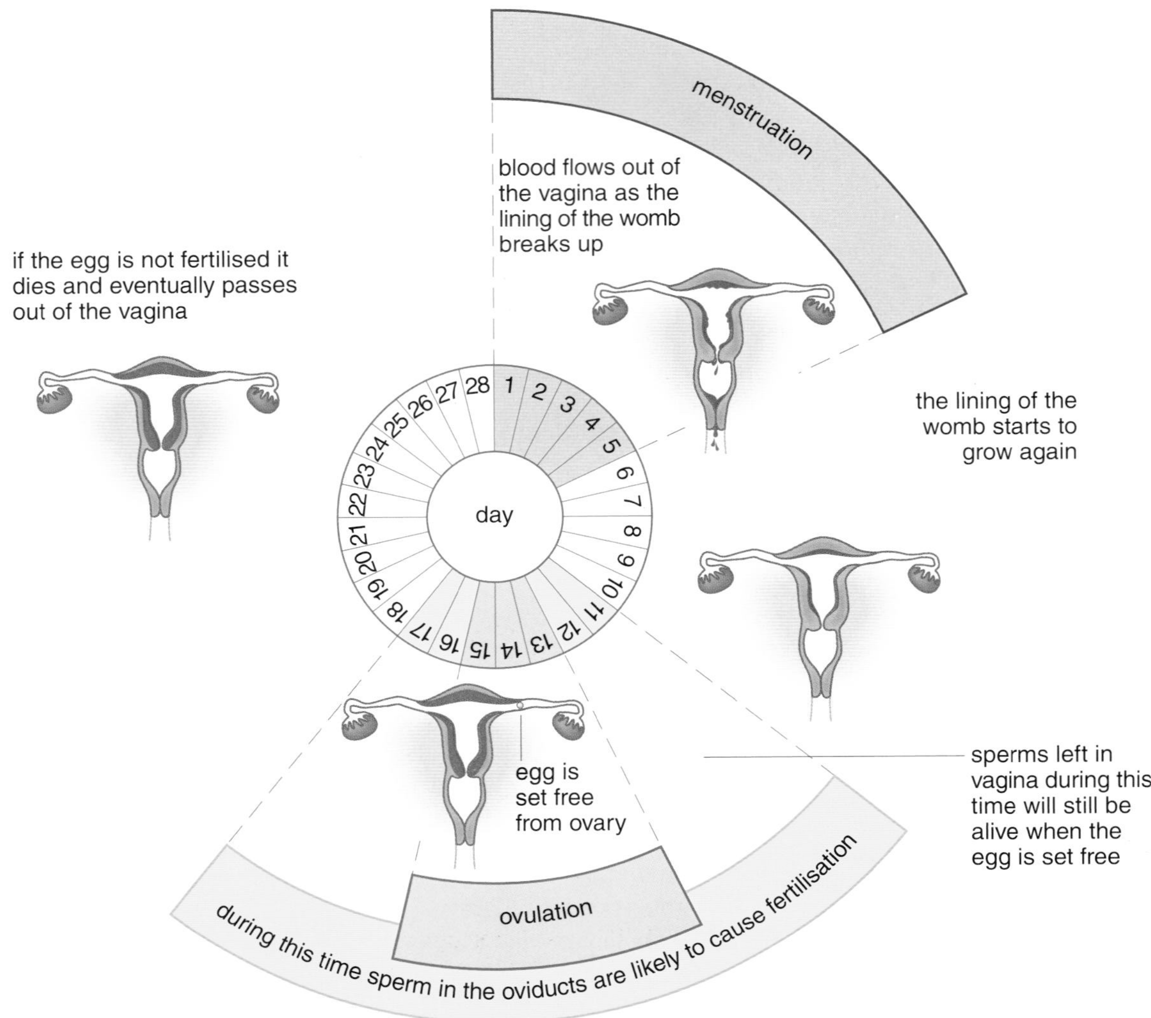
menstruation
blood flows out of the vagina as the lining of the womb breaks up
if the egg is not fertilised it dies and eventually passes out of the vagina
the lining of the womb starts to grow again
day
1 2 3 4 5 6 7 8 9 10 11 12 13 14 15 16 17 18 19 20 21 22 23 24 25 26 27 28
egg is set free from ovary
sperms left in vagina during this time will still be alive when the egg is set free
ovulation
during this time sperm in the oviducts are likely to cause fertilisation

Figure 6

period is called day 1 and usually it lasts about 5 days. The length of the menstrual cycle varies but is usually about 28 days. The events of the menstrual cycle are brought about by several hormones.

Responsible sexual behaviour

Sexual intercourse is a natural process but the biological end product is designed to be the production of a baby. Therefore intercourse is best reserved for a stable, caring relationship where the individuals are mature enough to be able to care for a child.

In addition there are some diseases that can be passed on during sexual intercourse which can be damaging to individuals. Some of these are caused by bacteria, others are caused by viruses. These include **gonorrhoea**, which is caused by a bacterial infection. These bacteria can cause a discharge from the reproductive organs and a burning sensation when you urinate. If it is untreated it can cause problems in the joints of the body and sterility. Early treatment with antibiotics can kill the bacteria.

AIDS is another sexually transmitted disease caused by the HIV virus. In addition to intercourse it can also be passed on through use of intravenous needles from an infected person, or through infected blood. The virus damages the immune system and so the body cannot defend itself against other infections. AIDS is fatal. There are some treatments available but they can only prolong life, they cannot cure the disease. The best method of prevention is to only have a sexual relationship with one partner who isn't infected and to use a condom during intercourse, although even this may not give complete protection.

Many people in a sexual relationship do not want to have children at that time. Methods of preventing conception of a child are called **contraception**. The different methods work in a variety of ways, and individuals, with advice from their doctors, choose the method most appropriate for them at that stage in their life. Natural methods rely on abstaining from intercourse at times when pregnancy is most likely to take place, especially around the middle of the menstrual cycle. This method has the advantage that it does not involve the use of any chemicals, but many people find the restriction on sexual intercourse difficult to deal with and it is not totally reliable.

Mechanical methods of contraception rely on preventing the gametes from meeting. These methods include the condom and the diaphragm. They are sometimes also called barrier methods. **Condoms** are widely available and relatively easy to use provided they are placed over the erect penis early enough before any sperm are produced. The **diaphragm** is a circle of rubber inserted into the top of the vagina to prevent the sperm travelling into the uterus and oviducts. However it must be obtained from a doctor or family planning clinic since it needs to fit correctly and the woman has to be shown how to use it correctly.

The main chemical method of contraception is the **pill**. This uses hormones to block ovum production and so there is no ovum to fertilise. This is a widely used method of contraception and if the pill is taken in the correct manner it is a very successful contraceptive. Sometimes women can forget to take a pill and this may mean that they could develop an ovum and possibly become pregnant. The contraceptive pill is only available from a doctor or family planning clinic since there are health risks associated with its use and doctors therefore need to monitor women's blood pressure when they are on the contraceptive pill. Doctors also suggest that over the age of 35 women consider using other forms of contraception.

If people have had children and do not want any more, or are sure that they never want children, then the longer term solution is surgical. In women this involves an operation where the oviducts are cut to prevent the sperm reaching the ova. In males the operation is called a **vasectomy** and involves cutting the tubes that carry the sperm. After recovery from the operation the semen is checked over a period of several months to check there are no sperm present. All other functions of the male reproductive system operate in the same way as before the operation – the only difference is that there are no sperm in the semen.

Questions

1 Draw a table to show the main types of contraceptives and how they work. Also give any advantages or disadvantage associated with each method.

Fertility research and problems

Most people have no problems in conceiving if they want a family but a minority, about 10 % of the population in the western world, find that they do have a problem. Recent developments in fertility research now provide some methods and hope of alleviating this problem. For some couples the problem is with the female reproductive system, for others it is the male reproductive system, and for some there are problems with both systems.

The reasons for female infertility are summarised in Figure 7.

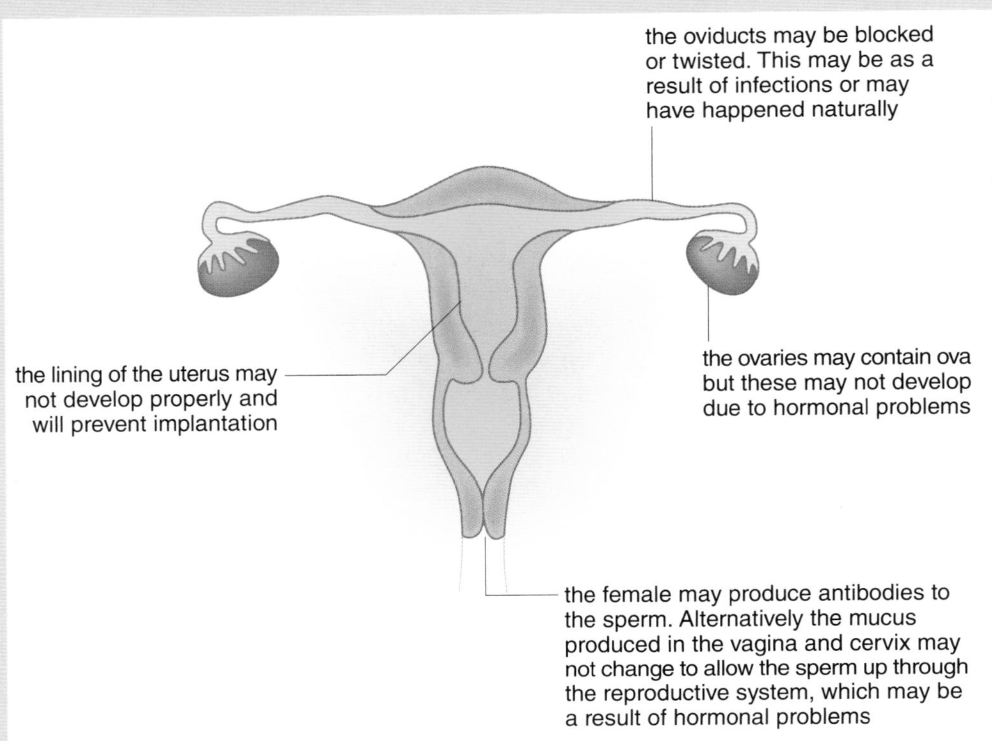
the oviducts may be blocked or twisted. This may be as a result of infections or may have happened naturally
the lining of the uterus may not develop properly and will prevent implantation
the ovaries may contain ova but these may not develop due to hormonal problems
the female may produce antibodies to the sperm. Alternatively the mucus produced in the vagina and cervix may not change to allow the sperm up through the reproductive system, which may be a result of hormonal problems

Figure 7 Causes of female infertility

In males the process of sperm formation takes about 60–70 days and this can be affected by the general health of the male. Smoking and excessive alcohol intake may cause changes in the hormones that control sperm production. As a result fewer sperm may be produced or there may be an increased number of abnormal sperm, for example those without tails. The temperature at which sperm development occurs is also thought to be a factor. Sperm develop better in conditions about 1°C below normal body temperature. These factors may lead to a decreasing chance of a sperm successfully fertilising an ovum.

To overcome these difficulties there are several processes that help to increase the chances of fertilisation. The method used depends on what is causing the problem in individual cases.

1 Use of **fertility drugs**. These are given to the woman and affect her ovaries, causing them to produce more ova. It has sometimes led to the development of multiple babies, but in more recent years the process has been refined so this does not happen so often.

2 **In vitro fertilisation** (test-tube babies). This techniques involves giving the woman fertility drugs to ensure that she produces several ova. These ova are then collected from the woman's ovaries by surgical techniques just before they would normally be ovulated. This means that when they are added to sperm from their partner there is a good chance of fertilisation. This process takes place in a petri dish, rather than a test-tube. The embryos that develop are monitored until they have divided several times, where upon several of them are implanted back into the woman's uterus. The woman is given other hormones prior to implantation to ensure that her uterus is ready for the embryos. The number of embryos implanted into the uterus has now been reduced to two by most clinics. In the past some clinics implanted more embryos to increase the chances of at least one successful implant, but in a few cases all the embryos successfully implanted and multiple births resulted.

One of the problems arising from this technique is that there are more embryos produced than are used and there is debate about what to do with these spare embryos. In Britain some of these are used with the parents permission for research, but this is only allowed on embryos that are up to 14 days old.

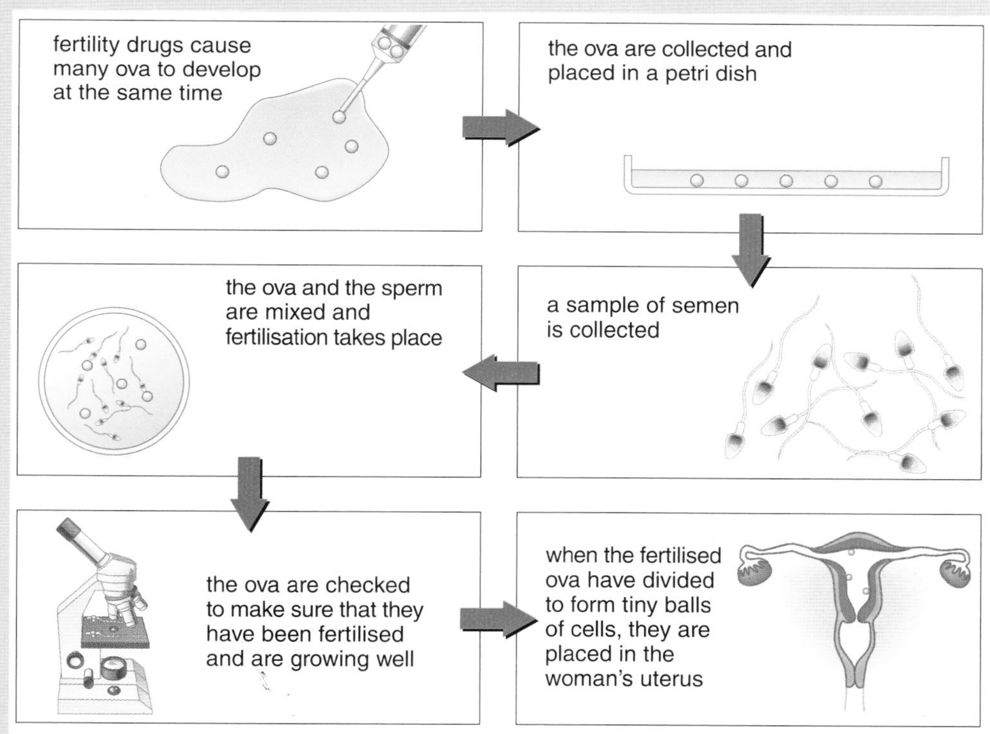
fertility drugs cause many ova to develop at the same time
the ova are collected and placed in a petri dish
a sample of semen is collected
the ova and the sperm are mixed and fertilisation takes place
the ova are checked to make sure that they have been fertilised and are growing well
when the fertilised ova have divided to form tiny balls of cells, they are placed in the woman's uterus

Figure 8 In vitro fertilisation

Reproductive techniques used in farm animals

If an animal such as a cow has a high milk yield or other desirable characteristics it may be an advantage to the farmer if he obtained several ova from that cow and once they were fertilised, used other cows to develop the calves. The process involves using fertility hormones to produces more ova in the cow. She is then artificially inseminated with bull's semen and some of the ova are fertilised and start to develop into embryos in the cow's uterus. After about six weeks these are washed out of the uterus, collected, and then transferred into other cows where they develop until they are born. These recipient cows are given hormones prior to transfer of the embryos to make sure that their uteruses are ready for the embryos.

Artificial insemination can also be used along with hormone treatment to result in a group of animals all giving birth at the same time. This may allow the farmer to make better provision for the animals at the time of birth and lead to better survival and treatment of the mothers and their offspring. To do this reproductive hormones are placed in coils which are put into the vaginas of a group of animals. The coil is left in place for a period of time and when it is removed its removal leads to ovulation in these animals at the same time. They can then be artificially inseminated at the same time and the birth of their offspring will take place within a short time of one another (see Chapter 23).

Websites

http://www.bbc.co.uk/science/teenspecies/index.shtml
Body changes, behaviour, interactive tour of the teenage body.

Exam questions

1 During puberty many changes occur in the human body.

a) Give **two** changes that occur in girls at puberty. *(2 marks)*

b) Give **one** change which occurs in boys but not in girls. *(1 mark)*

2 The diagram shows part of the male reproductive system.

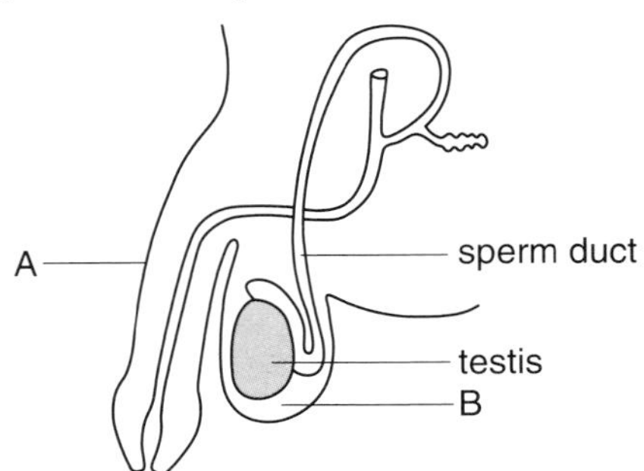

a) Name parts A and B. *(2 marks)*

b) Give **one** function of the

(i) testis. *(1 mark)*

(ii) sperm duct. *(1 mark)*

3 a) The diagram shows part of a human female reproductive system.

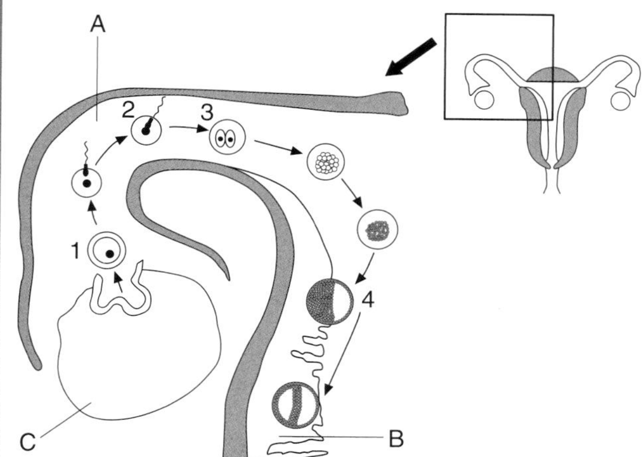

(i) Name parts A, B and C. *(3 marks)*

(ii) Name the processes occurring at 1, 2 and 3. *(3 marks)*

(iii) Describe the process occurring at 4. *(2 marks)*

b) The diagram shows a baby just before birth.

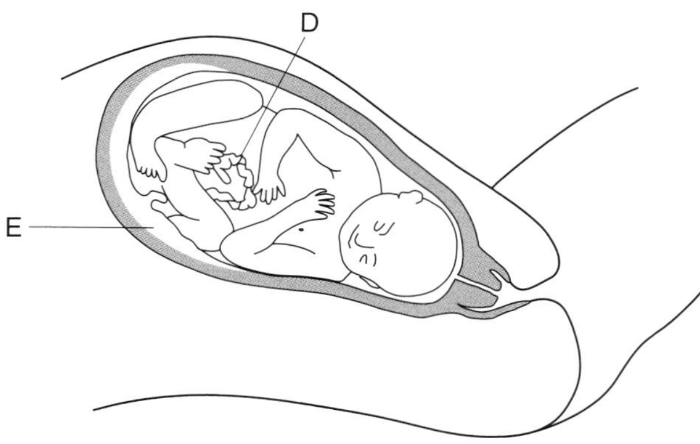

(i) Name parts D and E. *(2 marks)*

(ii) Give **three** changes which occur during birth. *(3 marks)*

(iii) Suggest why babies, born to mothers who smoke, have a lower birth weight than those born to non-smokers. *(2 marks)*

c) The diagram shows a male reproductive system after surgery.

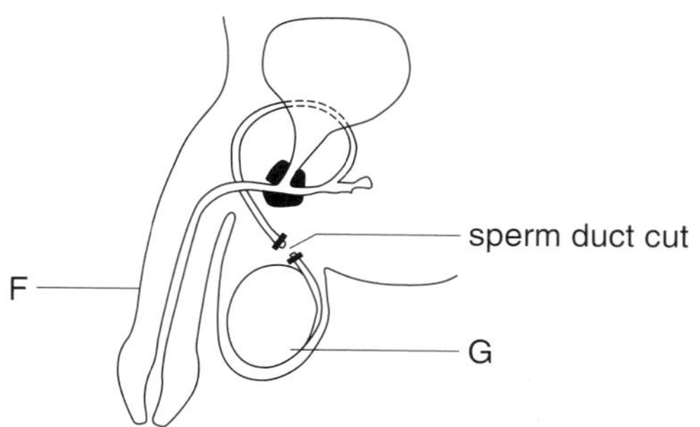

(i) Name parts F and G. *(2 marks)*

(ii) Copy the diagram and shade the part where sperm are made. *(1 mark)*

(iii) **Use the diagram** to explain how this surgery acts as a method of contraception. *(2 marks)*

4 The diagram summarises *in vitro* fertilization.

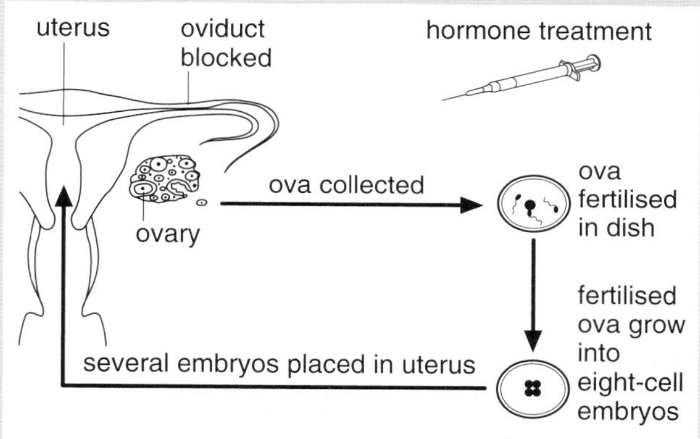

a) Explain why a blocked oviduct prevents a woman becoming pregnant. *(1 mark)*

b) Why are hormones given to the woman at the start of IVF treatment? *(2 marks)*

c) Suggest why the fertilised ova are allowed to grow into eight-cell embryos before being placed into the uterus. *(1 mark)*

d) Give one reason why several embryos are placed into the uterus. *(1 mark)*

Chapter 20

Cell Division and Cancer

Learning objectives

By the end of this chapter you should:

- Be able to give an outline of the processes of mitosis and meiosis
- Be able to state where these processes take place in humans
- Be able to give some of the similarities and differences between the two processes
- Be able to state that cancer is abnormal cell division
- Be able to give some of the triggers that can lead to cancer
- Be able to state the main difference between benign and malignant tumours
- Be able to explain why early detection of cancers is important
- Be able to state the three main methods of treatment of cancer

Cell division

Cells have a limited life span and therefore must be able to reproduce to ensure continuity of function and of the organism. To achieve this cells divide in a process called **cell division**. There are two types of cell division – **mitosis** and **meiosis**.

Cells must all contain genetic information in the form of chromosomes so that they have the instructions on how to carry out protein synthesis. Therefore at the start of both types of cell division the number of chromosomes must be doubled. The chromosomes are made of the chemical **DNA** and this initial stage involves **DNA replication**. After this the two types of cell division proceed in different ways.

Mitosis

This takes place in all animal cells to increase the numbers of cells, either during growth or to replace cells. In addition the same process takes place in some plants and in single celled organisms such as bacteria and yeast during asexual reproduction. In humans there are normally 46 chromosomes in a cell and the end result of mitosis is two cells each with 46 chromosomes. Cells with 46 chromosomes are called **diploid** because they have two copies of each chromosome. The end result of mitosis is two diploid cells that are *identical* to each other.

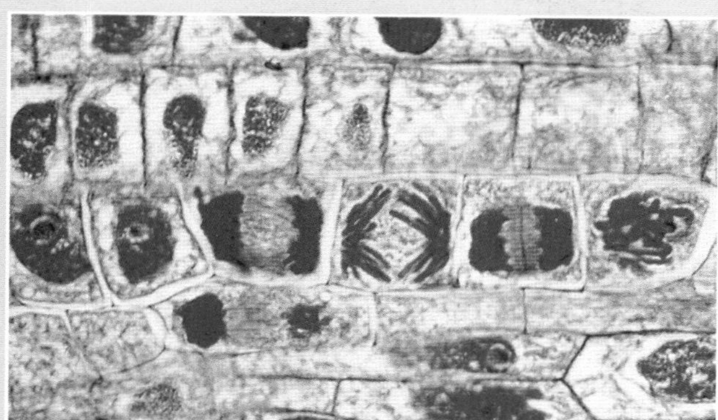

Figure 1a This photo shows cells at various stages of mitosis

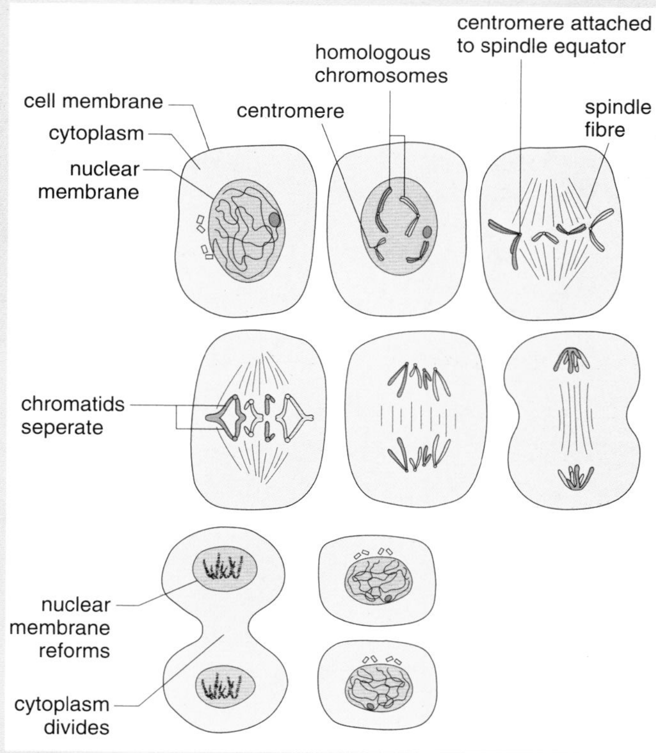

Figure 1b Mitosis

The main stages in mitosis are:

1 DNA replication – i.e. copying of the chromosomes (to produce chromatids).
2 Separation of the chromosomes so that half goes to one end of the cell and the other half to the opposite end of the cell. (The chromatids line up in the middle of the cell and are pulled by their centromeres along the spindle fibres to opposite ends of the cell.)
3 Nuclear membranes are formed around the two groups of chromosomes.
4 Division of the cytoplasm and formation of a membrane to give two separate cells (in plant cells new cell walls are also formed).

Meiosis

This process takes place only to produce *gametes*. Therefore it occurs in the testes and ovaries in humans. The end result is the production of four gametes from each cell that carries out this process in the testes or ovaries. Each of these gametes has 23 chromosomes. The gametes are described as **haploid** because they have half the chromosomes of a normal cell. However this means that when the gametes (sperm and ovum) join together the diploid number of chromosomes (46) is restored. The other main difference between this process and mitosis is that each gamete is *genetically different* due to **independent assortment**. This means that during separation there is a mixture of chromosomes, with some coming originally from the mother and others coming originally from the father. There is however one copy of each type of chromosome present. Figure 2 shows details of the process.

The main stages in the process are:

1 DNA replication – i.e. copying of the chromosomes.
2 Separation of the chromosomes so that half goes to one end of the cell and the other half to the opposite end of the cell.
3 Division of the cytoplasm and formation of a membrane to give two cells, each with 46 chromosomes.
4 A further separation of the chromosomes in each of the two cells, to give four sets of 23 chromosomes in total.
5 Division of the cytoplasm and formation of a membrane of each cell, to give four cells in total, each containing 23 chromosomes.

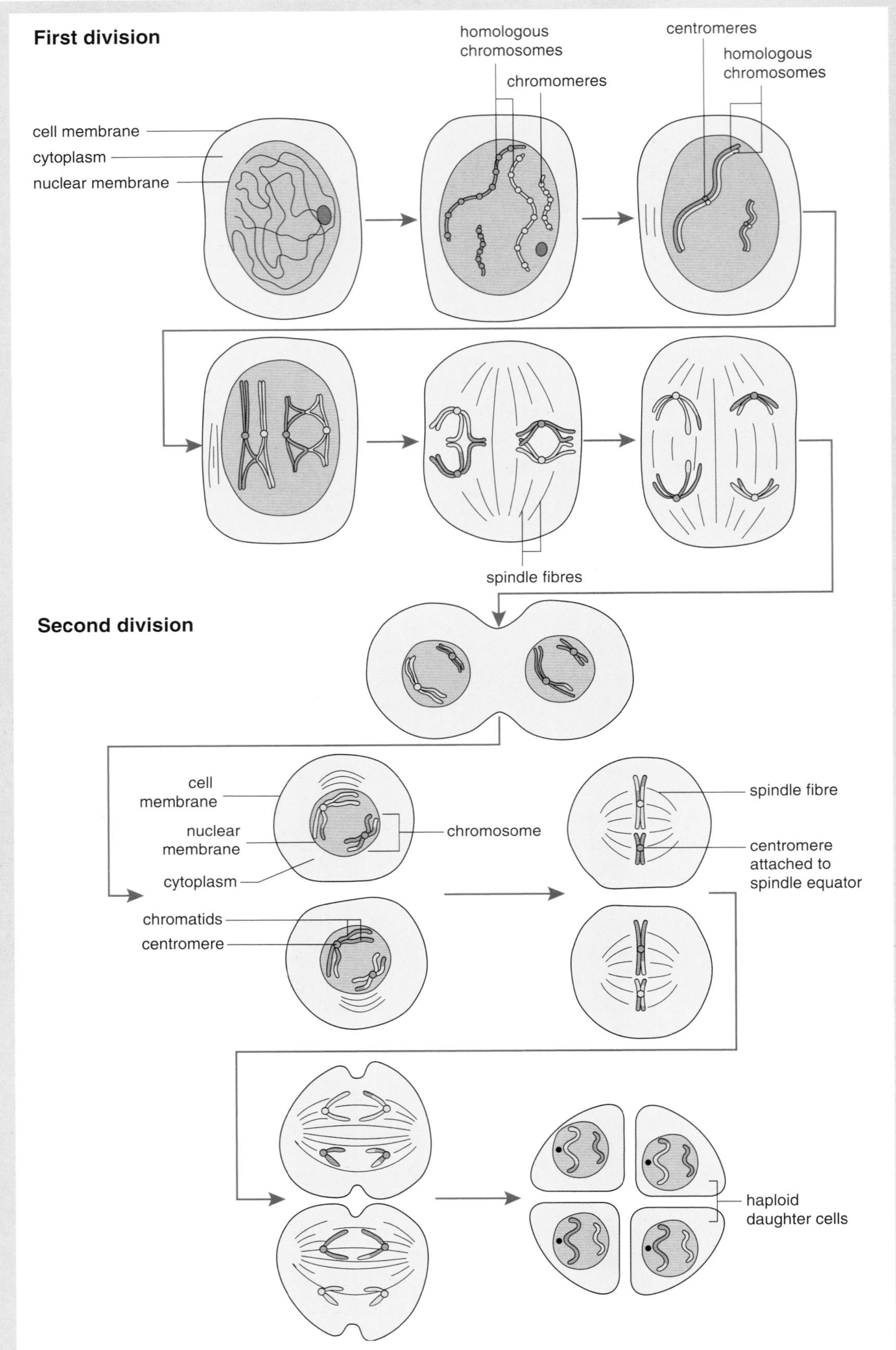

Figure 2 Meiosis

Cancer

This disease is produced by uncontrolled cell division. Mitosis occurs, but the usual constraints do not occur and the process continues unchecked. In addition the cells start to change and in some cases the cells develop thicker cell membranes and very large nuclei.

These changes can be used to detect cancer, for example in some screening programmes such as in smear tests carried out for cervical cancer. Screening programmes can aid early detection of cancers before a lump or more obvious sign of the disease occurs. They can be carried out for breast and prostate cancer in addition to cervical cancer.

The earlier a cancer is detected the better the chances of successful treatment and recovery, since there are fewer cancer cells to deal with and there is less likelihood of the cancer having spread to other parts of the body. Cancer can occur in any type of cell. Cancer cells cause damage because they disrupt the functioning of the normal cells in that region and the normal cells can no longer carry out their function. Cancers that spread and cause disruption are called **malignant**. Others remain in one place and do not disrupt normal function. These are called **benign** tumours.

The causes of cancer are not fully understood but there are some substances that are known to be **carcinogenic** (cancer causing). These include:

- Smoking which leads to a dramatic increase in the risk of lung cancer and cancers of the respiratory tract.
- Ultraviolet light which leads to an increased risk of skin cancer.

In addition viruses cause some cancers in animals and are thought to be linked with some forms of cancer in humans. There also seems to be a genetic link in some cancers which means that individuals in that family are more likely to suffer from certain forms of cancer.

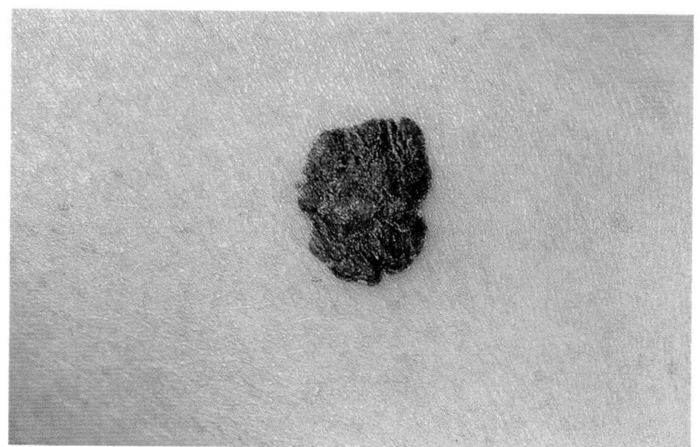

Figure 3 Skin cancer

Treatment of cancer falls into several categories depending on the type of cancer involved.

1 **Surgery** – this involves removal of the cancer cells. This method is sometimes followed by the use of one of the other two treatments to ensure all the cancer cells have been removed or killed.

2 **Radiotherapy** – this involves using X-rays or other forms of radiation to kill the cells, with the radiation being directed at a particular area affected with cancer.

3 **Chemotherapy** – this is where chemicals are used to kill the cancer cells. The drugs used are quite powerful, so they can also kill normal cells and cause some side effects.

All these treatments have a much greater chance of success when the numbers of cancer cells are low. In addition the treatment of cancers detected at an early stage will be less severe and recovery therefore easier. Methods are also being developed to increase the effectiveness of these treatments, for example, in the case of chemotherapy, to try to develop ways of delivering drugs so that they are targeted at the cancer cells and therefore do not affect normal cells. This would also lead to a reduction in the dose of drugs needed. There have been many developments in recent years, which have greatly increased the survival and quality of life of people who have cancer, and research continues to build on these advances.

Questions

1 Why do cells need to divide?

2 Give two smilarities and two differences between mitosis and meiosis.

3 What is cancer?

4 Explain the benefits of early detection of cancer.

Websites

http://www.cancerhelp.org.uk
Information about cancer.

http://www.cancerbacup.org.uk/
Information, questions, resources.

Exam questions

1 The number of people developing skin cancer is increasing.

a) Give **one** cause of skin cancer. *(1 mark)*

b) Suggest **one** way to reduce the risk of developing skin cancer. *(1 mark)*

c) Give **one** way skin cancer can be treated. *(1 mark)*

2 When cells get worn out, they are replaced by new ones. The process of cell division that produces new cells sometimes goes out of control. This is shown in the diagrams.

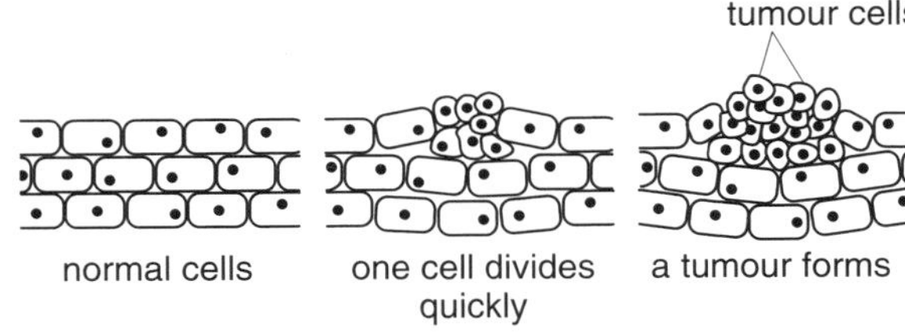

a) What is abnormal cell division called? *(1 mark)*

b) Give **two** ways, shown in the diagrams, that tumour cells differ from normal cells. *(2 marks)*

Chapter 21

Genetics

Learning objectives

By the end of this chapter you should:

- Know how to interpret and complete monohybrid crosses
- Know the principle of the test cross (back cross) and be able to complete a test cross using genetic diagrams
- Understand how sex is determined in humans
- Understand that some diseases, including cystic fibrosis and Down's syndrome, are inherited
- Understand sex-linkage and be able to use genetic diagrams involving sex-linkage

We are all aware that young animals and plants resemble their parents. Sometimes the family likeness is so great that it is easy to match offspring with their parents. The passing on of family characteristics from parents to offspring is called **inheritance**. **Genetics** is the scientific study of inheritance.

Gregor Mendel – the founder of genetics

Much of our understanding of genetics is based on the work carried out by Gregor Mendel. Mendel was born in Austria in 1822 and as a young man joined the church. As a monk in a large monastery he developed an interest in the breeding of the garden pea, plants that were common in the monastery garden. Mendel noticed that the garden pea had many characteristics that varied from plant to plant. These characteristics included pea shape and pea colour. The peas in the garden were either green or yellow and they could be round or wrinkled. Mendel carried out a range of breeding experiments in which he **crossed** (mated) plants carrying particular characteristics that he was interested in. By careful observation of the offspring produced, he was able to draw conclusions about the nature of inheritance.

Figure 1 Gregor Mendel

One characteristic of pea plants that Mendel was interested in was plant height. Pea plants occur in their normal tall form or in a much shorter dwarf variety. One breeding cross that Mendel carried out was a cross between tall and dwarf plants. Before he carried out this cross he allowed the tall plants to breed with each other for a period of time to ensure they always produced tall plants. He did the same with the dwarf plants by allowing only dwarf plants to breed together until he was sure that they would only have dwarf offspring. The parent plants he used were then referred to as **pure breeding**.

When Mendel crossed the tall plants with the dwarf plants (the parental generation) he found that all the plants in the first, or **F1 generation** (the offspring) were tall. However, when he crossed these F1 plants with other F1 plants their offspring (the second or **F2 generation**) were a mixture of tall and dwarf plants. Furthermore, as he carried out many crosses that produced hundreds of F2 plants he worked out that approximately 75% of these were tall with 25% dwarf.

Explanation of the monohybrid cross

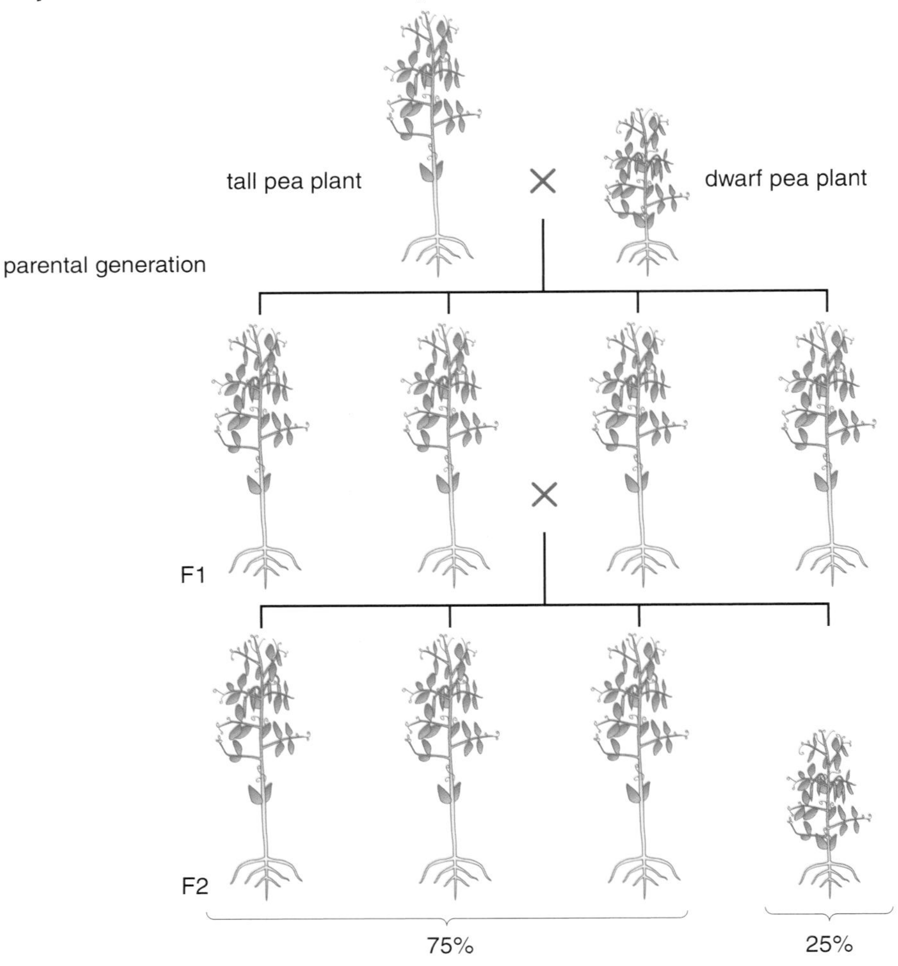

Figure 2 Mendel's results

As only one factor was considered in this cross (height of pea plants) it is referred to as a **monohybrid** cross. Mendel decided to give the characteristics he was observing symbols. He used the symbol **T** for the tall plants and the symbol **t** for the dwarf plants. He used a capital for the tall state, as it appeared to dominate the dwarf condition. Mendel suggested that there was some factor for tallness in the tall plants and an alternative factor for dwarfness in the short plants. We now know that Mendel's 'factors' are **genes** and that they are carried on the chromosomes. As chromosomes occur in pairs the genes also occur in pairs as shown in Figure 3. The two contrasting forms of a gene, i.e. T and t, are called **alleles**. Alleles are different forms of the same gene.

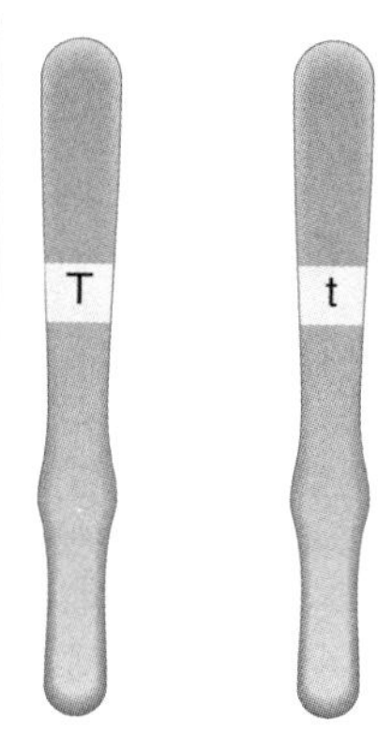

In this example the two alleles of the gene are different. The individual is heterozygous for the characteristic concerned

Figure 3 Chromosomes showing the position of one gene on a pair of chromosomes

Alleles occur in the same position on the chromosome. As the parental plants were pure breeding, Mendel suggested the tall plants only carried the tall factors (genes) and the dwarf plants only carried dwarf factors. These plants containing only one type of allele are **homozygous** (TT or tt). When both types of alleles are present the individual is **heterozygous** (Tt).

The paired symbols used in genetics are referred to as the **genotype** and the outward appearance (tall or short) is the **phenotype**.

Mendel also deduced that when gametes are produced only one factor from each parent passes on to the offspring. This is fully explained by our understanding of meiosis, as we know that only one chromosome, and therefore one allele, of each pair can pass into a gamete.

This was Mendel's **law of segregation**. The two members (alleles) of each pair of genes separate during meiosis, with only one of each pair being present in a gamete.

The F1 plants in our cross must have received one T allele from their tall parent and one t allele from the dwarf parent. The F1 plants were therefore Tt (heterozygous). Although all these plants contained both the T and the t allele they were all tall. This can be explained by considering the T allele **dominant** over the **recessive** t allele. The recessive condition will only be expressed, or visible, in the phenotype when only recessive alleles are present in the genotype (e.g. tt).

Figure 4 shows that when the F1 plants were interbred a ratio of 3:1 (tall:dwarf) was produced.

This ratio is achieved because the two alleles (T and t) of one parent will be produced in equal numbers during meiosis and they have an equal chance of combining with the T or the t allele produced by the other parent during fertilisation.

Mendel completed his work without being aware of the existence of chromosomes or genes. He also had no knowledge of chromosome behaviour in meiosis. Although he published his work in 1866 it did not get the credit it deserved and remained largely ignored. It was only at the start of the 20th century when chromosomes were discovered under the microscope that the significance of his findings was appreciated. Although additional research and knowledge has increased our understanding of genetics in recent times, it is important to note that this knowledge has built on Mendel's findings as opposed to contradicting them.

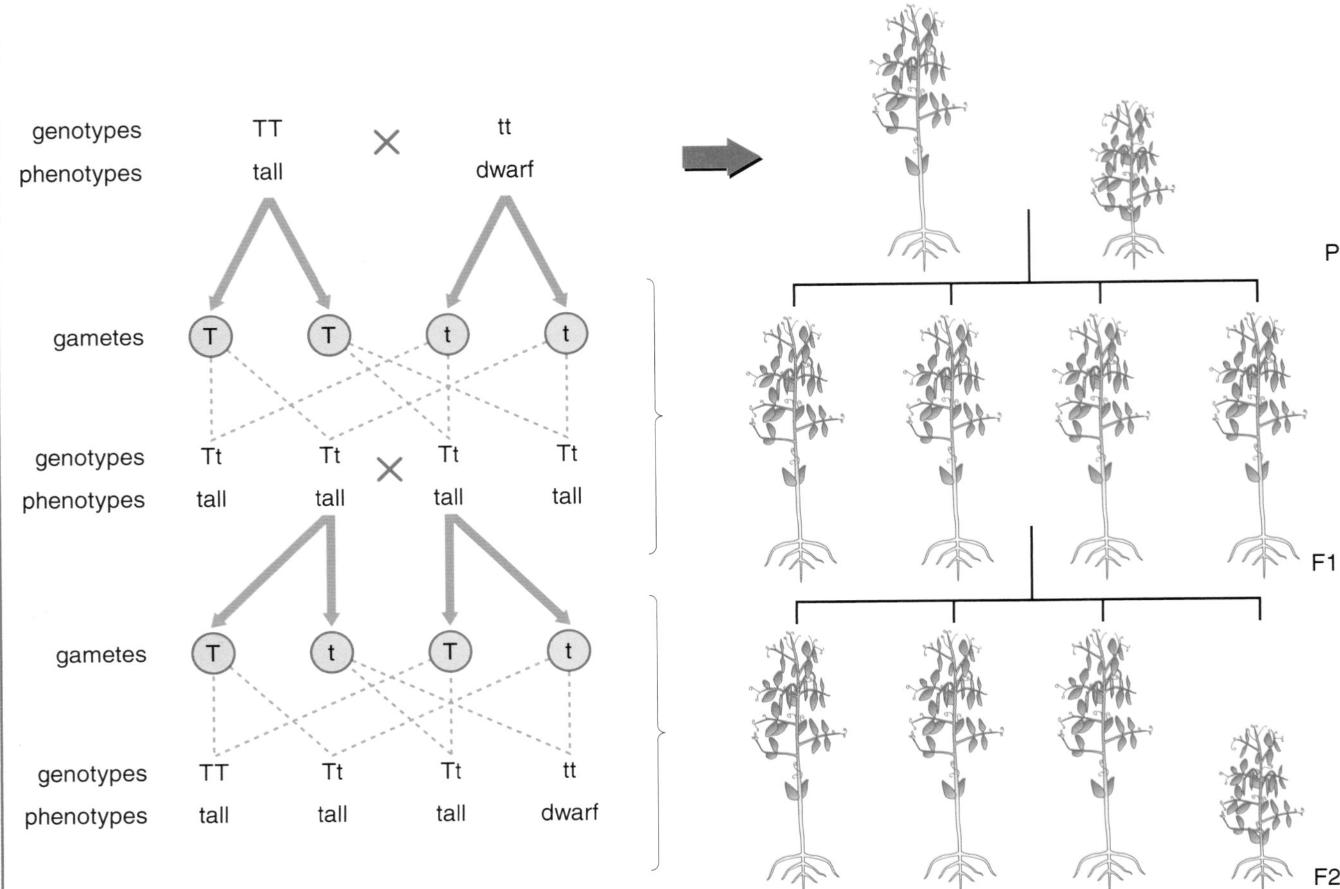

Figure 4 Explaining Mendel's results

Although the inheritance of most human characteristics is complex, often involving many genes and even chromosomes for a single characteristic, some human features do show monohybrid inheritance. Examples include eye colour and the ability to roll the tongue.

When completing genetic diagrams it is helpful to use a small grid called a **Punnett square**. Figure 5 uses Punnett squares to show examples of the monohybrid crosses that can occur in humans.

Some important points about genetic crosses

- Ratios will only be accurate when large numbers of offspring are produced. This is because it is totally random which gametes, and therefore alleles, fuse during fertilisation.
- It is common practice to use the same letter for both the dominant and recessive alleles, with the dominant allele being the capital and the recessive allele written in lower case.
- If a 3:1 ratio is present in the offspring of a particular cross, both of the parents involved will be heterozygous for the character being considered.
- If a 1:1 offspring ratio is produced in a cross, one parent will be heterozygous and the other homozygous recessive.

mother's gametes

father's gametes	B	B
b	Bb	Bb
b	Bb	Bb

100% of offspring have brown eyes

100% of offspring are heterozygous Bb

mother's gametes

father's gametes	B	b
b	Bb	bb
b	Bb	bb

50% of the offspring are heterozygous Bb and will be brown-eyed

50% are homozygous bb and will be blue-eyed

mother's gametes

father's gametes	B	b
B	BB	Bb
b	Bb	bb

So there is a 75% chance of these two heterozygous brown eyed parents having a brown-eyed child, and a 25% chance of having a child with blue eyes. This gives the ratio 3:1 brown:blue.
This percentage chance applies at each conception, therefore it is possible for all of the children to have blue eyes

75% of the offspring have brown-eyes

25% of the offspring are homozygous bb and have blue-eyes

Figure 5 The inheritance of eye colour in humans (B = brown, b = blue)

The test cross (back cross)

A tall pea plant can be either homozygous (TT) or heterozygous (Tt). Both genotypes give exactly the same phenotype. Sometimes, in agriculture or in the breeding of domestic animals, it is important to know the genotype of a particular animal or plant that is showing the dominant phenotype. To identify the unknown genotype a **test** or **back cross** is carried out.

The animal or plant in question is crossed with a homozygous recessive individual. If offspring are produced in sufficient numbers it is possible to identify the unknown genotype.

In the example of the pea, a tall plant could be homozygous (TT) or heterozygous (Tt). To identify the unknown genotype of the plant it is crossed with a homozygous recessive plant.

If the unknown genotype is TT

parental	phenotype	tall	×	dwarf
	genotype	TT		tt
gametes		(T)		(t)

Punnett square

	t
T	Tt

offspring	
genotype	all Tt
phenotype	all tall

If the unknown genotype is Tt

parental	phenotype	tall	×	dwarf
	genotype	Tt		tt
gametes		(T)(t)		(t)

Punnett square

	t
T	Tt
t	tt

offspring		
genotype	50% Tt	50% tt
phenotype	50% tall	50% dwarf

So if any dwarf plants are produced the unknown parent was heterozygous (Tt).

Figure 6 The test cross

Sex determination in humans

Sex in humans is another characteristic that is genetically determined. Humans have 46 chromosomes in each cell (except gametes) consisting of 22 pairs of normal chromosomes and one pair of sex chromosomes. The **sex chromosomes** determine the sex of each individual. Males have one X and one Y sex chromosome whereas females have two X chromosomes. A complete set of chromosomes is known as a **karyotype**. Figure 7 shows the karyotypes of the human male and female.

During meiosis the female will provide one X chromosome for each gamete, but half the male's sperm will have an X chromosome and half will have a Y chromosome. As there will be an equal chance of an X or a Y chromosome from the male being involved in fertilisation there will be equal numbers of males and females produced. Again, the random nature of fertilisation must be emphasised. We all know of large families consisting of only sons or only daughters. Work out the chance or probability of parents having five children, all of whom are male.

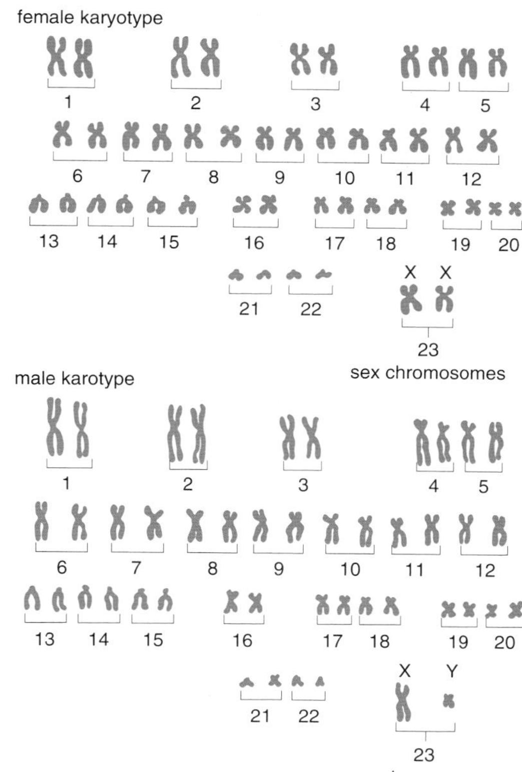

Figure 7 The complete set of human chromosomes

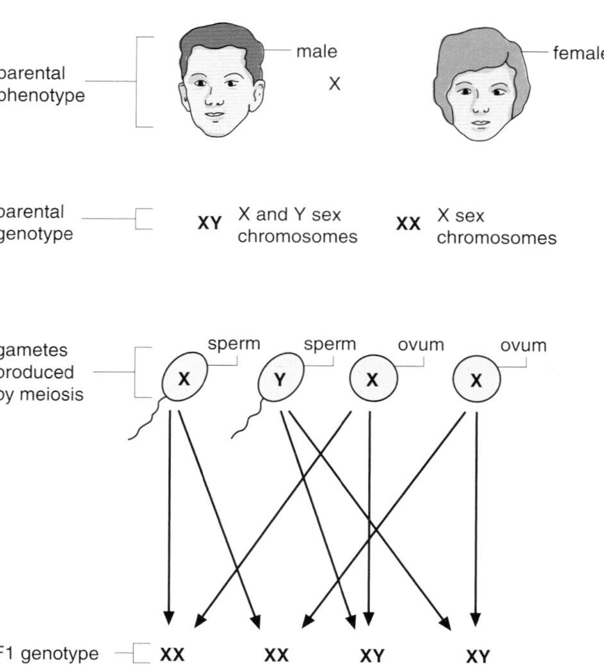

Figure 8 Human sex chromosomes

Inherited diseases

The passing on of genes can also be harmful as some diseases are inherited. Examples include cystic fibrosis and Down's syndrome. The way in which each of these conditions is inherited will be discussed in turn.

Cystic fibrosis

Individuals with cystic fibrosis have a genetic condition that causes problems with breathing and also with the digestion of food. The cystic fibrosis allele is recessive. Children who are born with cystic fibrosis must have two recessive alleles. Almost always, the parents of children with cystic fibrosis do not actually have the condition but are heterozygous. They are **carriers** in that they carry the cystic fibrosis allele but do not show the condition. The allele that causes cystic fibrosis is produced as a result of a mutation.

The Punnett square shows a cross between two heterozygous parents.

		Mother's gametes	
		C	c
Father's gametes	C	CC	Cc
	c	Cc	cc

C = normal
c = cystic fibrosis

Offspring				
	genotype	25% CC	50% Cc	25% cc
	phenotype	25% normal	50% carriers	25% cystic fibrosis

Figure 9 The inheritance of cystic fibrosis

Down's syndrome

Down's syndrome is also an inherited human condition. This condition is not caused by a recessive allele but is caused by an error in the formation of gametes during meiosis. In humans, gametes normally have 23 chromosomes (one from each of the 23 pairs). Occasionally gametes are formed with 24 chromosomes. This usually happens in the formation of eggs but not sperm. If the affected gamete is fertilised, resulting in pregnancy, the new individual will have 47 chromosomes in all his or her cells.

There are a large number of conditions or diseases that are either caused directly by the chromosomes and genes that an individual possesses, as in the examples above, or there is at least a strong genetic component. Several of the conditions that have been highlighted in earlier chapters are thought to have possible genetic factors. These include diabetes and heart disease. As our knowledge of inheritance and genetics increases it is hoped that we will eventually be able to reduce the incidence of genetic disease in the population in the years to come.

Some human conditions including the disease haemophilia occur almost exclusively in one sex, normally in males. These conditions are said to be **sex-linked**. The next section studies the genetics of sex-linked conditions.

Sex-linkage

The X and Y chromosomes are not only responsible for sex determination. They also have genes that code for a number of body functions. Each of the 22 normal (non-sex) pairs of chromosomes has the same gene present on both chromosomes at the same position (see Figure 3). The alleles may be different (alleles for the tall or the dwarf condition) but the gene (gene for height) is present on both. However, in the sex chromosomes the X is much larger than the Y and carries different genes to the Y.

This is particularly important in males as they have only one X chromosome. Therefore any recessive allele carried on an X chromosome in a male will show its effect in the phenotype – there is no dominant allele to mask its effect, as is the situation with females who have two X chromosomes. Haemophilia and red-green colour blindness are sex-linked conditions that are almost exclusively

H = normal allele h = haemophiliac allele

Cross 1 haemophiliac male × normal female

parental genotype X^h Y × $X^H X^H$

gametes (X^h) (Y) (X^H)

Punnett square

	X^H
X^h	X^HX^h
Y	X^HY

Offspring		
genotype	50% X^HX^h	50% X^HY
phenotype	50% carrier females	50% normal males

Cross 2 normal male × carrier female

parental genotype X^H Y × X^H X^h

gametes (X^H) (Y) (X^H) (X^h)

Punnett square

	X^H	X^h
X^H	X^HX^H	X^HX^h
Y	X^HY	X^hY

Offspring				
genotype	25% X^HX^H	25% X^HX^h	25% X^HY	25% X^hY
phenotype	25% normal females	25% carrier females	25% normal males	25% haemophiliac males

These crosses show why haemophilia is usually found only in males. Very occasionally, females may inherit the condition.

Figure 10 The inheritance of haemophilia

found in males only. Females seldom show sex-linked conditions but they are often carriers. In sex-linked conditions carriers are females who have one dominant and one recessive allele on their X chromosomes. In the female the recessive allele does not affect the phenotype as it is masked by the dominant allele.

Haemophilia is a condition where individuals who are only carrying the recessive allele are unable to make all the products required to clot their blood. Individuals with red-green colour blindness are unable to distinguish between the colours red and green.

Questions

1 Explain the difference between genotype and phenotype.

2 The ability to roll your tongue is caused by the presence of a dominant allele. Is it possible for two parents, both of whom can roll their tongue, to produce a child who is unable to do so? Use a genetic diagram to explain your answer.

3 A pedigree diagram shows the way in which a genetic condition is inherited in a family. The pedigree diagram in Figure 11 shows that one of the children has cystic fibrosis.

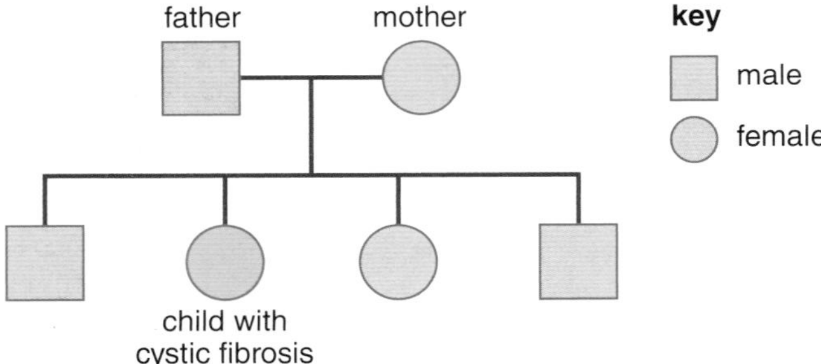

Figure 11

Use the diagram and your knowledge to answer the following questions.

a) What is the genotype of the child with cystic fibrosis? Use the symbol c to represent the cystic fibrosis allele.

b) What are the possible genotypes for the other children in the family? Explain your answer.

c) Genetic counsellors can advise parents about the likelihood of them having children that have an inherited disease. What is the probability that the next child of these parents will have cystic fibrosis?

4 Colour blindness is caused by a recessive sex-linked allele. Explain why it is unlikely, but not impossible, for girls to be colour blind.

Websites

http://web.ukonline.co.uk/webwise/spinneret/genes/genetx.htm
Genetic diagrams are explained with good examples.

http://web.ukonline.co.uk/webwise/spinneret/genes/crosses/gendia.htm
Good examples of crosses and an interactive worksheet to test your knowledge.

http://www.sonic.net/~nbs/projects/anthro201/disc/
Good explanation of Mendel's experiments.

http://www.revise.it/reviseit/content/GCSE/biology
Explanations of key terms and examples of crosses.

Exam questions

1 Brown coat colour in mice is dominant to white coat colour.

Let B represent the allele (gene) for brown coat colour.

Let b represent the allele (gene) for white coat colour.

a) What is the genotype of a heterozygous brown mouse? *(1 mark)*

b) What is the genotype of a homozygous white mouse? *(1 mark)*

c) Use a Punnett square to show the possible genotypes of the offspring of these two mice. *(2 marks)*

2 a) The diagram shows a cross between two people with brown eyes. The allele for brown eyes (B) is dominant to the allele for blue eyes (b).

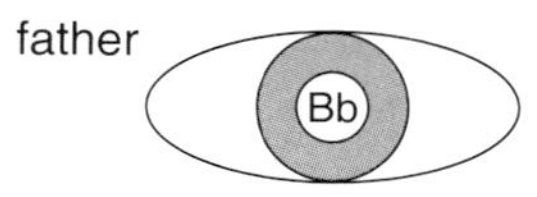

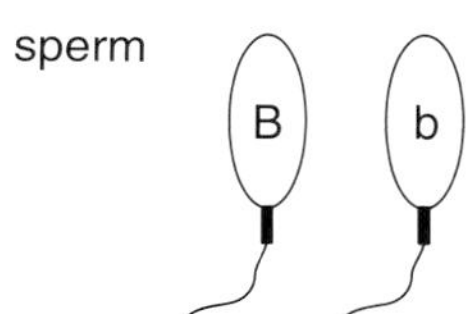

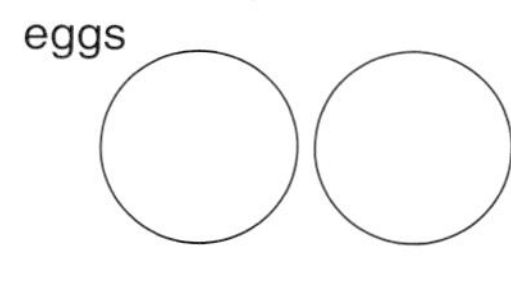

(i) Copy and complete the eggs to show the alleles carried in the sperm and eggs. *(3 marks)*

(ii) Copy and complete the Punnett square to show this cross.

		Mother	
Father	B		
	b		

(3 marks)

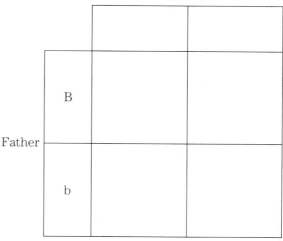

(iii) Draw a circle round the homozygous recessive child. *(1 mark)*

(iv) What is the ratio of brown eyes to blue eyes in the children? *(1 mark)*

(v) What is the phenotype of the mother? *(1 mark)*

(vi) Name the structures on which the alleles are found. *(1 mark)*

(vii) Where are these structures found in the cell? *(1 mark)*

b) The drawing shows striped and black-bodied flies.

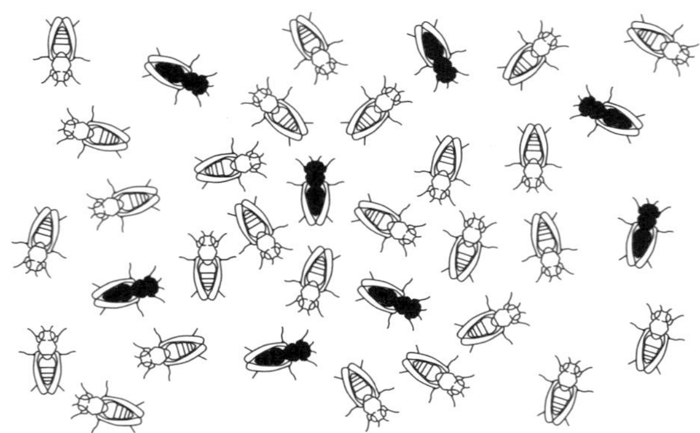

(i) Copy and complete the table by counting the number of striped and black-bodied flies

Body type	Number
Striped	
Black	

(2 marks)

(ii) Calculate the percentage of black-bodied flies. Show your working. *(2 marks)*

(iii) Suggest which body type is recessive. *(1 mark)*

3 Down's syndrome is an inherited condition of humans where all the body cells have 47 chromosomes.

The diagram shows two sperm cells and two egg cells (ova).

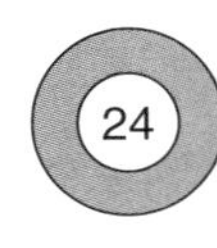

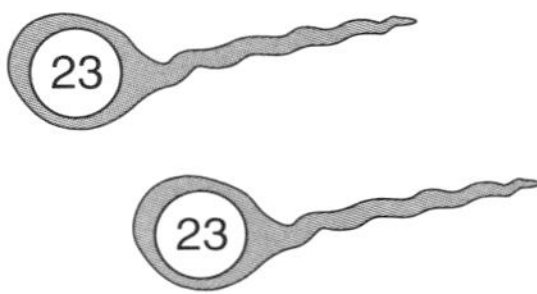

a) Copy the diagram and use a line to link two cells on the diagram to show how an individual with Down's syndrome could be produced. *(1 mark)*

b) Name an inherited disease of humans. *(1 mark)*

c) Sex in humans is determined by X and Y chromosomes.

What pair of chromosomes are present if a person is female? *(1 mark)*

4 a) In the sweet pea plant when a red-flowered plant is crossed with a white-flowered plant, the offspring are red-flowered plants.

Let R represent the allele (gene) for red flowers.

Let r represent the allele (gene) for white flowers.

Copy and complete the diagram by writing the correct letter or letters in each circle. Two circles have been completed for you.

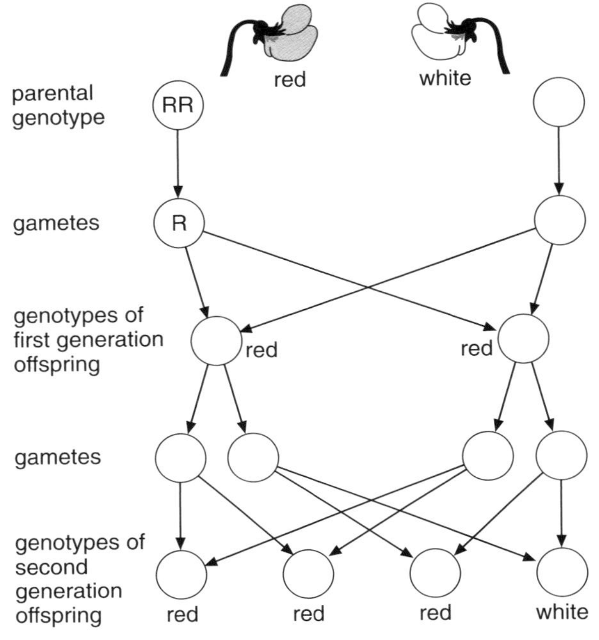

(4 marks)

b) Seeds were collected from another sweet pea plant. The following spring the seeds were planted and when they produced flowers the colours were recorded. The table shows the number of plants obtained with each flower colour.

	Flower colour	
	Red	White
Number of plants	60	60

(i) What is the ratio of red-flowered plants to white-flowered plants? *(1 mark)*

(ii) Draw a Punnett square to show how two plants produced the red and white offspring in this ratio. *(4 marks)*

5 The Punnett square shows how colour-blindness could be inherited by the children of a mother who has normal sight and a father who has normal sight.

The allele for normal sight is **N** and the allele for colour-blindness is **n**.

		Father's gametes	
		X^N	Y
Mother's gametes		X^NX^N	X^NY
		X^nX^N	X^nY

a) Copy and complete the Punnett square to show the gametes of the mother. *(1 mark)*

b) Explain why the alleles are only shown on the X chromosome. *(2 marks)*

c) What is the chance of the first child being a colour-blind boy? *(1 mark)*

d) Name a term used to describe a girl who is heterozygous for colour-blindness. *(1 mark)*

e) Name a human disease which is inherited in the same way as colour-blindness. *(1 mark)*

6 a) Haemophilia is a genetic disorder which is sex-linked.

The diagram shows a family tree.

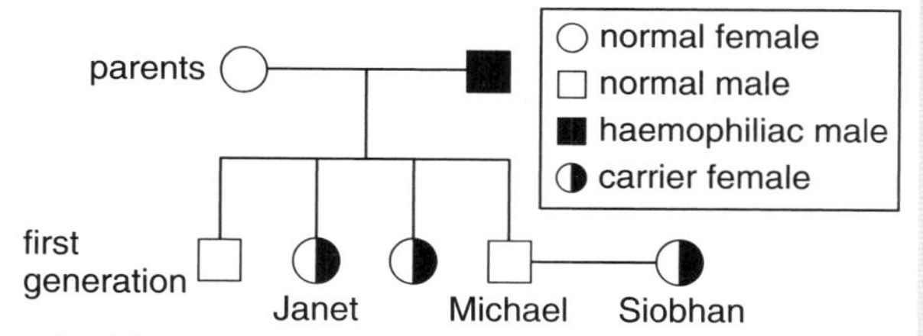

Let X represent an X chromosome
X^h represent an X chromosome carrying the haemophiliac allele
Y represent a Y chromosome

(i) Give the genotypes of the parents. *(2 marks)*

(ii) Give the phenotype and genotype of Janet. *(2 marks)*

(iii) Explain how Michael is a normal male even though his father is a haemophiliac. *(2 marks)*

(iv) Complete the Punnett square to show the possible offspring of Michael and Siobhan.

	Michael's gametes	
Siobhan's gametes		

(3 marks)

(v) What proportion of the offspring will have haemophilia? *(1 mark)*

(vi) Why are there fewer haemophiliac females than males? *(1 mark)*

Chapter 22

DNA – The Hereditary Material

Learning objectives

By the end of this chapter you should know:

- The structure of DNA
- How DNA controls protein synthesis
- That mutations are changes in an organisms DNA makeup
- The use of genetic engineering to manufacture important proteins
- DNA replication – making new DNA

We have learnt in the previous chapter that an organism's characteristics are passed down from generation to generation by genes. We also know that a large number of genes are packaged together into chromosomes. Approximately fifty years ago a major scientific advance was the discovery of the structure of the molecule that was actually responsible for determining our genetic makeup. This molecule is called **deoxyribose nucleic acid** or **DNA**. A chromosome consists of long strands of DNA.

The structure of DNA

DNA consists of three main components that are regularly repeated throughout the length of the molecule. These sub-units are **deoxyribose sugar, phosphate** and nitrogenous **bases**. There are four different bases involved – **adenine, guanine, cytosine** and **thymine**. The DNA is constructed very much like a ladder. The rungs of the ladder are the bases and the supporting sides are formed of repeating units of the sugar and phosphate. Figure 1 shows that the bases link the two sides together and the DNA 'ladder' is twisted round on itself to form a **double helix**.

Each repeating section of DNA that consists of a phosphate, sugar and a base is called a **nucleotide**. Figure 2 shows that the bases are linked in such a way, called **base pairing**, that only adenine can combine with thymine, and only cytosine and guanine can combine.

What makes one piece of DNA, or one gene, different from another is the way in which the bases are arranged along the length of the DNA.

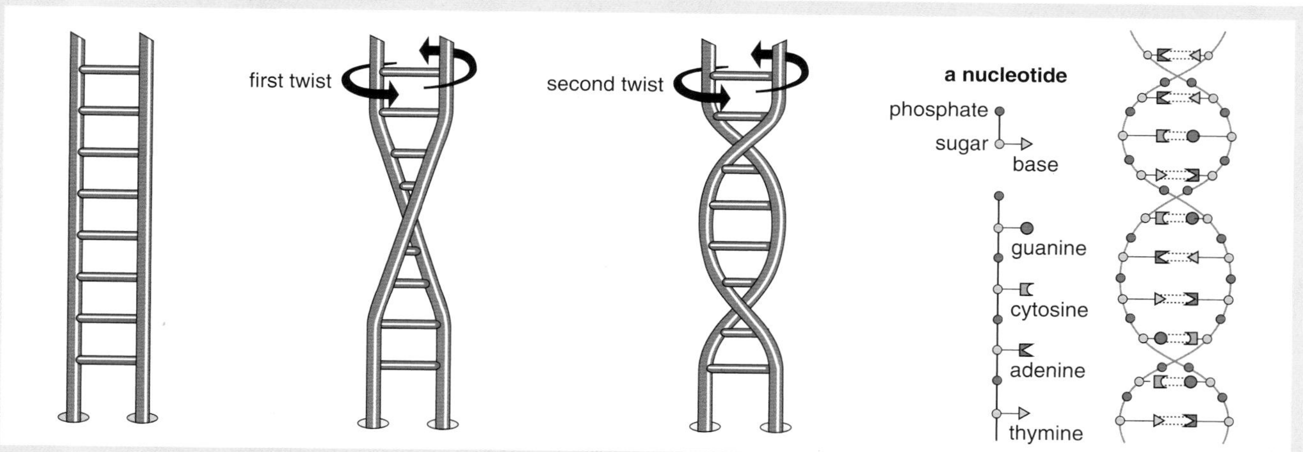

Figure 1 The structure of DNA

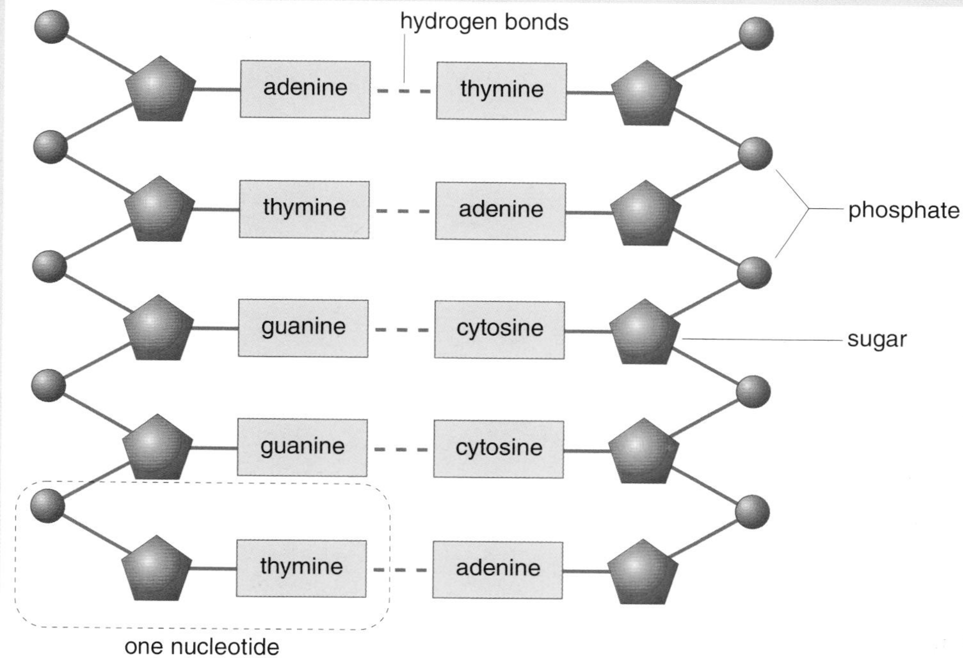

Figure 2 Base pairing in DNA

How does DNA work?

DNA works by coding for protein structure. The DNA determines what proteins are made in cells. Enzymes are very important proteins that control the reactions that take place in a cell. By controlling the manufacture of enzymes, DNA controls how cells develop and work. This in turn controls the overall development of the whole organism.

The bases along one side of the DNA molecule form the **genetic code**. When this code is used to produce proteins, the bases are 'read' in sequences of three. Each group of three bases is called a **base triplet** or a codon. Each base triplet codes for a particular amino acid as shown in Figure 3. As a protein is a large number of amino acids linked together it is important that the order of the DNA bases produces amino acids in the correct sequence. By this complex arrangement of bases a protein consisting of many amino acids is built up. The process is referred to as **protein synthesis** and the DNA provides the blueprint or plan. Figure 3 shows four base triplets coding for their respective amino acids. Note that the first and fourth amino acids are the same. This is because the base triplets on the DNA were also the same. Proteins are made from many more base triplets than are shown in Figure 3.

A section of DNA that codes for a particular protein is referred to as a gene. If the protein consists of many amino acids and is very large it will obviously require a large number of bases to code for it.

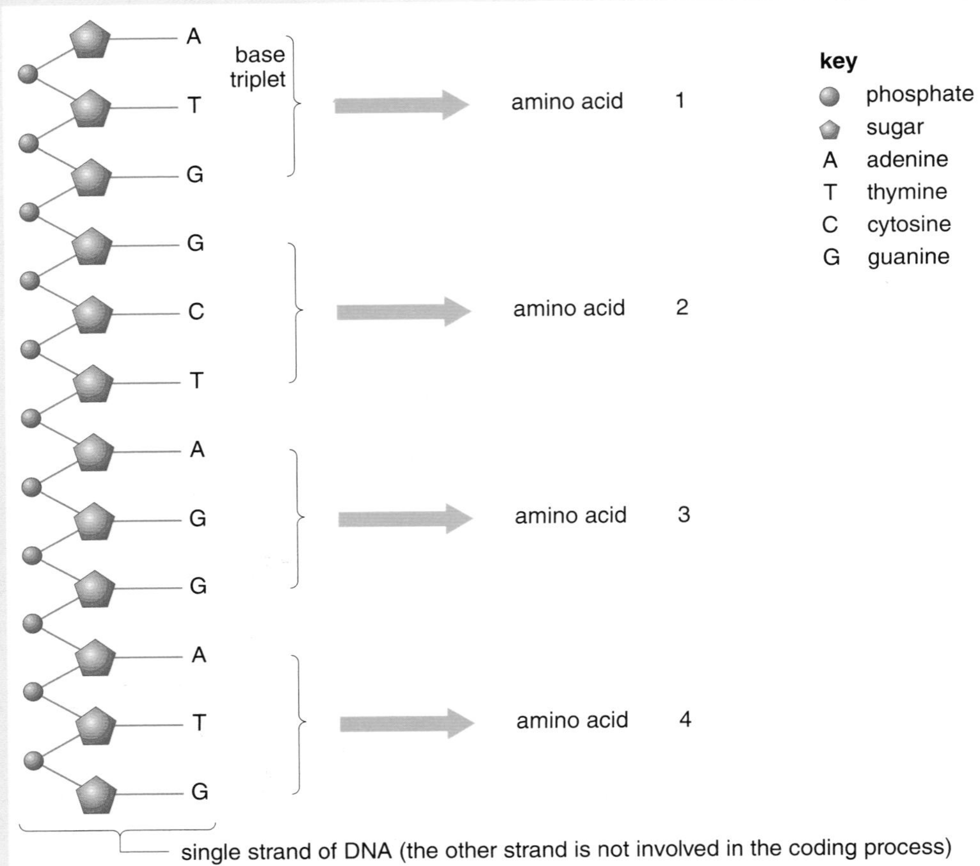

Figure 3 Protein synthesis – making protein from DNA

Questions

1 Use Figure 3 to work out the length of DNA required (in number of bases on the coding strand) to code for a protein consisting of 177 amino acids?

Working out the structure of DNA

By the early 1950s there was considerable interest in the structure of DNA as scientists were becoming aware of how important a molecule it really is.

In 1950 Erwin Chargaff found that although the arrangement of bases in the molecule varied there was always an equal amount of adenine and thymine. He also found that the volume of guanine was the same as the volume of cytosine.

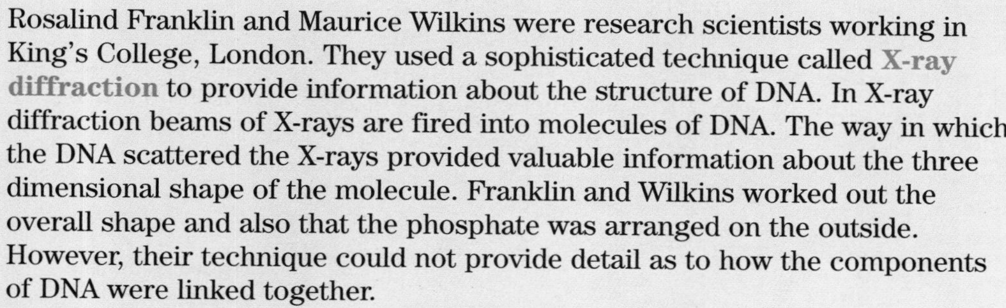

Questions

2 Explain Chargaff's results.

Rosalind Franklin and Maurice Wilkins were research scientists working in King's College, London. They used a sophisticated technique called **X-ray diffraction** to provide information about the structure of DNA. In X-ray diffraction beams of X-rays are fired into molecules of DNA. The way in which the DNA scattered the X-rays provided valuable information about the three dimensional shape of the molecule. Franklin and Wilkins worked out the overall shape and also that the phosphate was arranged on the outside. However, their technique could not provide detail as to how the components of DNA were linked together.

Building on the work of Franklin and Wilkins and others, including Chargaff, the molecular structure of DNA was worked out by James Watson and Francis Crick at Cambridge in 1953. Using all the information that was available they built a three-dimensional model of the molecule. As well as working out the arrangement of the bases Watson and Crick deduced that the molecule was organised as a double helix.

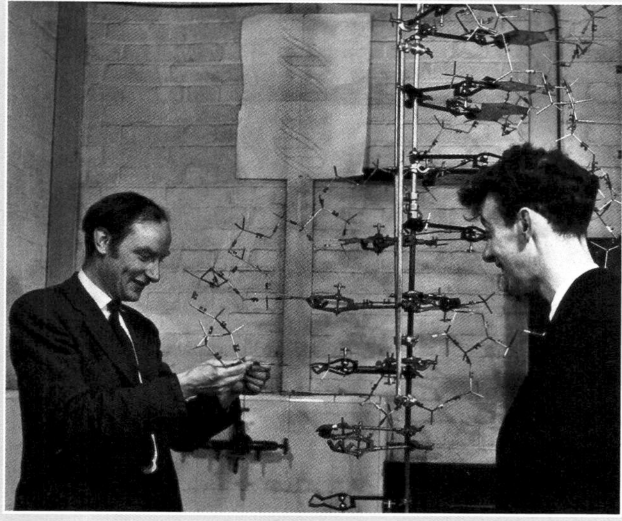

Figure 4 Watson and Crick with their model of DNA

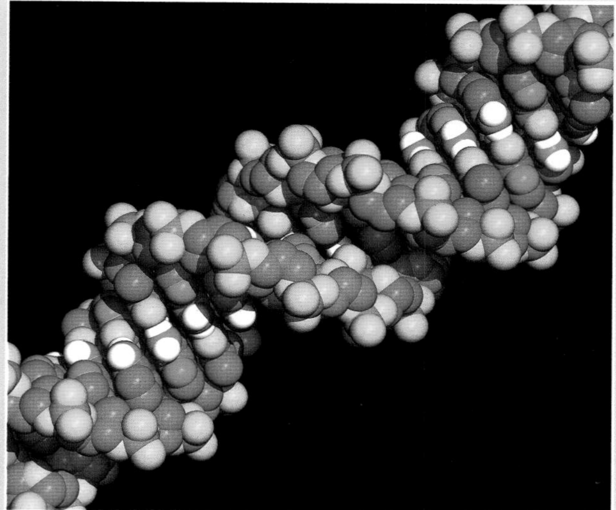

Figure 5 Model of DNA

Genetic engineering

The speed of increasing scientific knowledge is such that within fifty years of working out the structure of DNA, scientists were able to manipulate and change the DNA in living organisms. **Genetic engineering** involves taking a piece of DNA, usually a gene, from one organism and adding it to the genetic material of another organism. Commonly DNA that codes for the desired product is incorporated into the DNA of bacteria. This is because bacterial DNA is easily manipulated and also because bacteria reproduce so rapidly that large numbers will quickly be produced with the new gene. As a result the bacteria will produce a valuable product, such as a drug or hormone that may be difficult or expensive to produce by other means. Once the new genetic material is built into the bacteria they are allowed to reproduce rapidly in suitable growing conditions and are cultured in special fermenters or bioreactors that maximise the production of the desired product.

One of the best examples of genetic engineering providing essential products for man is in the production of genetically engineered human insulin. Diabetes is becoming increasingly common and as a result many more people require insulin than did in the past. Before the development of genetic engineering the insulin was obtained from the pancreases of domestic animals such as pigs and cattle.

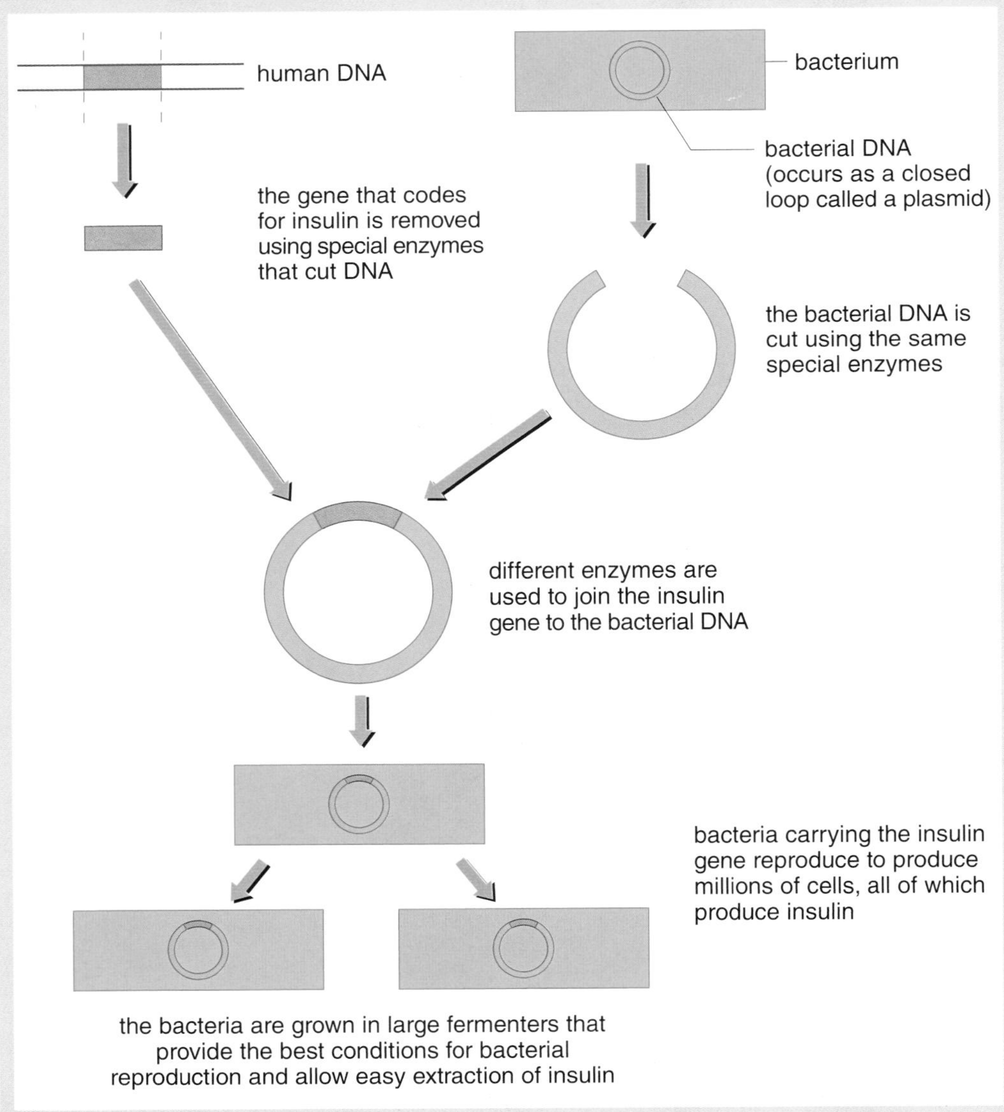
human DNA
bacterium
bacterial DNA (occurs as a closed loop called a plasmid)
the gene that codes for insulin is removed using special enzymes that cut DNA
the bacterial DNA is cut using the same special enzymes
different enzymes are used to join the insulin gene to the bacterial DNA
bacteria carrying the insulin gene reproduce to produce millions of cells, all of which produce insulin
the bacteria are grown in large fermenters that provide the best conditions for bacterial reproduction and allow easy extraction of insulin

Figure 6 Genetic engineering – making insulin

The amount of insulin available was limited by the number of animals brought to the abattoirs for slaughter and it was also a slow extraction process. An additional complication was the fact that the animal insulin differs in structure to human insulin and is therefore not quite as effective. Genetically engineered human insulin overcomes these problems and this method produces the large quantities of insulin that are required today.

Genetic engineering – the way forward?

Genetic manipulation is now used in more ways than just the production of important medicines or products. In some varieties of commercial animals and crops, beneficial genes can be inserted into the chromosomes at an early stage to produce genetically modified (GM) products. These GM products may grow faster or have other beneficial properties such as increased protein or reduced fat levels. The use of GM crops is a very controversial area and it has stimulated much heated debate, much of it uninformed. However, most people agree that genetic engineering is a branch of science that offers many possibilities but that progress in this field requires careful consideration and appropriate safeguards.

Mutations – changing the code

Genetic engineering involves deliberately changing the DNA code. Occasionally the DNA changes accidentally as a result of a **mutation**. Two mutations already discussed in earlier chapters cause haemophilia and Down's syndrome. Haemophilia is the result of a **gene mutation**. In a gene mutation an individual gene is affected. In haemophilia a change in the DNA means that the affected individual is unable to produce Factor 8, an essential chemical required for the clotting of blood. In some gene mutations the change in DNA structure may be as little as one base. Nonetheless a change in even one base can have a very large effect on an individual.

People with Down's syndrome have 47 chromosomes in their cells instead of the usual 46. This mutation is caused by the faulty segregation of chromosomes in meiosis during gamete formation. Normally the 23 chromosomes in each sperm or egg cell consist of one chromosome from each of the 23 pairs of chromosomes that are found in human cells. Down's syndrome arises because in one pair the chromosomes do not segregate properly and both chromosomes from a pair enters a gamete. This particular gamete (usually an egg as opposed to a sperm) will have 24 chromosomes. When an egg with 24 chromosomes is fertilised by a sperm with 23 the cells of the new individual will have 47 chromosomes. As the mutation that causes Down's syndrome affects the number of chromosomes in a cell it is called a **chromosome mutation**.

The mutations described above are harmful as is the mutation that causes skin cancer, described earlier in the book. Some mutations have no effect at all and some are beneficial. Examples of beneficial mutations will be discussed in later chapters.

DNA replication

For the DNA to work as a code it is important that it is able to pass from cell to cell during growth. DNA replication ensures that exact copies of DNA are produced and that these are present in all new cells produced during growth and repair. During the process of replication the DNA double helix unzips to provide two single stands. This happens because the hydrogen bonds holding the two stands together break. Following separation each of the strands will have a sequence of unpaired bases running along its length. These unpaired bases on each strand pair up with free nucleotides that are found inside the cell. When this takes place they follow the rules of base pairing in that adenine only combines with thymine and guanine only combines with cytosine. When this process is complete each of the new DNA molecules will coil to form a double helix and the cell will now have double the amount of DNA than it had prior to replication. When the cell divides one DNA molecule will enter each of the new cells produced. The process of DNA replication occurs prior to the formation and separation of chromatids in mitosis.

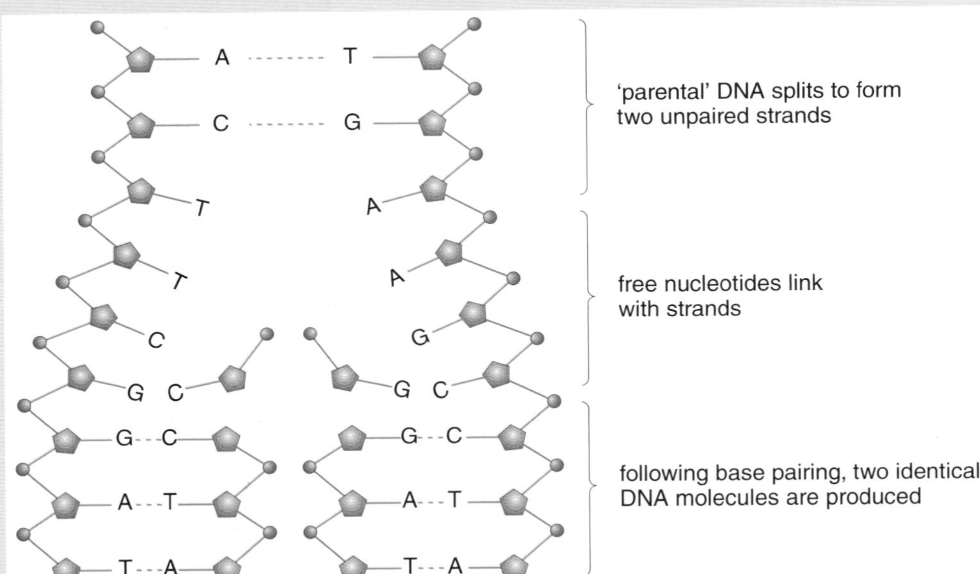
A T
C G
T A
T A
C G
G C G C
G C G C
A T A T
T A T A
'parental' DNA splits to form two unpaired strands
free nucleotides link with strands
following base pairing, two identical DNA molecules are produced

Figure 7 The replication of DNA

Websites

http://www.bbc.co.uk/schools/gcsebitesize/biology/inheritance/dnarev4.shtml
Summary of key points of DNA replication.

http://web.ukonline.co.uk/webwise/spinneret
Some good models of base pairing.

Try some searches of your own. Search under 'Watson + Crick'. There are some good sites summarising the discovery of DNA.

Exam questions

1 The diagram shows part of a molecule of DNA. The letters represent the bases of the molecule, which pair up in a specific way.

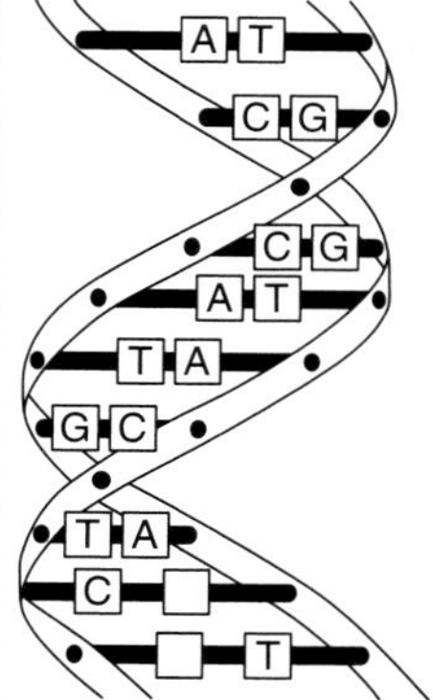

a) Use the information in the diagram to state which bases are missing. *(1 mark)*

b) What term describes the shape of the DNA molecule? *(1 mark)*

c) In cells, which structures contain DNA? *(1 mark)*

d) What is the function of DNA in cells? *(1 mark)*

2 a) The relative amounts of the bases in DNA, in different animals, are shown in the table.

Source of DNA	Amount of base/arbitrary units A	G	T	C
Man	30.9	19.9	29.4	19.8
Salmon	29.7	20.8	29.1	20.4
Sheep	29.3	21.4	28.3	21.0

(i) What pattern is shown by the ratio of the bases found in each animal? *(2 marks)*

(ii) Where is DNA found in the cell? *(1 mark)*

(iii) Copy the diagram and draw a circle round a base pair. *(1 mark)*

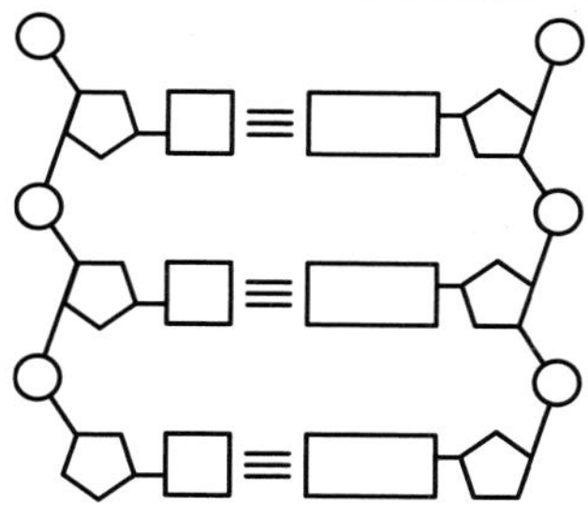

(iv) What is the shape of the DNA molecule? *(1 mark)*

(v) Explain the significance of the arrangement of the bases in the DNA molecule. *(2 marks)*

b) The diagram shows how human insulin can be obtained from genetically engineered bacteria.

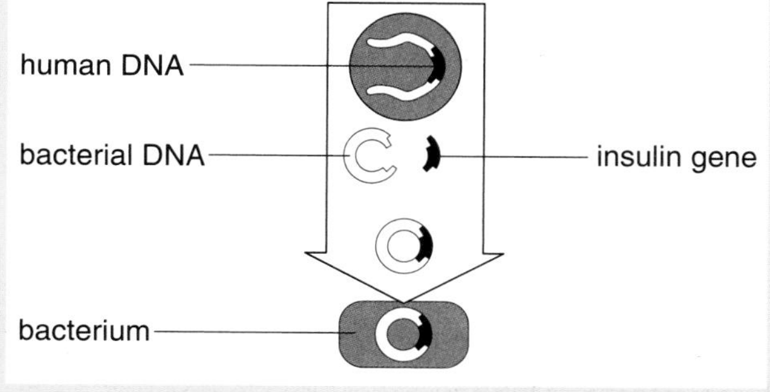

Use this information to help describe how large quantities of human insulin can be produced by bacteria. *(4 marks)*

3 a) Chromosomes are lengths of DNA which determine the proteins that a cell makes. The diagram shows how DNA controls protein synthesis.

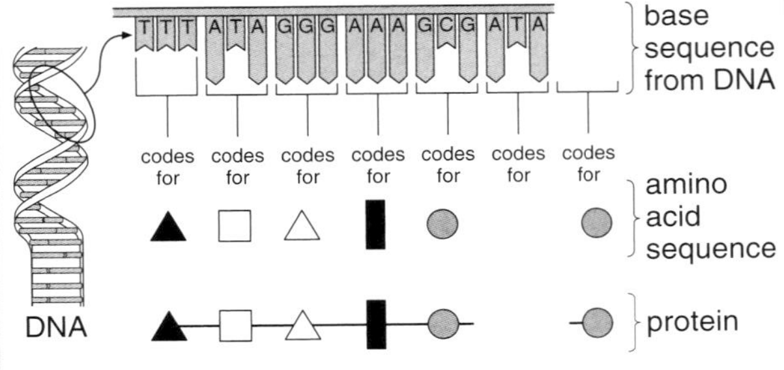

(i) [A] Give the sequence of bases for the last amino acid. *(1 mark)*

[B] Draw the symbol for the missing amino acid in the sequence and in the protein. *(1 mark)*

A mutation resulted in the sequence of bases TTT, in the diagram above, being changed to AAA.

(ii) What effect would this have on the amino acid sequence? *(1 mark)*

(iii) Give **one** cause of mutations. *(1 mark)*

b) The flow diagram shows the steps in the manufacture of insulin by genetic engineering.

(i) Suggest what illustrations should replace A, B and C using the symbols in the key. The first and last steps have been illustrated for you.

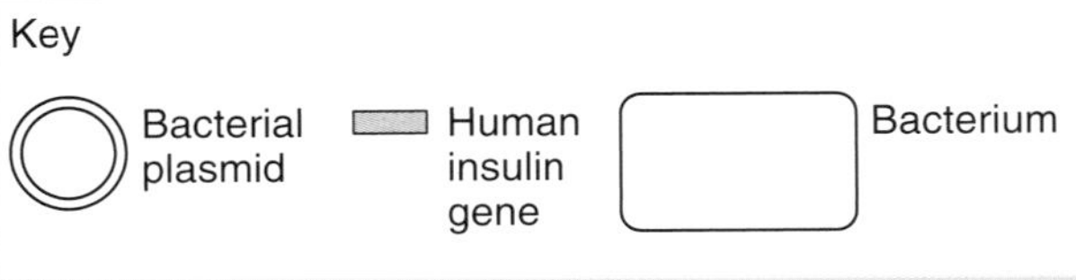

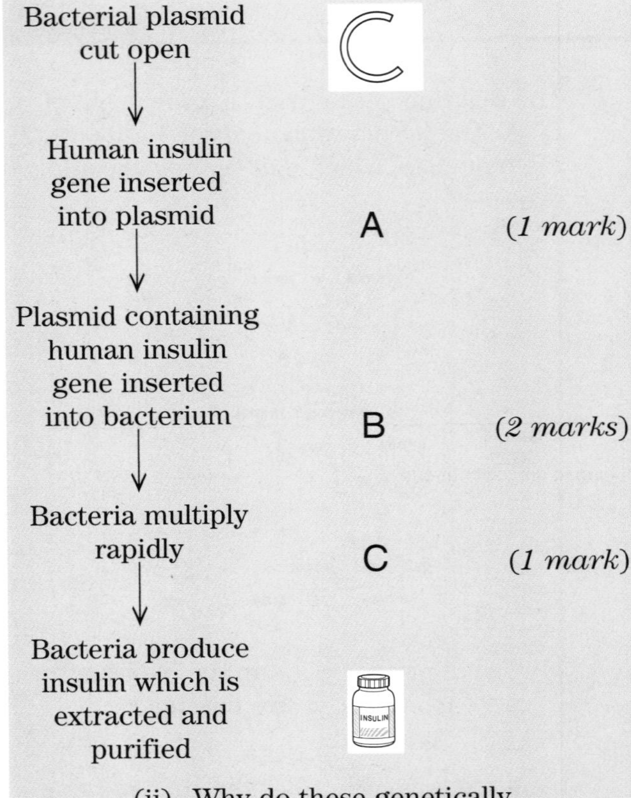

(ii) Why do these genetically engineered bacteria produce insulin? *(1 mark)*

4 a) The diagram shows one strand from a section of DNA.

The base Adenine (A) on one strand always binds with the base Thymine (T) on the other strand.

The base Guanine (G) on one strand always binds with the base Cytosine (C) on the other strand.

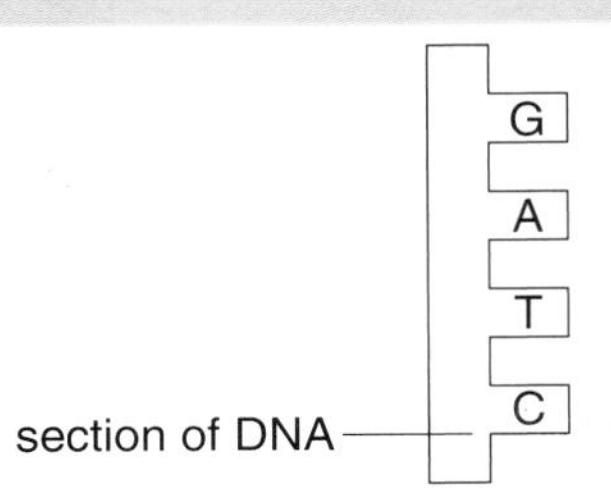

(i) Using this information draw the other strand to show the complete section of DNA. *(2 marks)*

(ii) When a length of DNA was analysed, it was found to contain 33 Adenine bases. How many Thymine bases would be found in the same length of DNA?

(1 mark)

b) The diagram shows some stages in the production of human growth hormone by genetic engineering. The process is similar to the production of human insulin.

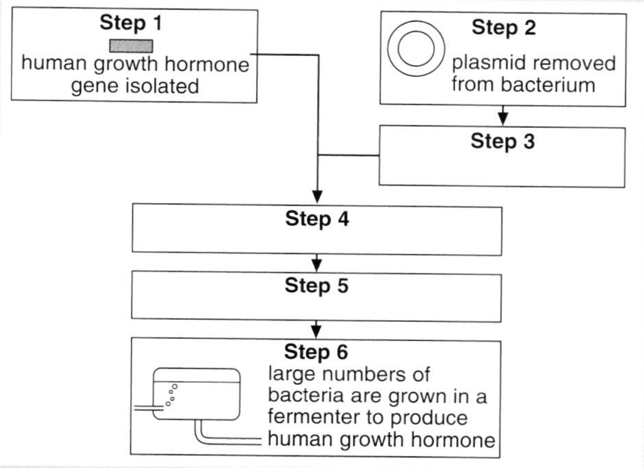

Describe what happens at Steps 3, 4 and 5.

(3 marks)

5 The diagram shows the base pairs which make up a strand of human DNA.

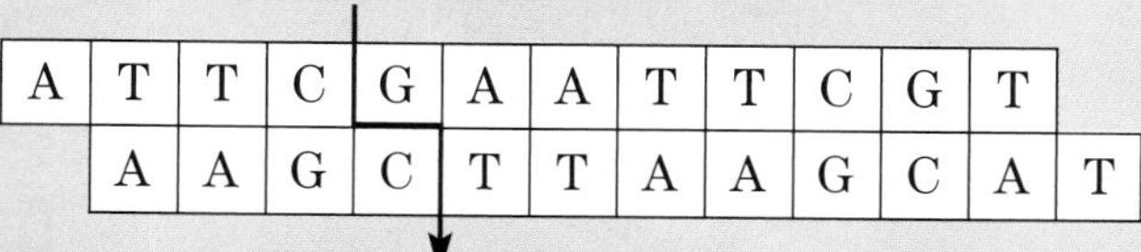

Enzymes cut DNA at specific bases. One enzyme, starting from the left-hand side, will cut this DNA strand at the end of a sequence ending with C.

a) Draw all the fragments which would be produced.

The first fragment has been done for you.

A	T	T	C	
	A	A	G	C

(2 marks)

Fragments of human DNA code for different proteins e.g. insulin.

The diagram shows some stages in the production of human protein by genetic engineering.

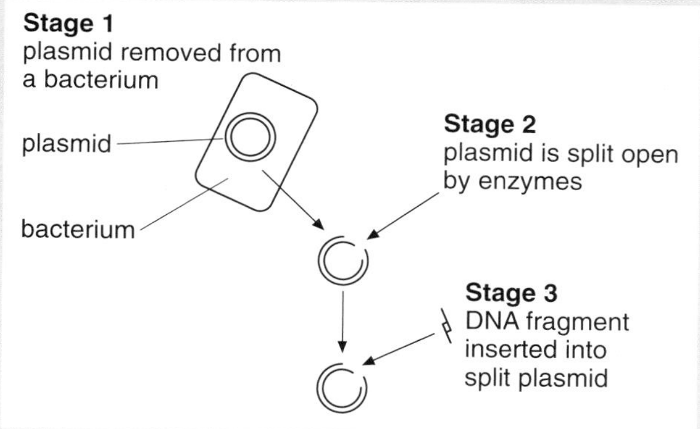

b) The diagram below shows the cut ends of the split plasmid.

Complete the diagram by inserting the fragment from (i) which fits this plasmid.

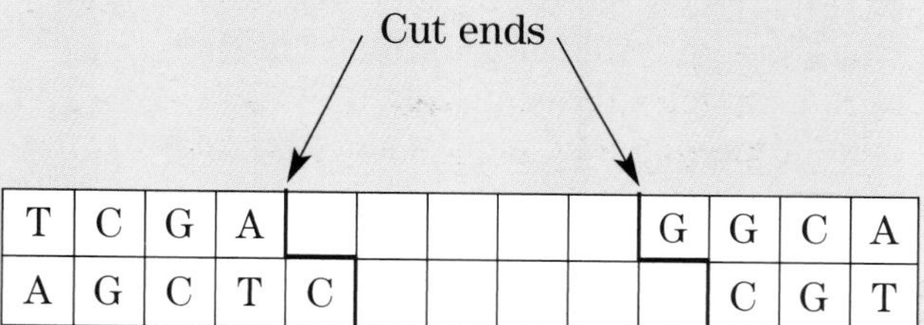

(1 mark)

c) Complete the sequence of stages in the production of this human protein by describing what happens after the insertion of the DNA fragment into the plasmid in stages 4, 5 and 6

(3 marks)

Chapter 23

Variation in Living Organisms

Learning objectives

By the end of this chapter you should know:

- That variation in living organisms has both a genetic and environmental basis
- That sexual reproduction is a source of genetic variation, while asexual reproduction produces clones
- Examples of cloning including, cuttings, runners and tissue culture in plants and the splitting of embryos in animals

Living organisms that belong to the same species, or type, vary from each other in a large number of ways as a general rule. Members of the human species differ in height, weight, eye colour, intelligence, hair type and in many other ways.

Variation is usually caused by differences in the **genetic** makeup (genotype) or by **environmental** factors. Differences between individuals for a particular characteristic are often due to a combination of genetic and environmental factors. However, some types of variation may be due to only one of the two causes.

Figure 1 Variation in humans

Height in humans is affected by both genetic and environmental influences. The genotype will determine the potential height that an individual can attain, but he or she will only grow to that height if there is a good diet and good overall health. By comparison eye colour is purely genetic and cannot be affected by any environmental condition. Any differences in the appearance of identical twins must be environmental as they have identical genotypes.

Genetic variation

Sexual reproduction, through a combination of meiosis in the production of gametes (sex cells) and the random mixing of gametes during fertilisation, ensures that the genotypes of offspring from a particular set of parents will show variation. The process of meiosis ensures that each gamete produced by a parent has a different chromosome arrangement. In fertilisation it is purely random which male gamete fuses with which female gamete, therefore the offspring will have a new arrangement of genetic material.

Mutations that change the genetic makeup of organisms also cause variation.

Environmental variation

This is variation caused by the surrounding environment. Environmental variation is particularly obvious in plants. Plants that are growing in good light conditions with sufficient supplies of water and minerals will appear very different to plants growing with limited resources.

Continuous and discontinuous variation

Variation of a particular characteristic can be either continuous or discontinuous. In **continuous variation** there is gradual change in a characteristic across a population. Height is an example of continuous variation in humans. While people can be described as being tall or short or neither there is no clear cut-off height that determines tallness. Figure 2 shows a typical set of values for height in human males. Note that the histogram produced shows a **normal distribution**. A normal distribution is where most individuals are around the average or mean value and relatively few are found at either extreme.

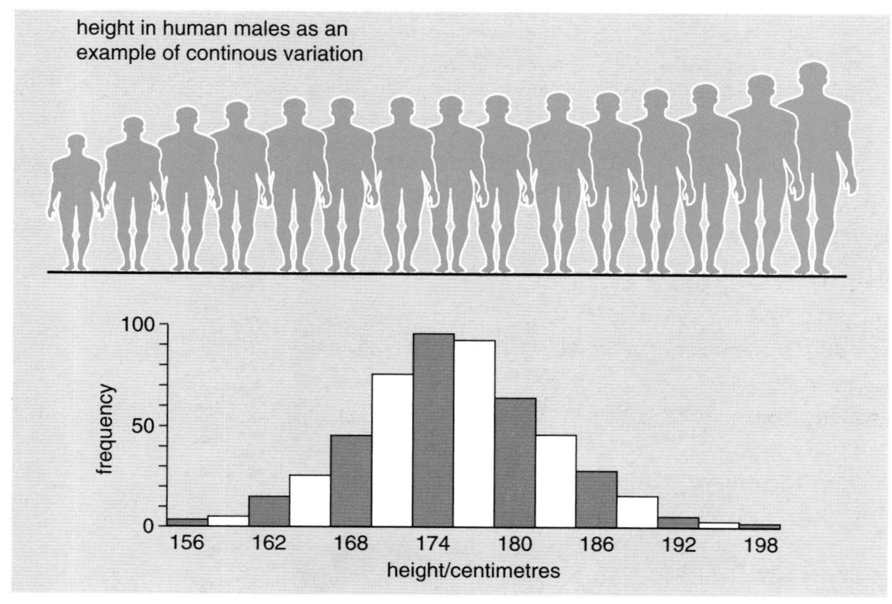

Figure 2 Height – an example of continuous variation in humans

In **discontinuous variation** the population can be clearly divided into discrete groups or categories. Examples include the ability, or inability, to roll the tongue and the presence, or absence, of ear lobes in humans. In each of these examples, individuals will fit into one of two categories. There will be no intermediates. In other examples of discontinuous variation there can be more than two categories, for example blood groups, but in all examples individuals can clearly be categorised into a group.

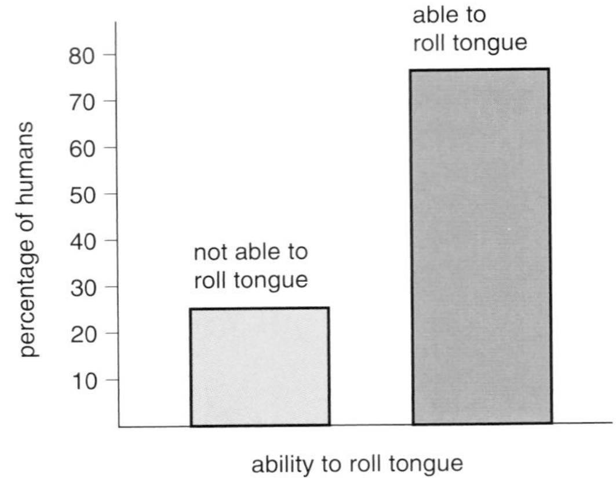

Figure 3 Tongue rolling – an example of discontinuous variation in humans

Although variation between individuals is a natural feature of living organisms, it is possible to decrease the variation between individuals for commercial reasons. Examples of this can be seen in vegetable and fruit production where it is often important to develop produce that has particular characteristics which make it attractive in the marketplace.

Cloning – the production of identical offspring

Plants can naturally reproduce by cloning, such as in the production of bulbs by daffodils or in the development of potato tubers. However, it is also possible to artificially clone with the purpose of producing large numbers of genetically identical offspring. Examples of the cloning of plants include the development of runners, which is a totally natural process, and the taking of cuttings by plant growers.

Runners and cuttings

The development of **runners** in strawberry plants produces new plants that can develop independently of the parent plant. Each of these new plants has an identical genotype to the parent. As the new plants are produced asexually they are genetically identical to the parent plants. Runners and other methods of asexual reproduction (propagation) in plants produce new plants in close proximity to the parent plant. This can build up a colony of genetically identical plants that have the characteristics to grow successfully in a particular area.

In artificial propagation gardeners and horticulturists can artificially propagate new plants. **Cuttings** are small parts that are removed from a parent plant. These can be parts of the stem or even as little as part of a leaf. Cuttings can develop new roots and grow into a fully developed plant genetically identical to the parent. Sometimes gardeners can encourage the development of cuttings by applying hormones that encourage root development. One parent plant can produce many offspring through cuttings and it is a popular way for gardeners to grow and propagate favourite plants.

It is often beneficial to keep cuttings in a moist environment until they are established

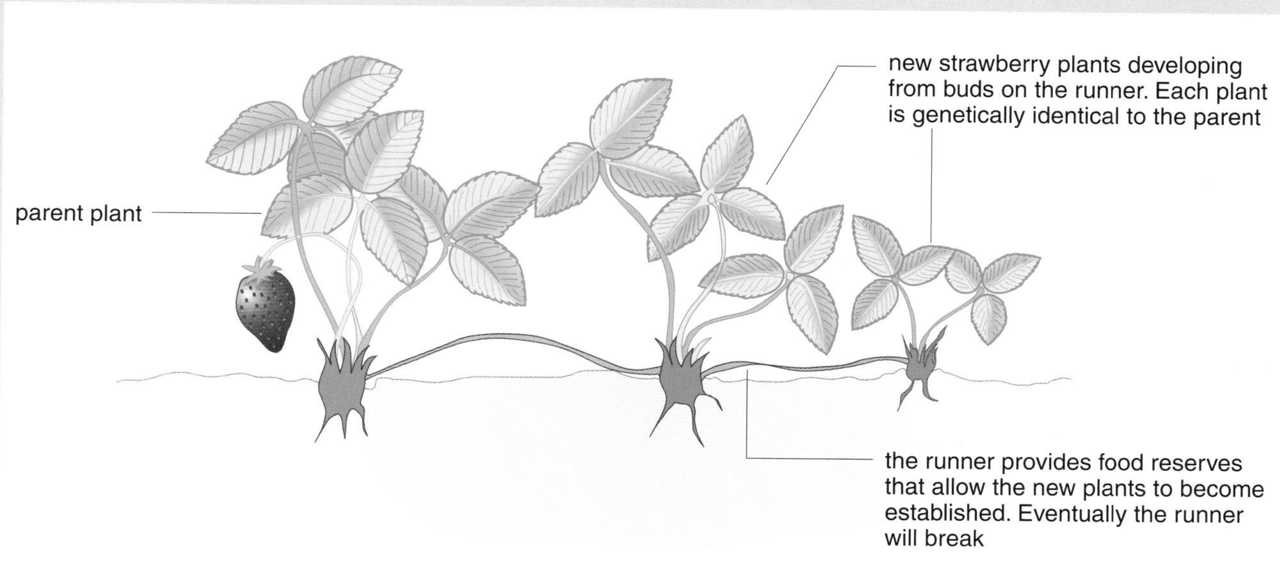
new strawberry plants developing from buds on the runner. Each plant is genetically identical to the parent
parent plant
the runner provides food reserves that allow the new plants to become established. Eventually the runner will break

Figure 4 Natural cloning in strawberries

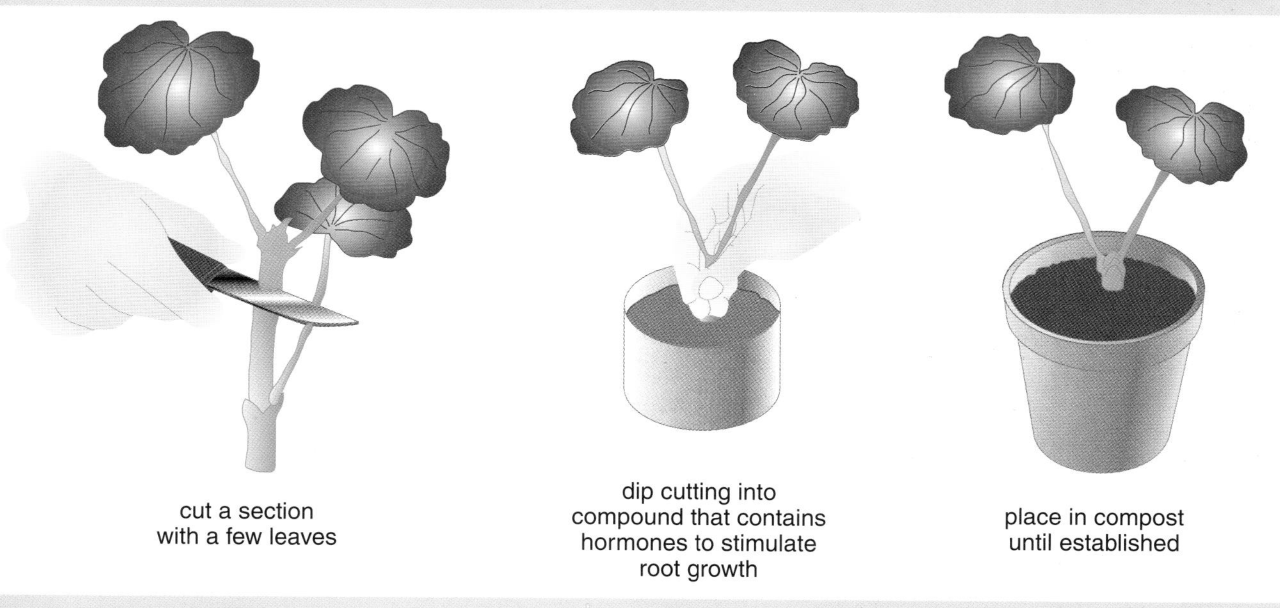
cut a section with a few leaves
dip cutting into compound that contains hormones to stimulate root growth
place in compost until established

Figure 5 Taking cuttings

Questions

1 Explain why it is necessary to keep cuttings in a moist environment.

Cloning plants by tissue culture

The cloning of plants by **tissue culture** is another effective method of producing large numbers of identical plants. It is more complex than taking cuttings, but even more effective, in that it can produce very large numbers of offspring. The process of tissue culture involves taking a very small piece of the parent plant, the **explant**, and placing it in an agar (jelly-like) medium that contains a range of essential nutrients.

Within a short period of time a small group of cells called a **callus** develops. Cells are removed from the callus and placed in a different agar medium. Again this growth medium contains essential nutrients for growth but it also contains hormones that encourage the development of the cells into miniature plants with properly differentiated roots and shoots. Once the tiny plants are established they are transplanted into a glasshouse where further growth continues. Figure 6 summarises some of the important steps in the cloning process.

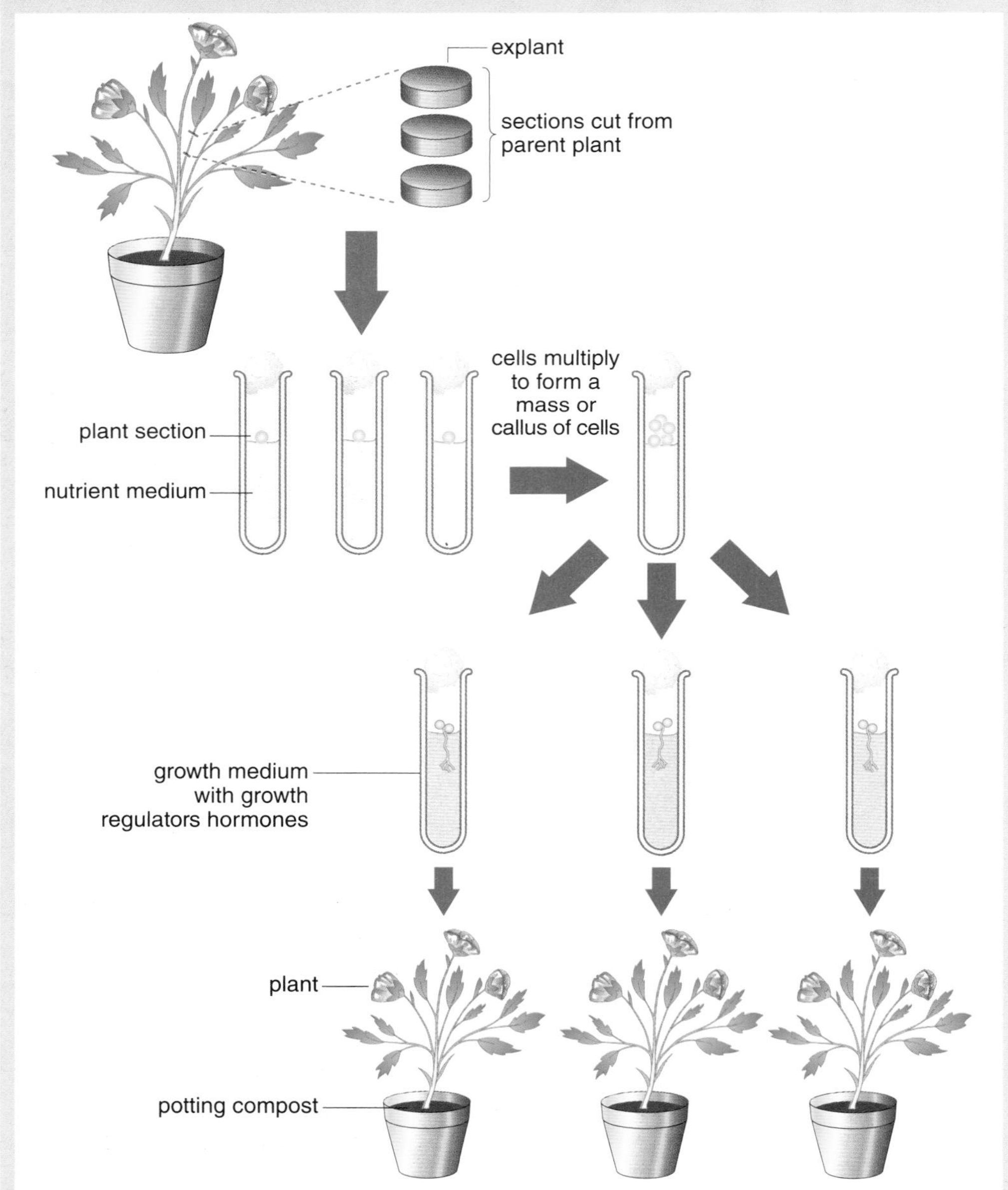

Figure 6 Plant cloning

Cloning has many advantages for crop producers. These include:

- It can produce pure strains of valuable or rare plants, many of which are difficult to propagate by other methods
- It produces large numbers in a short period of time
- Cloning is an effective method of producing disease free varieties
- It is relatively inexpensive
- As cloning is a laboratory based procedure it can take place all year round

Although cloning plants has many advantages it is a complex procedure and there are potentially some problems with its use. Laboratory conditions must be carefully regulated to provide the precise conditions required for cloning and it is particularly important to provide sterile conditions. As cloning produces identical plants they can be susceptible to disease spreading rapidly through the plants. In addition, the absence of genetic variation can lead to genetic weaknesses associated with inbreeding. A further disadvantage is that cloning will not work for all species.

Figure 7 shows a plantation of oil seed rape that has been produced by cloning.

While cloning has been widely used in plant breeding its use in animal breeding has been more limited. Although it has been demonstrated for some time that animal cloning is possible, (a good early example was Dolly, the first cloned sheep), animal and in particular, human cloning raises many moral and ethical concerns.

Figure 7 A field of cloned oil seed rape plants

Embryo transplants in agricultural animals – acceptable cloning?

Embryo transplantation is a technique used in the breeding of several types of agricultural animals including sheep, cattle and horses.

Embryo cloning in cattle

Sperm and eggs can be collected from high quality bulls and cows respectively. The cows can be treated with hormones in advance to make sure that they produce large numbers of eggs. Following fertilisation, usually by artificial insemination, the embryos are removed from the cow to allow the cloning process to take place. Cells are removed from at least one very young embryo that has not begun differentiating into particular body parts. These cells can be introduced into the wombs of other adult (surrogate) females and they will develop into identical high quality offspring as they all have the same genetic composition. Embryo transplants are an effective method of producing large numbers of genetically identical animals with economically desirable characteristics or traits. However, if the process is overused the genetic variability of the population will reduce. A reduction in genetic variability can lead to problems in the future.

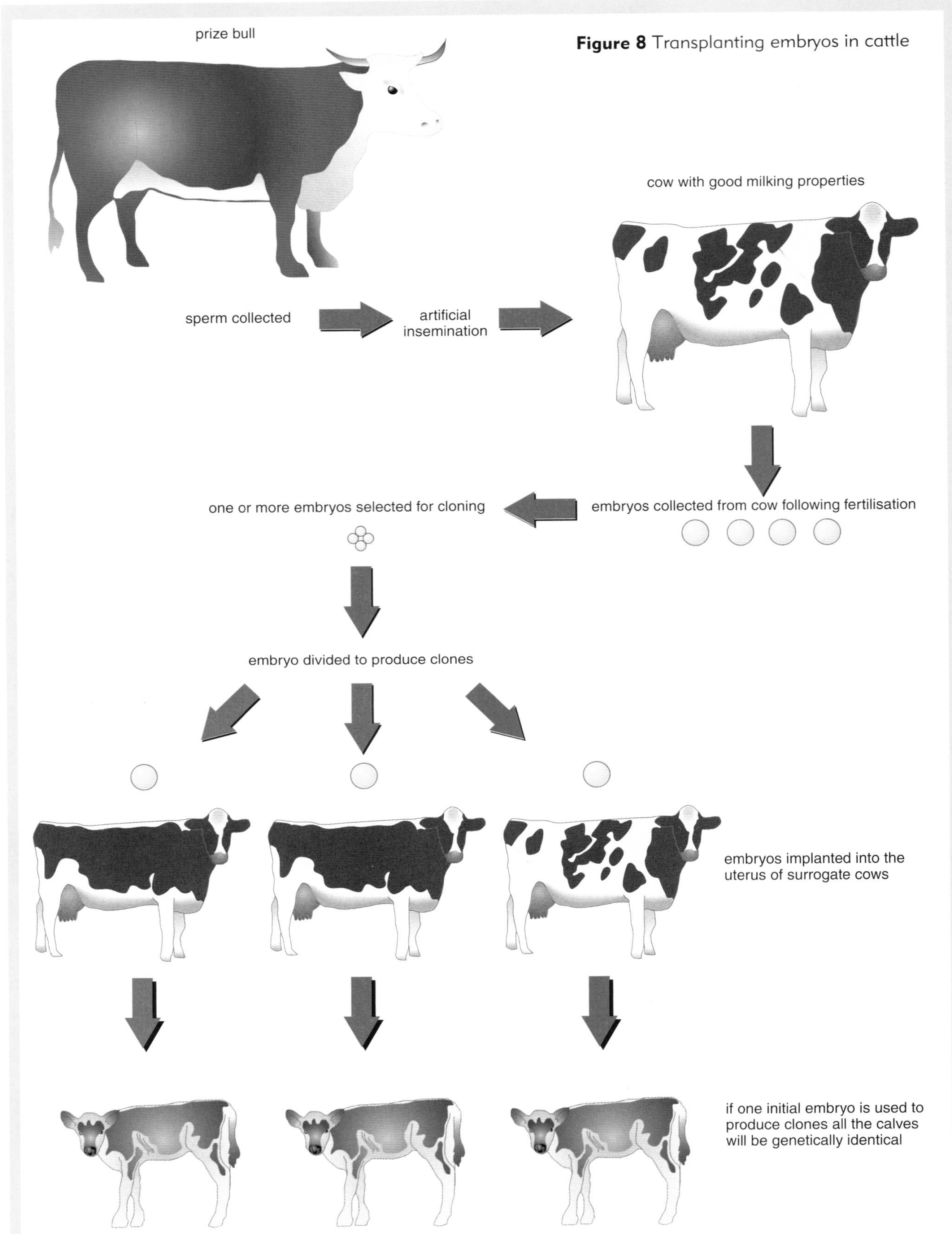
prize bull
sperm collected
artificial insemination
cow with good milking properties
embryos collected from cow following fertilisation
one or more embryos selected for cloning
embryo divided to produce clones
embryos implanted into the uterus of surrogate cows
if one initial embryo is used to produce clones all the calves will be genetically identical

Figure 8 Transplanting embryos in cattle

Websites

http://www.sac.ac.uk/animal/External/ABDWeb/Genetics/History.htm
Excellent account of the history of selective breeding.

Exam questions

1 The histogram shows the heights of a class of 16 year old boys.

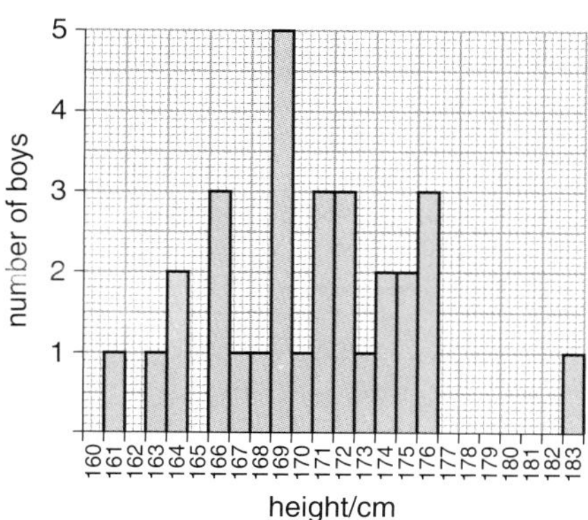

a) What is the most common height in the class?

(1 mark)

b) Calculate the difference in height between the tallest boy and the shortest boy in the class.

(1 mark)

c) Two factors produced variation in the height of the boys. One factor was environmental, name the other.

(1 mark)

d) Height is an example of **continuous** variation. What is meant by the term continuous variation?

(1 mark)

e) Give **one** example of **discontinuous** variation in humans.

(1 mark)

2 a) Tissue culture can be used to produce Bramley apple trees.

The diagram shows the basic steps of the technique.

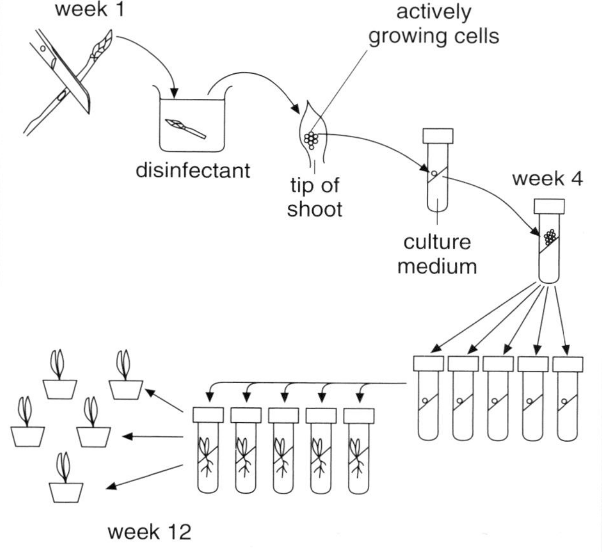

(i) Give **three** advantages of producing apple trees by this method rather than growing them from seed.

(3 marks)

(ii) What name is given to a group of organisms produced by this technique?

(1 mark)

Chapter 24

Selection and Evolution

Learning objectives

By the end of this chapter you should:

- Understand the link between variation and selection
- Understand natural selection and know examples of natural selection in action
- Understand the processes of evolution and extinction
- Understand the principle of artificial selection and its importance in plant and animal breeding

When there is a lot of variation between the animals or plants in a population it is likely that some of the individuals will be better equipped to prosper or survive in their environment. That is, they are better **adapted**. An example of variation linked to survival is shown in Figure 1, which shows the relationship between seed size in wild garlic and the percentage of seeds that germinate successfully and develop into young seedlings in a woodland.

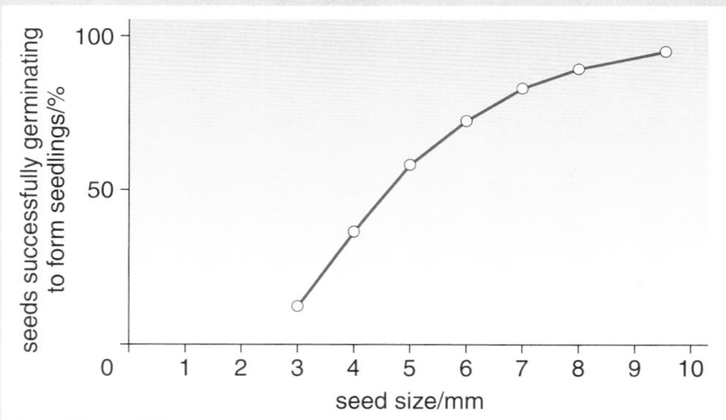

Figure 1 The link between seed size and successful germination in wild garlic

The ability of the seeds to germinate depends on the amount of resources they contain. Larger seeds will have more food reserves. The seeds that fail to germinate probably do so because they do not have enough food reserves to reach the soil surface and produce leaves to begin photosynthesising. You can probably think of many adaptations that might help plants and animals survive in particular situations.

Natural selection

In the natural world adaptations in living organisms are essential for survival and success in all habitats. They are even more important when organisms compete with each other for resources. This **competition** ensures that the best adapted individuals will survive. For example, the larger seedlings growing in a clump will be able to obtain key resources such as light, nutrients and water more easily than the smaller seedlings. As a result of this competition the stronger individuals will survive, possibly at the expense of the weaker ones. This competition for survival with the result that the better equipped individuals survive is the cornerstone of Charles Darwin's theory of **natural selection**.

Figure 2 Charles Darwin

Charles Darwin and the theory of natural selection

Charles Darwin (1809–1882) was a naturalist who devoted much of his life to scientific research. As part of his research he spent five years as a ship's naturalist on HMS Beagle as it travelled to South America. Darwin was greatly influenced by the variety of life he observed on his travels, and in particular, the animals of the Galapagos Islands. Darwin and another scientist, Alfred Wallace, who independently came to the same conclusions as Darwin, jointly presented their theories in a scientific paper titled 'On the Origin of Species by Means of Natural Selection' to the Linnean Society in London in 1859.

Darwin's main conclusions can be summarised as:

- All living organisms produce more young than can survive. In many species it is the availability of food that limits survival.
- There is **variation** between the individuals in a population.
- Consequently there is a **struggle for existence**.
- The better adapted individuals survive this struggle or competition. This leads to **survival of the fittest**.
- The **best adapted individuals are more likely to survive to breed**. Consequently they will be the ones that are more likely to pass their genes and characteristics (variations) on to offspring.

It is worthwhile looking at some examples of natural selection in action to highlight the key features of Darwin's theory. The first two examples given are recent and show how species can change genetically over short periods of time. The third example is one of the most studied examples of natural selection, the peppered moth.

Example 1 Antibiotic resistance in bacteria

When bacteria are treated with an antibiotic such as penicillin most of the bacteria are destroyed. However, a small number (the fittest) may survive, probably because they have a mutation that provides resistance. Very soon the resistant bacteria are the only ones surviving and they reproduce rapidly to produce a large number of bacteria, all of which are resistant to penicillin.

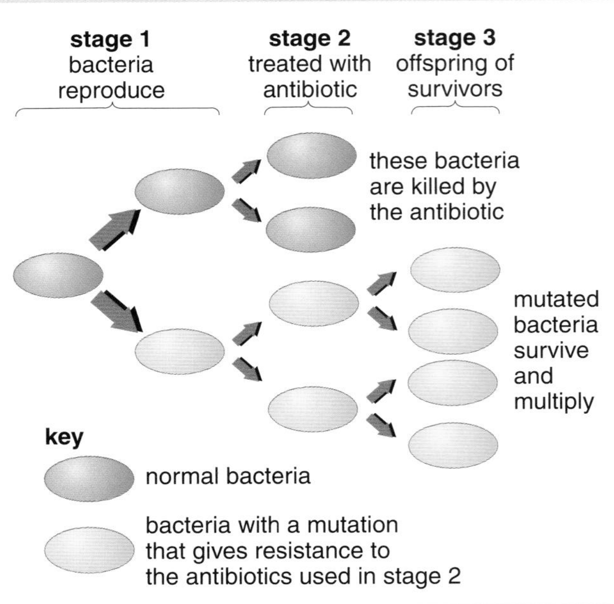
stage 1
bacteria reproduce
stage 2
treated with antibiotic
stage 3
offspring of survivors
these bacteria are killed by the antibiotic
mutated bacteria survive and multiply
key
normal bacteria
bacteria with a mutation that gives resistance to the antibiotics used in stage 2

Figure 3 Antibiotic resistance in bacteria

If a second type of antibiotic is used this may eliminate some of the bacteria resistant to penicillin. Many will be destroyed, but again a small number may have a different mutation and be able to survive this new antibiotic. If the sequence continues 'superbugs' that are resistant to all antibiotics can develop.

Questions

1 Why are superbugs more likely to be found in hospitals than in other large buildings that contain many people?

Example 2 Insecticide resistance in insects.

Insecticides are toxic chemicals that were developed to control insect pests. When they were first used they were very effective in controlling insect numbers. At some stage a few individuals were able to survive as they had the ability to break down the insecticide (as a result of mutations providing them with the genes required). These resistant insects could survive to breed and through time the number of resistant insects increase.

Example 3 The Peppered Moth

The peppered moth is a moth common in much of Britain. The moth has two very distinct forms. One has light coloured wings and the other form is black. A single gene controls the difference in colour, with different alleles of this gene causing the different appearances.

Up until the beginning of the industrial revolution in Britain very few of the black form of the moths were seen. This was because the black variety was easily spotted on the lichen-covered trees by predatory birds, and was more likely to be eaten. The lighter, speckled form of the moth was ideally camouflaged and was less likely to be eaten by birds. By 1850 less than one percent of the moths in some areas that were beginning to become industrialised were black. Within fifty years almost all the moths in these regions were black. This can be explained by the changes that the industrial revolution was causing to the environment. The bark of the trees in industrialised areas was becoming blackened due to the large volume of soot that was entering the atmosphere. In these areas the black form of moth became better camouflaged and adapted and it was the speckled form that was most easily picked off by the birds.

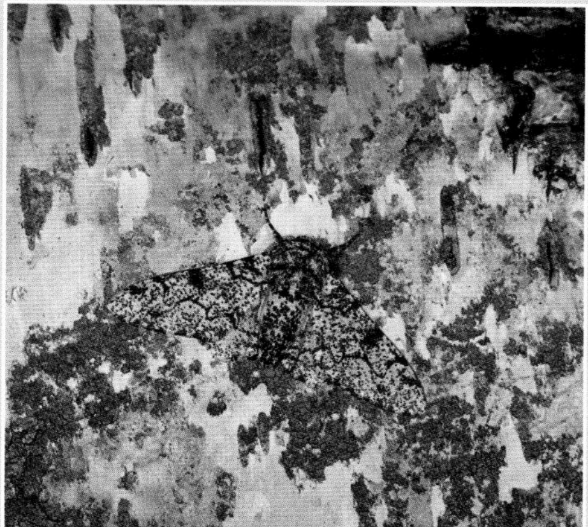

Figure 4 The lighter speckled moth is well camouflaged on the lichen covered tree, however it is not camouflaged on the blackened bark. The black moth is much better camouflaged on this bark

This is a very good example of natural selection in action. The mutation that produces the black form of moth happens fairly often but in non-industrial areas it is obviously harmful and moths with the mutation are quickly eliminated. The mutation became beneficial when the black form was better camouflaged and therefore the ratio of black to speckled forms increased.

Darwin and evolution

Darwin used the theory of natural selection to explain the process of **evolution**. Darwin suggested that species have changed gradually through time in response to changes in the environment. He was not the first to propose that organisms could evolve but his theory was based on much stronger scientific evidence than other earlier versions.

The finches that Darwin observed on the Galapagos Islands during his travels were very important in his thinking and in helping him develop his theory of evolution. Darwin studied 13 different varieties of finches and he noticed that they differed little except in the shapes of their beaks and in their diets.

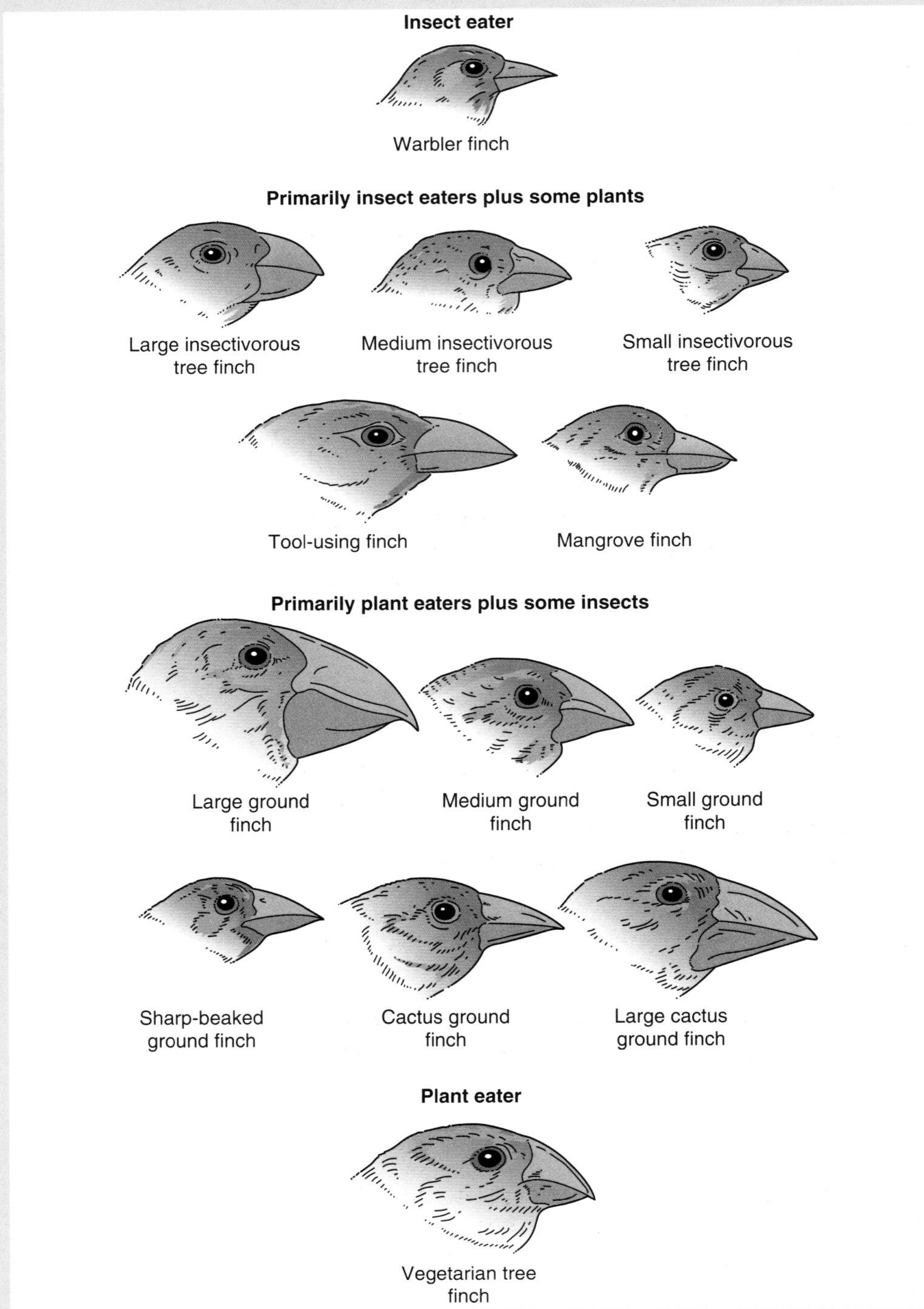

Figure 5 Darwin's finches

These finches were unique to the Galapagos Islands and some were only found on particular islands within the Galapagos group. Darwin suggested that many years before his visit a group of finches arrived on the Galapagos Islands from neighbouring South America. As the island group and the mainland are separated by 600 miles, many times greater than the finches flying range, he suggested that this was a freak event and the finches may have been blown by very strong winds. When they arrived the finches were isolated on islands that had very little other bird life. In time small variations in beak shape enabled some finches to eat other types of food that was found on the islands and this in turn reduced competition (*the struggle for existence*) between the finches for food. Because of this reduced competition for food the finches that could make use of other food types would be more likely to survive (*survival of the fittest*) and be able to pass their genes (and their beak variations) on to their offspring. Eventually a range of beak types, and species of finches, evolved that could make use of the wide range of food sources that the islands provide.

Controversially, Darwin suggested that the theory of evolution applied to all living organisms, including man. When his theory was first proposed there was considerable opposition to his ideas for a number of reasons. These included:

- It clearly contradicted the teaching of the church.
- There was no explanation as to how variation was caused and also how these variations were passed on to offspring. He had no knowledge of Mendel and his work or genetics.
- He could not demonstrate natural selection in action. Darwin could only observe the process of selection at a given point in time. He did not observe change actually occurring. He was not aware of examples such as the peppered moth.

The current position

Following the widespread publication of Mendel's work on genetics, many of the missing parts of the evolution jigsaw were in place, including the genetic basis of variation and inheritance. Our increased knowledge of how DNA works and the way in which mutations occur help provide a deeper understanding of the processes of natural selection and evolution.

Darwin's theory is further supported by the extensive fossil record and by other evidence including our greater understanding of living organisms and the relationships between them.

Although evolution can explain how organisms evolve and change through time, including the formation of new species, it can also explain the process of **extinction**.

Extinction

An animal or plant may be described as being extinct if there are no living examples left. The fossil record shows that many animals and plants have become extinct through time. The most famous examples include the dinosaurs and mammoths.

Most of the animals and plants that have become extinct have disappeared because they could not evolve fast enough to cope with a changing environment. The fossil record suggests that in the past, extinctions were often associated with climate change.

The woolly mammoth (Figure 6), a large elephant-like mammal may have become extinct at the time of the last ice age because the increasing size of the ice fields may have eliminated much of the mammoths' natural habitat.

Figure 6 Woolly mammoths

The activities of man have been directly or indirectly responsible for the extinction or near–extinction of many plants and animals.

This has been the result of the hunting or collection of animals or plants, however the loss of habitat may have an even more devastating effect. The threat to the giant panda due to the loss of the bamboo forests and, the daily extinctions that probably occur as much of the Amazon rainforest is cleared, are well known. However, there are many local examples where plants and animals have been driven to the verge of extinction or made extinct by the action of man.

A good example is the plight of the corncrake, a bird that used to be common over much of Northern Ireland. The increase in silage cutting and the reduction in the growing of hay helped eliminate the corncrake from Northern Ireland. In Ireland it is now restricted to a very small number of sites in the south of the country. The corncrake lays its eggs in hay fields or meadows with the fields providing shelter and food. The young chicks are well established and able to survive by mid/late summer when hay was traditionally cut. With silage being cut much earlier in the summer, and more often, the timescale for the rearing of chicks is too short.

Figure 7 A corncrake

As well as contributing to the extinction of many species, man has also manipulated the course of natural selection and evolution by deliberately selecting particular characteristics or traits in many plants and animals that are of use to man. This is the process of **artificial selection**.

Artificial selection (selective breeding)

Artificial selection to produce more productive and profitable crops and animals has been taking place for centuries. Typically characteristics that are advantageous are increased yield or food value, more attractive produce, better storage properties, hardiness and disease resistance.

Artificial selection in plants

The manipulation of selection in cereals has been used to create plants that bear very little resemblance to their early ancestors. Typically in cereals the process has been designed to produce plants that give high yield and are less susceptible to disease and harsh weather conditions. Figure 8 shows how selective breeding has been used to produce the modern variety of wheat.

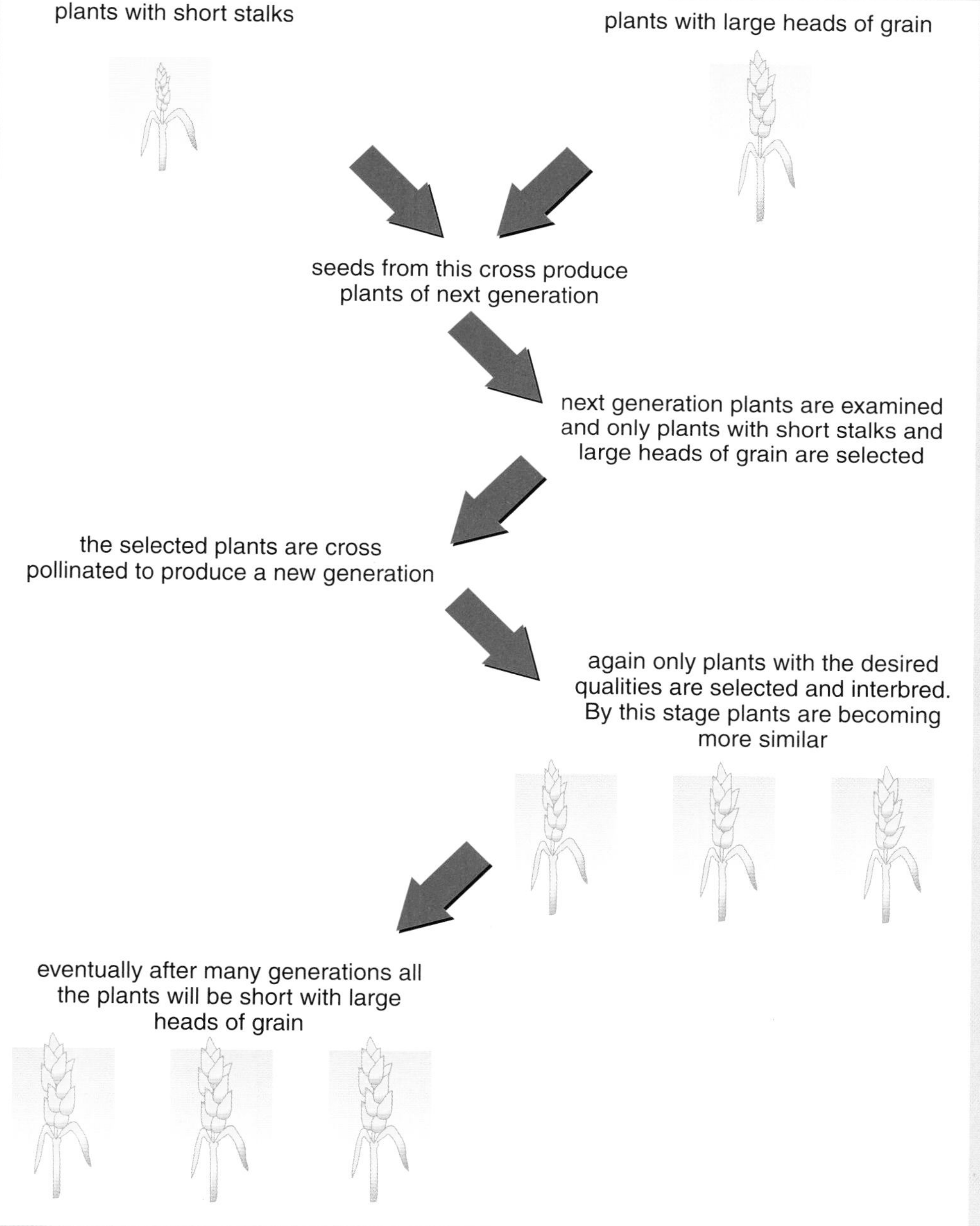
plants with short stalks
plants with large heads of grain
seeds from this cross produce plants of next generation
next generation plants are examined and only plants with short stalks and large heads of grain are selected
the selected plants are cross pollinated to produce a new generation
again only plants with the desired qualities are selected and interbred. By this stage plants are becoming more similar
eventually after many generations all the plants will be short with large heads of grain

Figure 8 Artificial selection in wheat

Figure 9 compares the wheat before and after selection.

Figure 9a Wheat used to consist of stalks of variable size. The number of seeds per plant also varied

Figure 9b A field of modern wheat, showing that all the stems are of a similar height and contain many seeds

The benefits of selective breeding in wheat are easy to identify. There is a greater yield per plant and the short modern plants are less easily damaged by wind. The uniform height means that harvesting is easier and quicker.

Selective breeding in animals

Selective breeding in animals uses the same principles as used with plants. Domestic animals have been bred to produce animals with high milk yields, good meat qualities and almost any other characteristic that affects the profitability or value of the animal. The number of varieties that can be produced is almost limitless, as can be seen in the breeding of dogs.

In recent times selective breeding has become more sophisticated with the use of artificial insemination to more tightly control the variety of genes that will be present in offspring.

The use of cloning as discussed in the previous chapter is an extreme example of selective breeding where the exact genetic make up of all offspring can be controlled.

Websites

http://www.bbc.co.uk/education/darwin
Useful summaries of natural selection, evolution and extinction.

http://www.nhm.ac.uk/museum/tempexhib/voyages/darwin_map.html
Information about Darwin's voyages and his discoveries.

Try your own search using the multiple criteria 'corncrake + Ireland'.

WWW

Exam questions

1 a) Variation within a species can give rise to plants which are adapted to their different environments. Seeds of *Potentilla* plants were collected and grown at the altitudes shown in the diagram. The drawings show the appearance of the plants after one year.

	grown at 200 m	grown at 1400 m	grown at 3000 m
Seeds collected at 200 m			
Seeds collected at 1400 m			
Seeds collected at 3000 m			

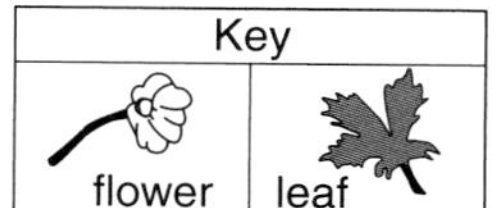

(i) Give **three** ways, shown in the drawings, in which the plants differ from each other.

(3 marks)

(ii) Describe the results for the seeds **collected** at 1400 m.

(1 mark)

(iii) Which plant is **least tolerant** when grown at an altitude different from the one at which its seeds were collected.

(1 mark)

(iv) If a **species** does not adapt to its environment what may eventually happen to it?

(1 mark)

b) Plant breeders use artificial selection to produce improved varieties of plants.

(i) Give **two** desirable characteristics which could be introduced into plants.

(2 marks)

(ii) Suggest how breeders could produce large numbers of identical plants:

[A] using laboratory techniques

(1 mark)

[B] without using laboratory techniques

(1 mark)

2 Natural Selection suggests that organisms better adapted to their environment survive and reproduce. They pass their characteristics to their offspring.

The diagram shows three stages in the development of antibiotic resistance in a population of bacteria.

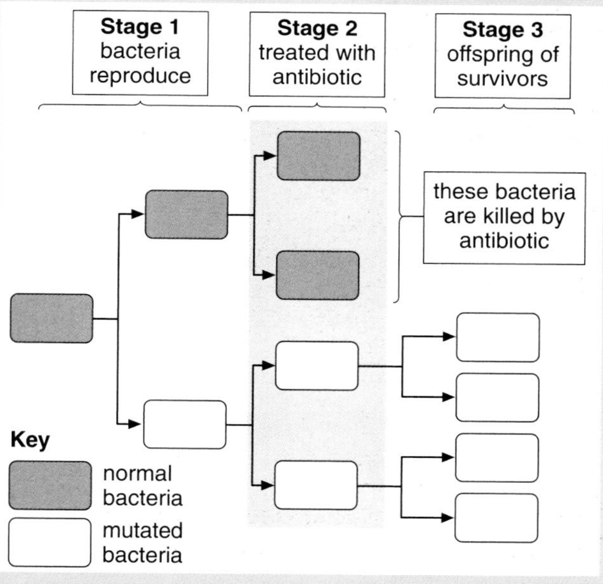

a) Describe and explain what has happened at stages 2 and 3.

(3 marks)

b) The diagram shows a quick growing *Brassica rapa* plant.

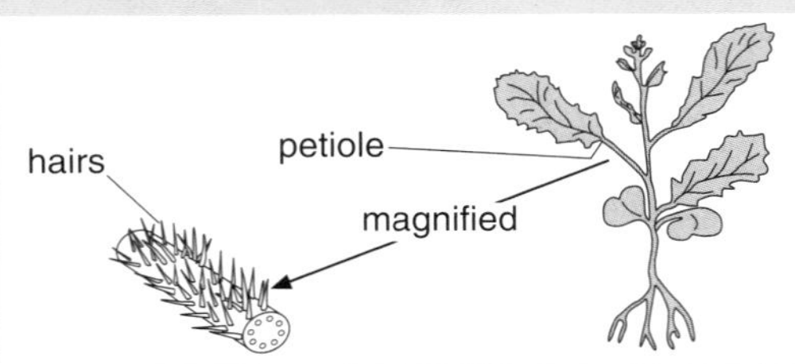

Pupils in a biology class investigated hairiness of petioles in three generations of this plant.

They selected the most hairy plants and self-pollinated them.

They collected the seeds and grew them.

They repeated this process to produce a further two generations of plants.

The table shows the results obtained.

Generation	Average number of hairs per petiole
1	29
2	43
3	63

(i) Describe the trend shown by the results of this investigation.
(1 mark)

(ii) Explain why the **average** number of hairs per petiole was used to compare the three generations.
(1 mark)

(iii) Explain how this investigation demonstrates **artificial** selection.
(1 mark)

(iv) Suggest **two** desirable characteristics that could be introduced into plants by artificial selection.
(2 marks)

(v) Asexual reproduction in plants produces genetically identical offspring. Give **two** methods a gardener may use to produce genetically identical plants.
(2 marks)

3 Warfarin, a poison used to kill rats, was first used in the 1950s. By 1980 many areas had populations of rats which were resistant to warfarin. The diagrams show how this resistance spreads through rat populations.

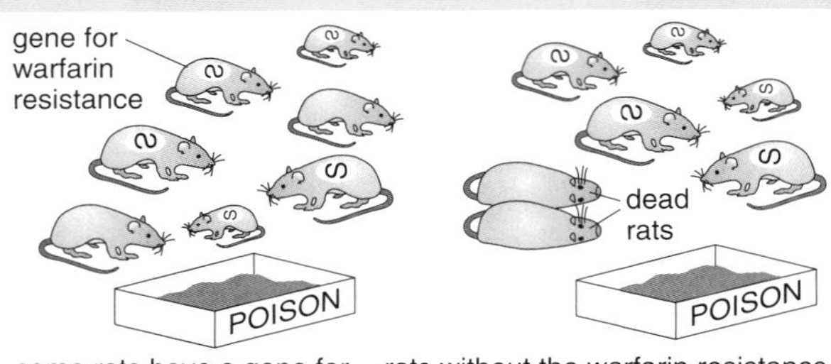

some rats have a gene for warfarin resistance | rats without the warfarin resistance gene are killed by the rat poison

a) What type of variation is shown by warfarin resistance in rats?
(1 mark)

b) Using the example of warfarin resistance explain what Darwin meant by survival of the fittest.
(3 marks)

c) Give one way in which genetic variations arise.
(1 mark)

d) Suggest what would happen to the numbers of each type of rat if the population of rats was treated with warfarin.
(2 marks)

e) Suggest what effect warfarin treatment would have on a population of rats, none of whom have the warfarin resistant gene.
(1 mark)

Chapter 25

Plant Reproduction

Learning objectives

By the end of this chapter you should know:

- The parts of the flower and their functions
- Self and cross-pollination
- Insect and wind pollination
- Fertilisation in the ovule
- Seed and fruit dispersal
- Seed structure
- Natural and artificial propagation

The flower is the organ of reproduction in a flowering plant. All flowers have the same general structure although there is considerable variation between species. Figure 1 is a section through the centre of a wallflower showing the arrangement of the main flower parts.

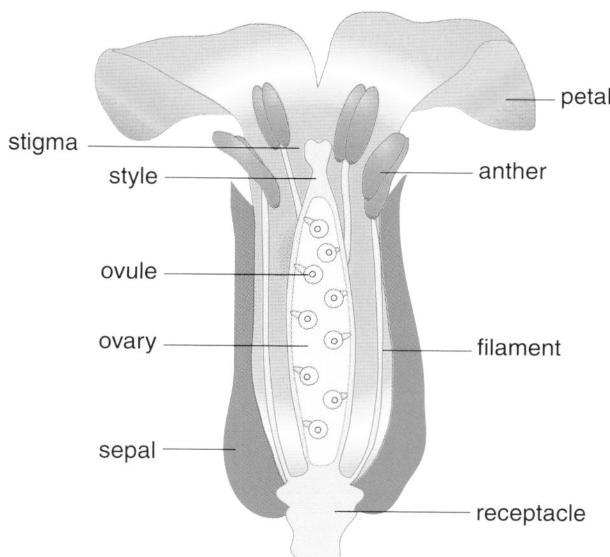

Figure 1 A wallflower

The parts of the wallflower and most other flowers are regularly arranged in circles or in whorls. The **sepals** form the outside layer of the flower. These protect the flower when in bud. In the wallflower the sepals are green but in some other plants they are brightly coloured. In the wallflower the four brightly coloured **petals** form a ring inside the sepals. In the wallflower and many other flowers the role of the petals is to attract insects. The **stamens**, the male part of the flower, are situated inside the petals and each stamen consists of a stalk or **filament** that supports the **anther**. The anthers produce **pollen grains**, which contain the **male gametes**.

The female part of the flower is in the centre. This is called the **carpel**. The carpel is subdivided into the **stigma**, the **style** and the **ovary**. The stigma is the top of the carpel and its function is to catch pollen grains during pollination. The ovary contains the **ovules** which contain the **female gametes**. At the base of the flower there is a **nectary**. This produces nectar, which attracts insects to the flower. Guidelines or markings on the petals help direct the insects to the nectary. The **receptacle** is the top of the flower stalk from which the parts of the flower arise.

Figure 2 shows a diagram of a sweet pea flower. It is not as regularly arranged as the wallflower, but you can still identify the characteristic arrangement with the carpel as the innermost part and the stamens, petals and sepals occurring progressively further away from the centre.

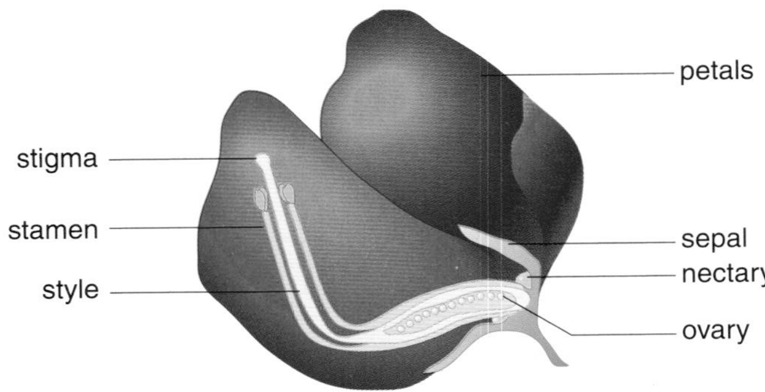

Figure 2 The sweet pea

Irrespective of the shape of the flower its prime function is sexual reproduction. The general sequence of events in this process is the same in all flowers.

The reproductive process

Reproduction in plants involves two distinct phases – **pollination** and **fertilisation**. Pollination is the transfer of a pollen grain from an anther to a stigma. Fertilisation occurs when the male gamete (the pollen grain nucleus) combines or fuses with the female gamete (the ovule nucleus) in an ovule.

Pollination

Pollen grains are produced and stored in the anther. When they are ripe the anther releases the pollen. The grains are so small that they resemble a fine powder. Pollination will only occur if at least one pollen grain can be transported to a stigma. Pollen grains cannot actively move so they require some mechanism to transport them. Normally the pollen grains are transported by either insects or by wind. Flowers of a particular species are adapted usually for either insect or wind pollination. Figure 3 shows diagrams of typical insect and wind pollinated flowers. The table summarises the main difference between flowers that are adapted for insect pollination and flowers that are adapted for wind pollination. The diagram and the table will make it easy for you to work out whether the wallflower is wind or insect pollinated.

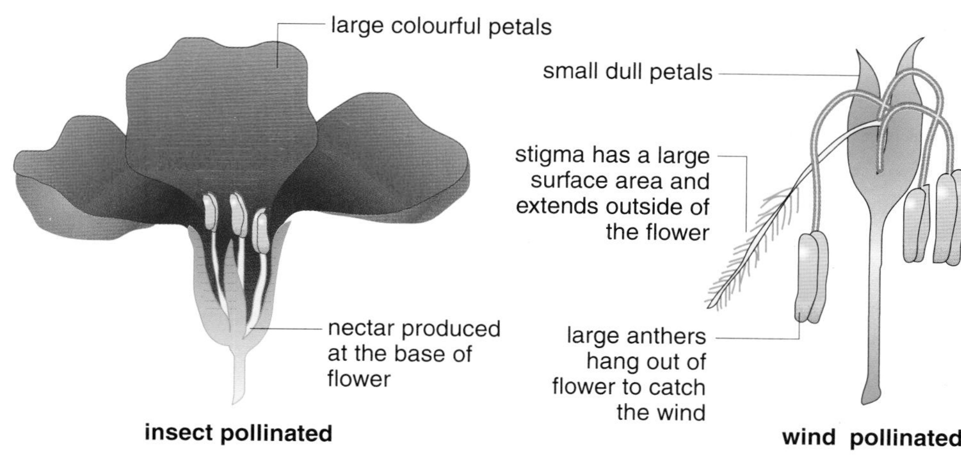

Figure 3 Insect and wind pollinated flowers

Insect pollinated flowers	Wind pollinated flowers
Brightly coloured petals. Petals often large and 'showy' to attract insects.	Petals not brightly coloured. Petals often small and few in number.
Anthers and stigmas positioned inside flower to be in best position to give or receive pollen when insect enters flower.	Anthers and stigmas large and hang outside flower. With the anthers outside the pollen can blow in the wind more easily. Large feathery stigmas hanging outside the flower are more likely to catch pollen.
Nectaries often present.	Nectaries absent.
May produce scent.	No scent produced.
Anthers produce relatively few large sticky pollen grains. Fewer can be produced, as there is less wastage with insect pollination. The sticky large grains will stick to insects better.	Anthers produce large numbers of small pollen grains. Many are produced, as few will reach their target when transported by wind. Small grains will be carried more easily by the wind.

Insect pollination is more likely to be successful as the movement of insects from flower to flower is less random than the direction and strength of the wind. A disadvantage is that insect pollination relies on a sufficient number of the right type of insects being present when the plants are in flower.

Self and cross-pollination

If pollen is carried from an anther to the stigma in the same flower, or to a stigma on another flower, on the same plant, **self-pollination** is taking place. If pollen is transferred to a stigma of a flower on a different plant (of the same species), **cross-pollination** will result.

Self-pollination is a much easier process, due to the short distances involved, often only a few millimetres. However, over three-quarters of all types of flowering plants are adapted for cross-pollination due to the advantages cross-pollination provide. Cross-pollination will provide genetic variation, as new plants produced will contain a combination of the genes from both parents. In self-pollination only one parent is involved.

To ensure that cross-pollination takes place plants must have adaptations to decrease the possibility of self-pollination taking place. These include:

- **Separate sexed plants.** Holly trees are either male or female i.e. in any one holly tree the flowers will either be male or female. Therefore they will only contain stamens or carpels in their flowers, but not both.
- **Male and female parts maturing at different times.** Plants that use this strategy have flowers in which the male and female parts mature at different times. Any one flower (or plant) at a specific time will effectively be male or female, as only the stamens or carpels will be mature, and can carry out their function. Cross-pollination occurs because other plants of the same species are maturing at different rates. There would be a problem if all the plants and flowers matured at exactly the same rate.

Questions

1 Why would it be a problem if all the plants matured at exactly the same time?

- **Structural adaptations to the flower.** Some types of plants have male and female flower parts that mature at the same time but can still prevent self-pollination. An example is the primrose. Primrose flowers exist in two forms (see Figure 4). In one form the anthers rise above the stigma (thrum-eyed flowers) whereas in the alternative form the stigma is above the anthers (pin-eyed flowers). Stigmas from a pin-eyed flower are at exactly the same height as the anthers in the thrum-eyed flower and vice-versa. If a bee visits a pin-eyed flower it will pick up pollen on its head region. When it visits a thrum-eyed flower its head will be at the same level as the stigma therefore it is easy for pollen to transfer.

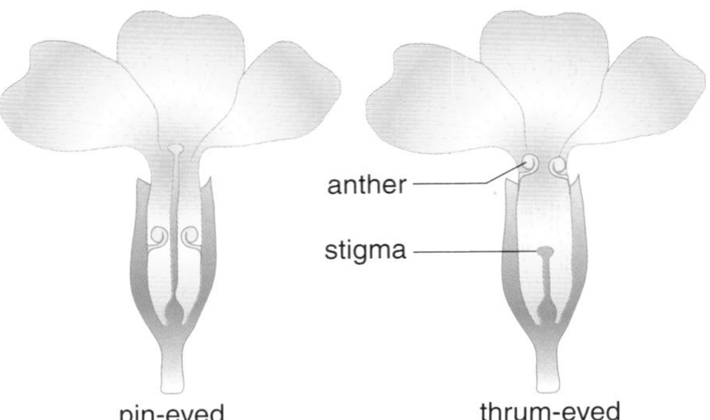

Figure 4 Pin-eyed and thrum-eyed primrose flowers

Questions

2 How is pollen transferred from a thrum-eyed flower to a pin-eyed flower?

In some plants the stigmas are raised above the level of the anthers. While this on its own is unlikely to prevent self-pollination, this will reduce the probability of it occurring, particularly by pollen falling onto the stigma from overhanging anthers, a situation that happens frequently in self-pollinated flowers.

Once the pollen grain has landed on the stigma pollination is complete. The next part of the process is getting the male and female gametes together to allow fertilisation to take place. This is discussed in the next section.

The link between pollination and fertilisation

After pollination the male gamete (pollen grain nucleus) must reach the female gamete (ovule nucleus) for the next part of the reproductive process to continue. When the pollen grain lands on the stigma it begins to grow a **pollen tube**. This tube grows down through the style and enters the ovary. It can then enter an ovule through the **micropyle**. When this happens the pollen grain nucleus passes down through this tube and fuses with the ovule nucleus. This is fertilisation and a zygote is produced. The zygote is the first cell of the new plant. The pollen grain nucleus and the ovule nucleus are haploid and have been produced by meiosis in the same way that animal gametes are produced. When fertilisation takes place the resultant zygote will be diploid.

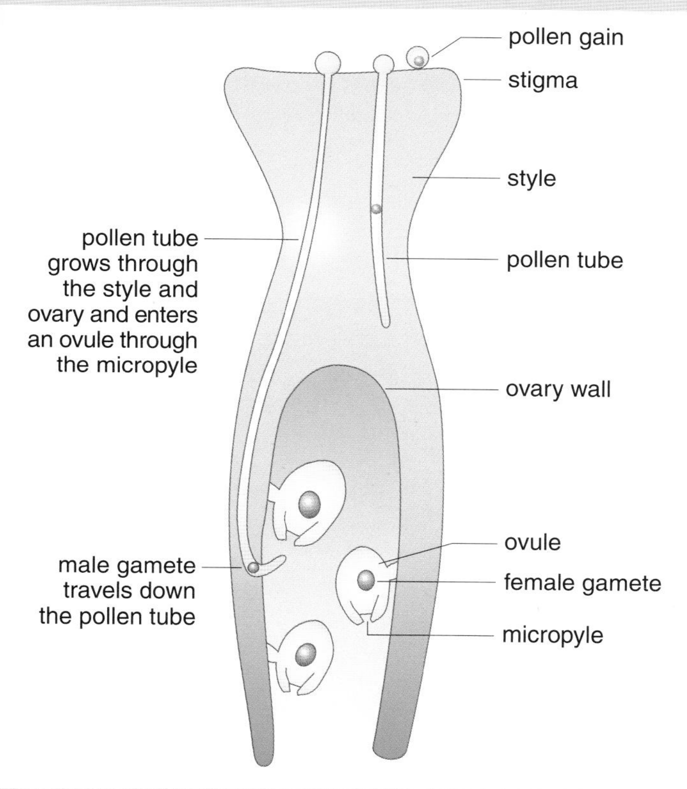

Figure 5 Fertilisation in a wallflower

Following fertilisation the ovule develops into a **seed** and the ovary becomes a **fruit**. You are probably familiar with a large number of seeds and fruits. For example, when you 'shell' peas and beans, the pod is the wall of the fruit and the peas and beans are the seeds. The pips of grapes and oranges are seeds within larger juicy fruits.

Questions

3 You split open a large pea pod expecting to find seven or eight peas inside but only find two, what is the most likely reason for this?

Seed and fruit dispersal

Once the seeds develop it is important that they are dispersed away from the parent plant. This is important for two main reasons:

- Dispersal allows new plants to grow well away from the parent plant, and from each other. As a result there will be less competition for resources.
- It allows the colonisation of new habitats.

Seeds and fruits are often adapted for a particular method of dispersal. The most common types are wind, animal, water and explosive.

Wind dispersal

Many common plants and trees rely on wind dispersal. Sycamore seeds have extended 'wings' that allow the seeds to spin and produce a 'parachute' effect when they fall from trees. This effect keeps the seeds in the air for longer and allows the wind to blow the seeds away from the tree. Ash and elm seeds also have extensions that work in similar ways.

Dandelions have very effective 'parachutes' that can catch the wind and allow the seeds to be blown considerable distances.

a)

b)

Figure 6 Wind dispersal a) dandelions and b) sycamore

Animal dispersal

As most animals are mobile and many can travel large distances in short periods of time they are capable of helping the process of seed dispersal. When birds and other animals eat fruit the seeds or pips may pass through their digestive systems and eventually be dropped well away from the parent plant. The tough coat of the seeds prevents them being digested. This is how the seeds in juicy fruits such as cherries and blackberries are usually dispersed. Alternatively, some animals (and humans) discard the less tasty parts, the core, which contains the seeds, after eating the fleshy parts. This is often enough to provide effective dispersal.

Some seeds and fruits are able to attach themselves to the fur of animals for transport. Two of the best examples are goosegrass and burdock. The fruits or seeds of these plants are usually either sticky or have small hooks on their surface.

a)
b)

Figure 7 Animal dispersal – a) burdock has barbs on their fruit which become attached to passing animals and fall off when the animals clean themselves, b) birds eat berries, the seeds pass through their digestive system and are deposited far from the parent plant

Water dispersal

Not surprisingly, the seeds of many water plants are dispersed by water currents. These seeds or fruits must be able to stay afloat for a period of time if they are to be effectively dispersed. However, water dispersal is important in some land plants. An excellent example is the coconut. Coconuts are able to float considerable distances and are very effective at colonising other islands that they are carried to. Coconut trees often grow at the sea edge, partially because this is where they get washed up, and also because any coconuts they produce can only be dispersed if they reach water.

Explosive mechanisms

As some types of fruit dry they twist and coil setting up tensions within the structure. Eventually the tension reaches a point where the fruits uncoil or split rapidly. The force of this can eject the seeds up to several metres. This type of self-dispersal can be seen in gorse, pea and wallflowers.

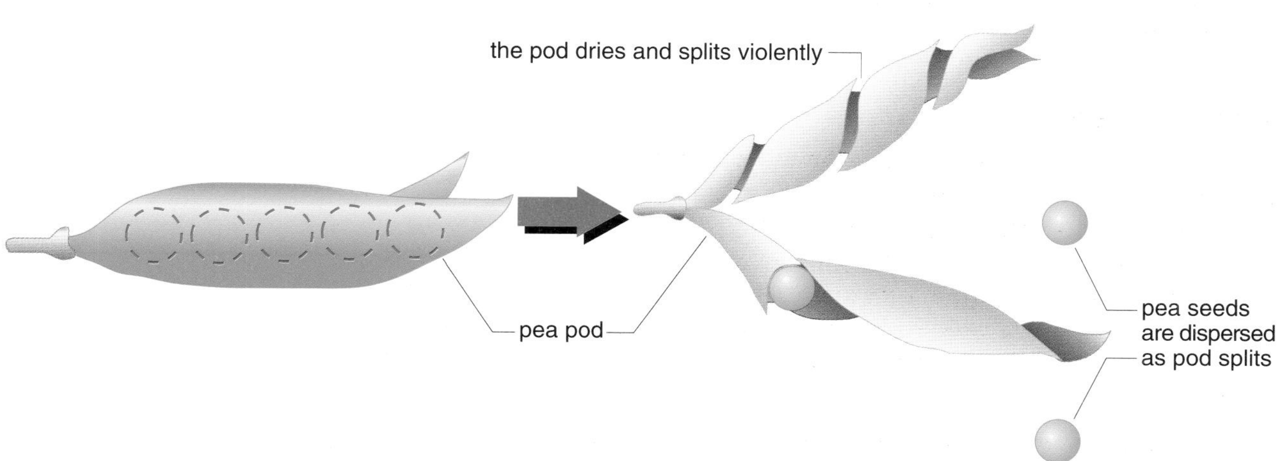
the pod dries and splits violently
pea pod
pea seeds are dispersed as pod splits

Figure 8 Explosive dispersal

Seed structure

The seed is a dormant stage that can eventually grow into another plant if it lands in a place that can provide all the required conditions. The conditions required for germination are moisture, oxygen and an adequate temperature. Many seeds are buried in the soil for a period of time before they germinate and grow. To grow into a young seedling each seed needs a reserve of food to supply the embryo as it develops and grows. Seeds contain one or more **cotyledons** which store food. In some seeds there is also an **endosperm**, another type of food store. The seed coat or **testa** protects the seed contents from microbial attack and also keeps them dry before they begin the germination process. When the seed germinates the **radicle** (young root) and **plumule** (young shoot) begin to grow. The radicle penetrates the testa first and is soon followed by the plumule. Figures 9 and 10 show the structure of a seed and the sequence of events that take place as the seed germinates.

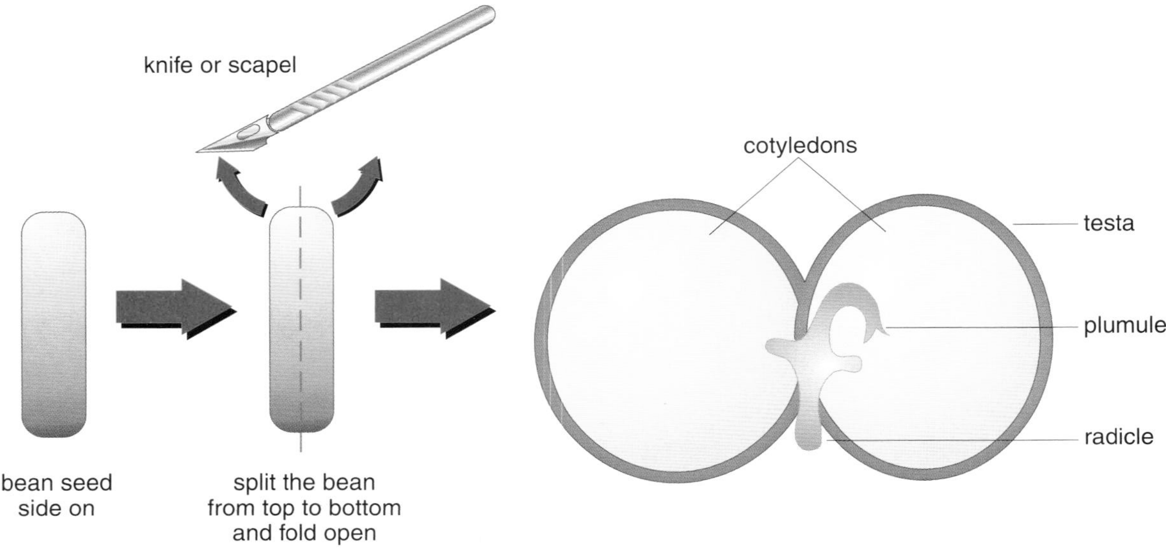

Figure 9 Examining the structure of a bean seed

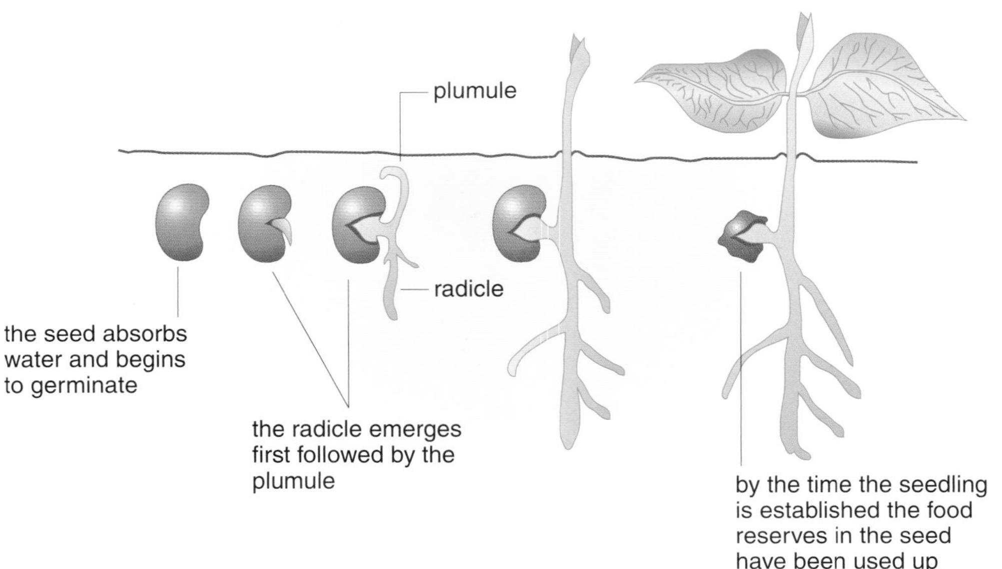

Figure 10 Seeds and germination

Natural and artificial propagation

Many plants can reproduce without involving flowers. This type of reproduction is asexual reproduction and is called propagation. Examples of propagation include the growth of new plants from tubers (potatoes) and bulbs (daffodils). The development of runners in strawberry plants is another example, each runner can produce new plants that can develop independently of the parent plant.

The taking of cuttings is an example of artificial propagation. Runners and cuttings were discussed in detail in Chapter 23.

Websites

http://www.revise.it/reviseit/content/GCSE/Biology/
This site summarises the key points well.

http://waynesword.palomar.edu/plfeb99.htm
This site includes some unusual examples of wind dispersal.

Exam questions

1 The photograph shows wallflower pollen grains.

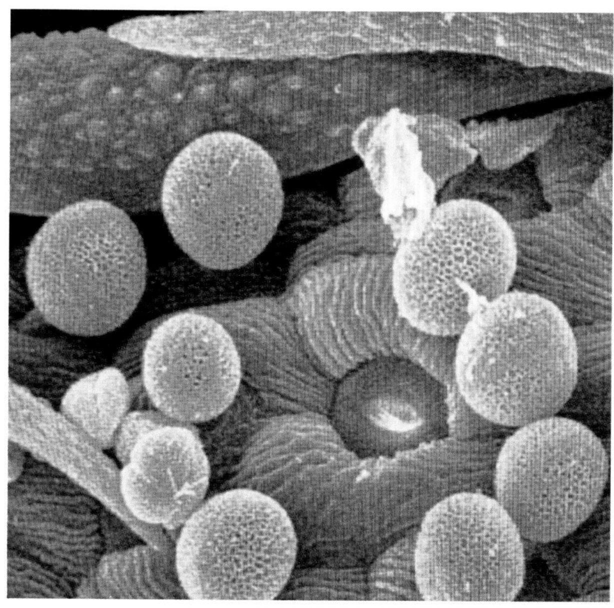

a) Name the part of the plant where pollen is made.

(1 mark)

b) What is pollination?

(1 mark)

Wallflower pollen grains are large and have a rough surface.

c) Suggest the agent for wallflower pollination.

(1 mark)

d) Describe what happens to a pollen grain between pollination and fertilisation.

(2 marks)

2 The drawings show the transfer of pollen between flowers.

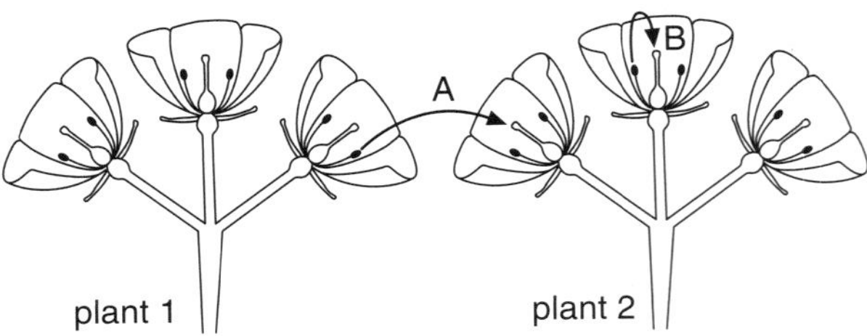

a) Identify the types of pollination shown by arrows A and B.

(2 marks)

b) The diagram shows a plant ovule just prior to fertilisation.

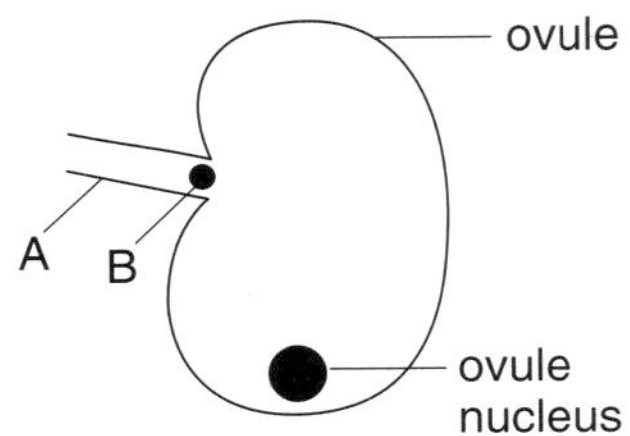

(i) Identify the structures A and B.

(2 marks)

(ii) If the adult plant has a diploid chromosome number of 36, how many chromosomes are present in the ovule nucleus?

(1 mark)

3 The diagrams show a strawberry flower and a grass flower.

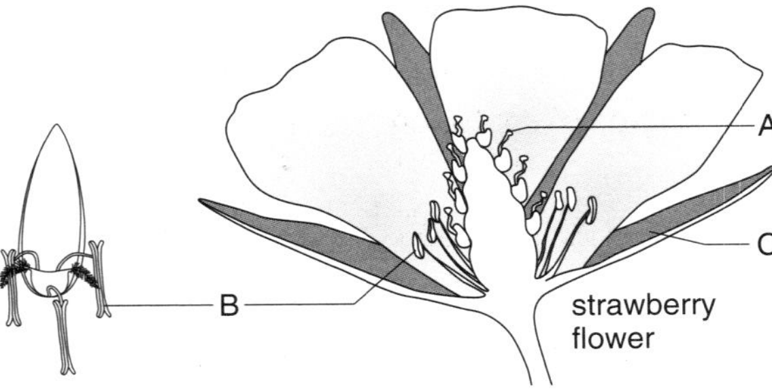

a) (i) Name parts A, B and C.

(3 marks)

(ii) Describe **one** way the grass flower differs from the strawberry flower.

(1 mark)

The strawberry flower is cross-pollinated.

(iii) Explain cross-pollination.

(3 marks)

(iv) Give **one** feature, shown in the diagram, which adapts the strawberry flower for pollination.

Explain how this helps to bring about cross-pollination.

(2 marks)

The diagram shows a magnified view of a carpel from the strawberry flower.

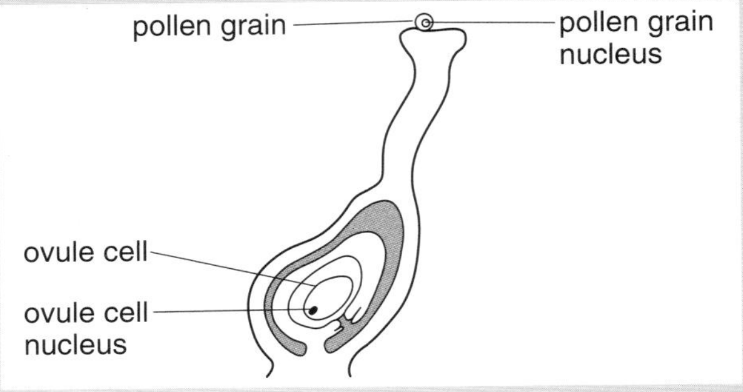

b) (i) Copy the diagram and draw the pathway taken by the pollen tube to the ovule.

(3 marks)

(ii) On your diagram, label the ovary.

(1 mark)

(iii) Describe the process of fertilisation in the strawberry.

(2 marks)

The diagram shows a section of a strawberry fruit.

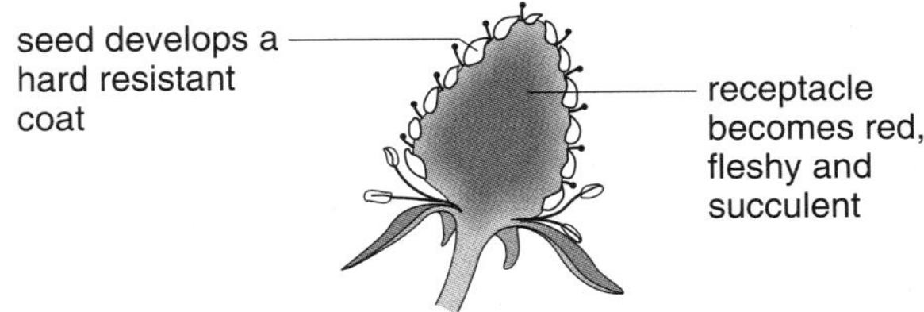

c) (i) Suggest how the strawberry fruit is adapted to be dispersed by birds.

(3 marks)

(ii) Give two other methods of seed dispersal.

(2 marks)

Chapter 26

Classification

Learning objectives

By the end of this chapter you should know:

- The main features, and examples of the main plant groups – algae, bryophytes (mosses), pteridophytes (ferns) and spermatophytes (angiosperms)
- The main features and examples of the main animal groups – annelids, arthropods (insects), molluscs, chordates (bony fish, amphibians, reptiles, birds and mammals)
- The main features of fungi, examples to include moulds and toadstools
- The main adaptations associated with life in water and on land

Living organisms are classified into groups on the basis of having a range of similar characteristics. Organisms in the same group, for example animals, all have a range of features in common that makes them animals as opposed to any other group. Animals, plants and fungi are large groups that can be further sub-divided many times. Each sub-division will produce smaller groups that have more and more characteristics in common. If we sub-divide enough we can differentiate between different species.

A **species** is a group of organisms that resemble each other and can breed together to produce fertile young. To avoid confusion over the names of organisms, each species is given a scientific name. The scientific name for the human species is *Homo sapiens*. One of the reasons for using scientific names is to avoid the confusion that can be caused by using local names. The common shrub *Ulex europaeus* can be known as gorse, whin or furze and a number of other local names. The students in any one class probably do not all know it by the same name. Check and see.

Figure 1 Gorse or whin or furze?

If there is this potential for confusion at a local level, think of the degree of confusion local or common names could cause at a global level.

It is possible to assign organisms to groups through the use of keys. The examination questions at the end of this chapter have examples of keys.

The main characteristics of three major groups of organisms, the plants, animals and fungi will be covered in the next few sections.

Plant classification

Plants are multicellular organisms with cellulose cell walls. They contain chlorophyll and produce food by photosynthesis. There are four major plant groups. These are the algae, the bryophytes (mosses), pteridophytes (ferns) and spermatophytes that include the angiosperms or flowering plants.

The Algae

These simple plants are usually found growing in water. They include the green algae that forms long chains of cells called filaments. Filamentous algae is usually found in freshwater but can also occur at the seashore. The cells in these filaments are typical, chloroplast containing, plant cells. The filament is the entire plant; they are not sub-divided into roots, stems or leaves and they do not contain any vascular tissue. The cells are completely undifferentiated.

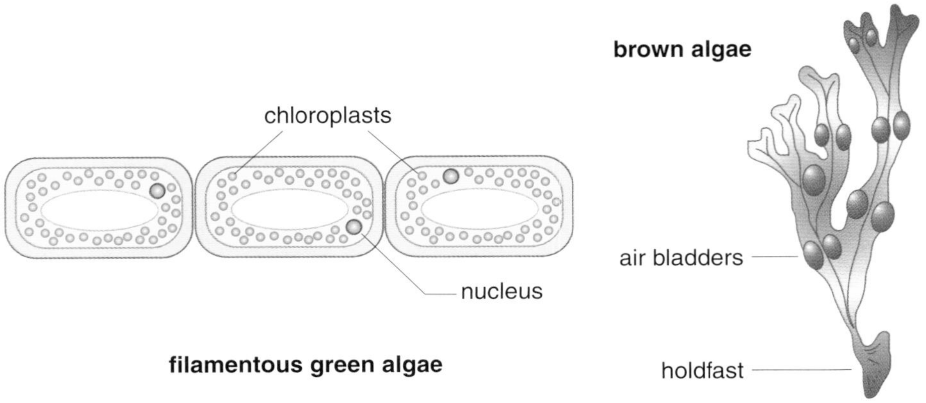

Figure 2 Algae

Brown algae (known as seaweed) are very common on rocky seashores. They often form dense carpets that cover much of the rocks between the high and low water marks. As with green algae they do not have leaves, stems or roots and they do not contain vascular tissue. However, the brown algae are more complex than the green algae. They have a holdfast that attaches the plant to the rock, a stem-like part called a stipe that attaches the holdfast to the main photosynthesising part called the thallus. Some species of brown algae have air bladders that help the plants float in order to gain more light for photosynthesis. Brown algae are unusual plants in that they are not green in colour. This is because they have different pigments to trap light compared to most green plants.

Bryophytes (mosses)

Mosses are land plants that occur in damp or moist areas. They are restricted to damp areas as their leaves do not have a cuticle and they have no roots that can absorb water. Although moss plants do not have roots they do have stems and leaves. They also have root-like structures called **rhizoids** that can help anchor the plant. In mosses water is absorbed all over the surface of the plant. Vascular tissue is not present and the loss of the support that it would provide is one factor that prevents mosses growing very high. Mosses reproduce by producing **spores**. The spores are produced in capsules that are supported on stalks allowing them to extend into the air above the leaves.

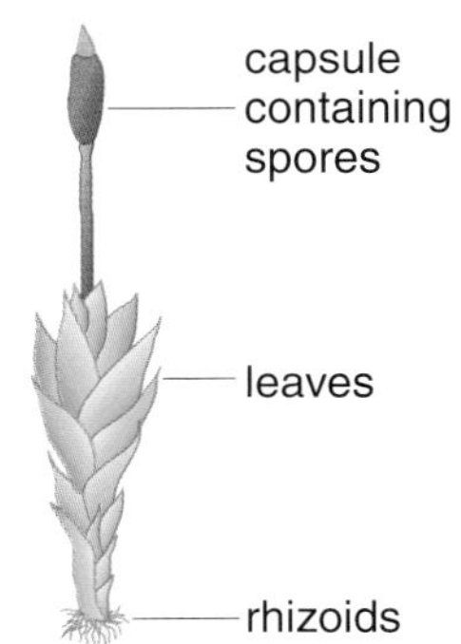

Figure 3 A moss plant

Pteridophytes (ferns)

Ferns have roots, stems and leaves. They have vascular tissue that gives both strength and the ability to transport water through the plant. The leaves have a cuticle which reduces water loss. The presence of roots, vascular tissue and a cuticle allows ferns to grow much taller than mosses and also to live in drier areas.

The fronds (leaves) of ferns can reach considerable sizes and ferns can grow as single plants or form large colonies as with bracken. Ferns also reproduce by producing spores. In ferns the spores are produced in groups or patches on the underside of the fronds in special structures called **sporangia**.

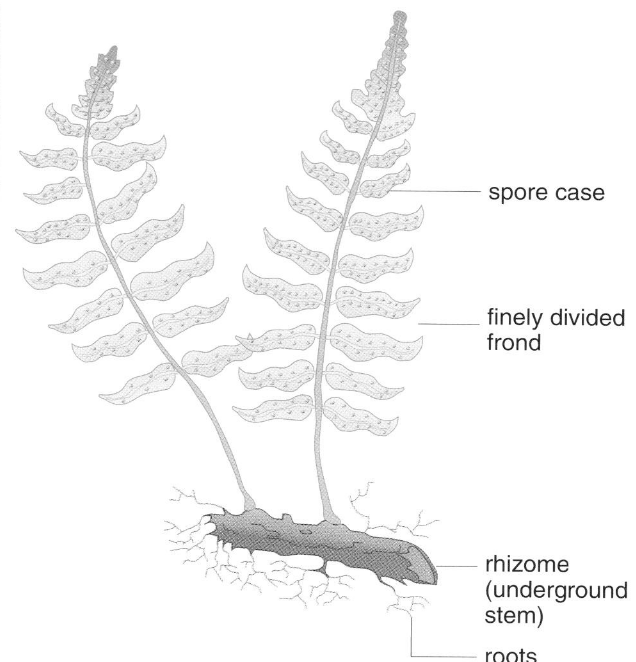

Figure 4 A fern

Spermatophytes (angiosperms)

Flowering plants or angiosperms belong to the most complex group of plants, the spermatophytes. The unique feature of angiosperms is having flowers as the reproductive structure and the production of seeds. Like ferns, flowering plants have roots, stems and leaves and have vascular tissue that provides both support and water transport.

Flowering plants are the dominant and most successful plants on land. They (and to a slightly lesser extent ferns) have adaptations that ensure successful life on land. Flowering plants can even grow in hot deserts, the hottest and driest places on Earth. The important plant adaptations to life on land include:

- The presence of roots, for anchorage and for obtaining water, often well away from the main part of the plant.
- The presence of vascular tissue, for support and water transport.
- A cuticle to reduce water loss. This is replaced by a waterproof bark in the stems of trees.
- A seed that is more resistant to drying out than spores.

These adaptations for life on land are at their most extreme in desert plants such as cacti. In addition to the above features, cacti have the ability to store large volumes of water in their succulent stems. Their leaves are modified to form spines. The spines reduce the surface area over which water can be lost and also discourage animals from feeding on the plants.

Figure 5 Cacti are highly adapted for conserving water

Animal classification

Animals are multicellular organisms that feed on organic material. Animals do not have cell walls and most are mobile. There are many more groups of animals than there are plants. Some of the major animal groups are discussed in the following sections.

Annelids

Figure 6 An earthworm

Earthworms are annelids. The body of an annelid is formed of many rings or segments that run along the length of the body. **Segmentation** is a characteristic feature of all annelids. Earthworms move by sliding over the surface of the ground. Each segment has little spikes called **chaetae** that allow the worm to attach itself to the ground.

Arthropods (insects)

Arthropods include the insects, spiders, crustacea (crabs and woodlice), millipedes and centipedes. The insects are the most numerous of the arthropods. There are more insects alive today than all the other animals added together.

All insects have an exterior **exoskeleton**, made of a substance called chitin. This exoskeleton provides good defence and stops the insect from becoming dehydrated. The body of an insect has three distinct regions, the head, the thorax and the abdomen. The head has specialised mouthparts, antennae that are sensory in function and a compound eye. The thorax typically has three segments. Each segment has a pair of jointed legs, giving three pairs in total. Most insects, e.g. the dragonfly, have two pairs of wings and these arise from the thorax.

Figure 7 Arthropods come in many shapes and forms

Molluscs

Snails and bivalves (shellfish) are molluscs. A common characteristic of molluscs is the presence of a shell. An exoskeleton in the form of a shell provides excellent defence against predators. This is particularly important in shellfish, many of which do not move, and would otherwise be easy prey.

Snails can live in water or on land, usually feeding on vegetation. In snails that live on land the shell also protects against water loss.

Bivalves almost always live in the water, filtering out small pieces of food carried by the water currents. Bivalves are so called because they have two shells, hinged together at one side. When feeding the hinge allows the shells to separate slightly allowing water (and food) to flow though. Mussels and clams are bivalves.

Annelids, arthropods and molluscs are **invertebrates**. These animals do not have a backbone and are referred to as invertebrates. In these groups a skeleton, if present, surrounds the body (exoskeleton). The next section deals with **vertebrates**, animals that have an internal skeleton.

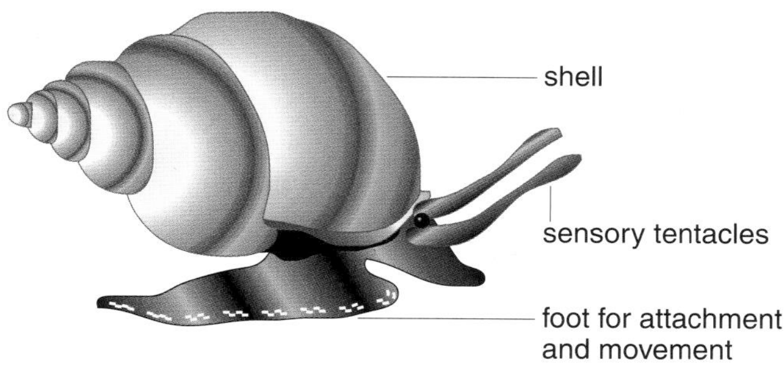

Figure 8 Molluscs

Chordates

Chordates (vertebrates) have an internal skeleton. These animals all have a backbone. The main chordate sub-groups are the bony fish, the amphibians, the reptiles, the birds and the mammals.

Bony fish

Bony fish have a backbone formed of bone. (Some other fish such as sharks have a backbone formed of cartilage – they belong to a different group from the bony fish.) Fish are found in both marine and freshwater habitats. They use their **gills** to absorb oxygen from the water.

Water enters the fish through the mouth and passes out through gills that are positioned on either side of the body at the back of the mouth. As new water continually passes through the gills, oxygen in the water diffuses into the blood vessels that run through the gills. The body covering in fish consists of waterproof scales. The scales prevent too much water from entering or leaving the body.

Questions

1 Using your knowledge of osmosis explain what would happen if fish did not possess a waterproof covering.

Movement in water is achieved by having a streamlined shape and also by the use of fins. The fins help keep the fish stable when swimming and also help in propulsion. In most fish the tail fin is most important in propulsion.

Many fish shed their sperm or their eggs into the water and this will result in **external fertilisation**. This is a very risky process as there will be a lot of wastage of sperm and eggs. Fish that use external fertilisation produce large numbers of eggs to make it more likely that at least some eggs will get fertilised.

Figure 9 A perch

Amphibians

This group includes the frogs and toads. Characteristically the young live in water and the adults can live on land. Adult amphibians have a moist skin that is not waterproof. As water loss can occur over the body surface frogs and toads are usually restricted to damp environments. Fertilisation is external in amphibians but although sperm and eggs are released directly into the water the adults are in very close contact when this occurs. The many eggs that are produced develop into frog spawn. The jelly covering stops the eggs from being washed away as well as providing protection. Figure 10 shows the life cycle of a frog and shows the changes that occur in the tadpole as it develops.

In adult amphibians gas exchange takes place both in the lungs and over the moist body surface. In the tadpoles gills are used.

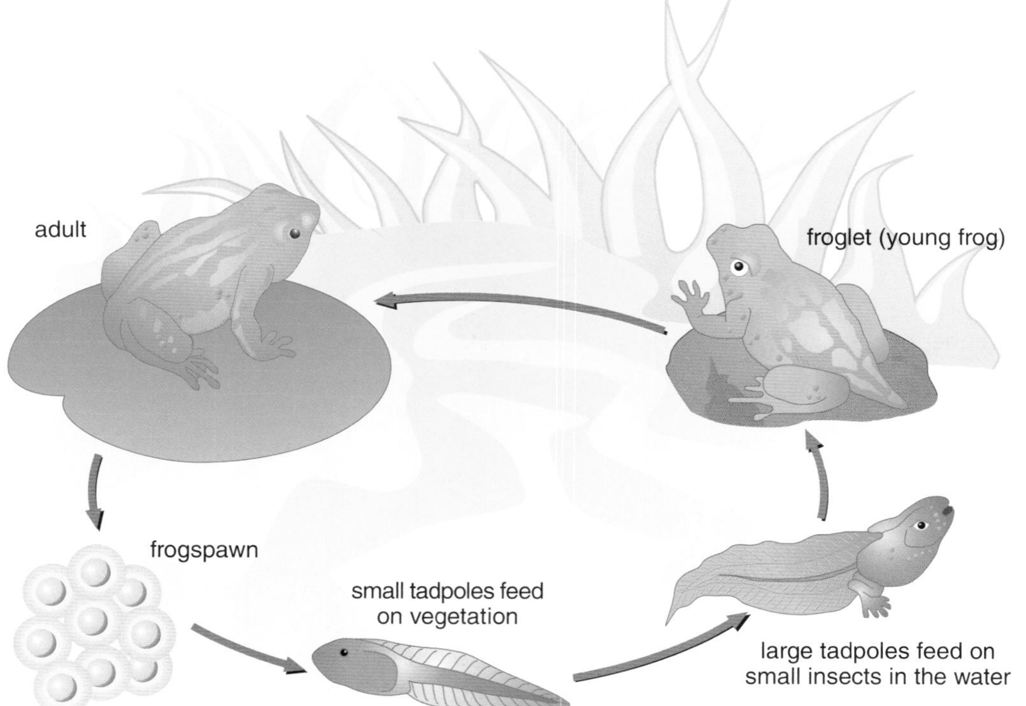

Figure 10 The life cycle of the frog

Reptiles

Reptiles are more effectively adapted for life on land than amphibians. Although many reptiles, for example crocodiles, spend much of their time in water many can live exclusively on land. Some desert lizards have become adapted to living in very dry and hot environments. A body covering of scales conserves water and also provides protection. The reproductive process in reptiles is much more specialised for life on land compared with amphibians. Fertilisation takes place inside the body of the female. As the chance of sperm and egg coming into contact is much greater in internal fertilisation, fewer eggs are produced. Eggs are laid on land and they are covered by a shell to prevent them drying out. Young reptiles that hatch are very vulnerable and they need a lot of parental care as they develop.

Figure 11 Reptiles, like this Eastern green mamba aand Nile crocodile, are adapted to life on land.

Figure 12 Birds have a number of characteristic features, including feathers, wings and beaks

Birds

Birds are also highly adapted for life on land. Like reptiles they produce a small number of shelled eggs that are laid on land. Fertilisation is also internal and parental care is important in protection and for teaching the young chicks to fend for themselves.

The development of wings has allowed birds to live in many habitats inaccessible to most other animals. A body covering of feathers gives an ideal insulating layer that reduces heat loss. Birds have a constant (warm) body temperature. This temperature allows enzymes to work at maximum speed ensuring that birds produce the energy required to meet their needs. The beak of the birds is a feature found in no other group.

Mammals

Some mammals are sea living, for example dolphins and whales, and some can fly, for example bats, but most are land dwelling. They form a very successful group that contains the dominant animals on the planet. Like reptiles and birds they have a range of characteristics associated with life on land. Internal fertilisation and the development of offspring (gestation) for a period of time inside the mother, before birth, ensure that the young animals are quite well developed before they experience the outside world. Parental care is important and mothers feed the young on milk produced in **mammary glands**. This uniquely mammalian feature gives mammals their name.

Figure 13 Mammals, and particularly primates like this De Brazza's monkey, show parental care

Like birds mammals have a constant body temperature. In humans this temperature is 37°C. The body temperatures of other mammals may differ slightly from the human temperature. Mammals have a body covering of hair or fur and this covering provides insulation in the same way that feathers do in birds. Mammals are the only animals to have an external **ear pinna**.

Chordates include animals that are specialised for living in all the different types of environments on Earth. Chordates have successfully colonised the water, the air and land. Some of the chordate features associated with life in water and on land are outlined below.

Life in water (e.g. fish)

- streamlined shape
- fins for stability and propulsion
- gills for breathing

Life on land (e.g. mammals)

- thick skin to reduce moisture loss
- internal fertilisation
- skeleton to provide support and allow for movement

In this section we have seen that many animal groups are adapted for life on land. Reptiles and insects, in addition to mammals, are ideally suited for life on land. Their adaptations might be slightly different to the ones listed for mammals but they are based on the same principles. For example insects and reptiles do not have skin but they have a waterproof cuticle and waterproof scales respectively. Similarly mammals such as whales are adapted for life in water. Their adaptations are slightly different to those found in fish. Try to find out what adaptations mammals such as dolphins or whales have that allow them to live successfully in water.

As well as adaptations for life in water, land and air, animals will usually be adapted for the particular environmental conditions in which they live. Animals living in hot or cold climates are adapted in very different ways to control their body temperature. It is often possible to tell from the appearance of an animal what environmental conditions they live in. Figure 14 shows pictures of desert and arctic foxes. Differences in colour and thickness of fur are important adaptations in each animal's respective environment.

Figure 14 The desert and arctic fox

Questions

2 Why is there a difference in ear size in the two foxes?

Fungi

The fungi are the third major group of organisms we are going to examine. They are quite plant-like in appearance, but sufficiently different from plants to be placed in a separate group.

Moulds that can be found on fruit, jam or bread are fungi. A **mould** is formed of thread-like hyphae that grow through the food or organic material in which the fungus lives, absorbing nutrients as they go. This type of nutrition is called **saprophytic nutrition** and fungi are referred to as saprophytes. Fungi release enzymes into the food and after the enzymes digest the food they then absorb the nutrients. As discussed in the chapter on nutrient cycling fungi are important in the decay process as they grow into and break down dead organisms. They also can cause decay in food unless we take measures to stop it. Fungi do not contain chlorophyll and they rely totally on saprophytic nutrition.

Fungi reproduce by producing spores from special spore producing structures that extend above the food medium. When we observe fungi such as bluemould or mucor in jam the part we see consists mainly of the spore producing structures – most of the fungus is growing through the jam itself.

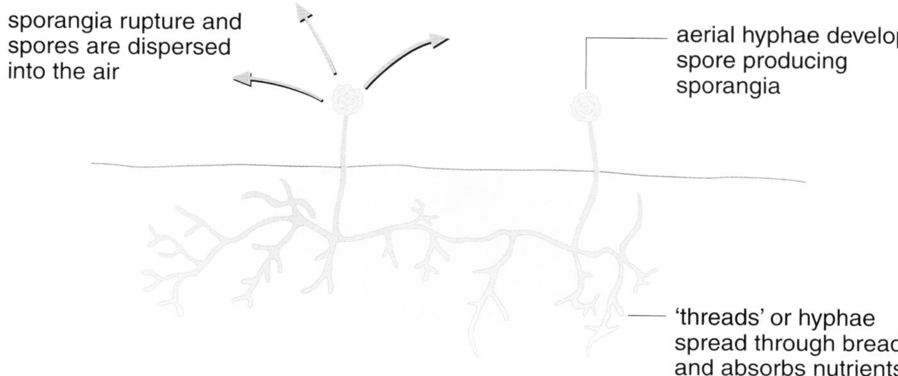

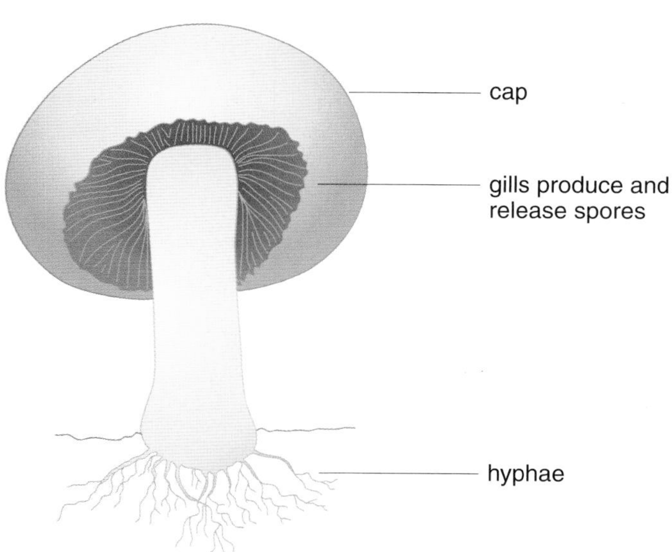

Figure 15 Fungi

Toadstools and mushrooms are fungi that feed in exactly the same way as bluemould and mucor. The toadstool or mushroom itself is an elaborate spore producing structure with the main part of the fungus in the ground. The spores are released through filaments, called gills, on the undersurface of the umbrella-like cap. These structures ensure that the spores are released well above the ground surface allowing them to be dispersed by wind currents.

Websites

http://www.herb.lsa.umich.edu/kidpage/factindx.htm
Lots of information about fungi. There are very good articles on the importance of classification and on the role of fungi in decomposition.

Exam questions

1 Use the key to identify the four fish A, B, C and D in the diagram.

diagrams not to scale

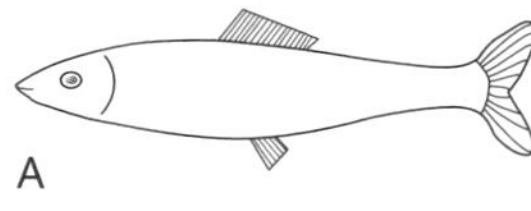
A

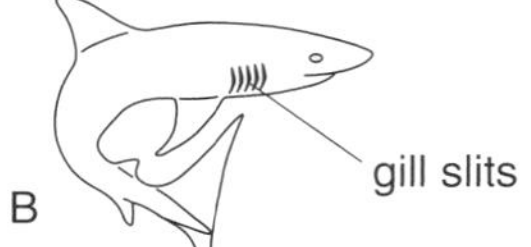

B

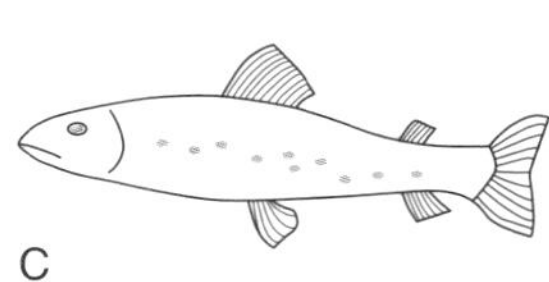
C

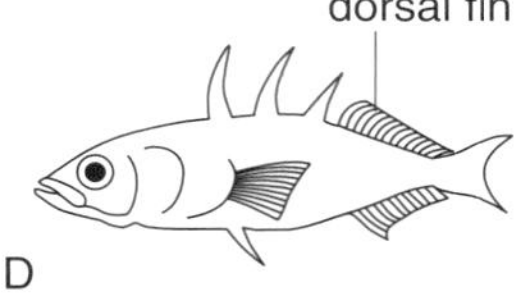

D

1	Five gill slits showing	Basking shark
	No gill slits showing	Go to 2
2	Three spines in front of dorsal fin	Stickleback
	No spines in front of dorsal fin	Go to 3
3	Two fins showing	Trout
	Four fins showing	Flying fish

(3 marks)

2 The diagrams show five leaves (not to scale).

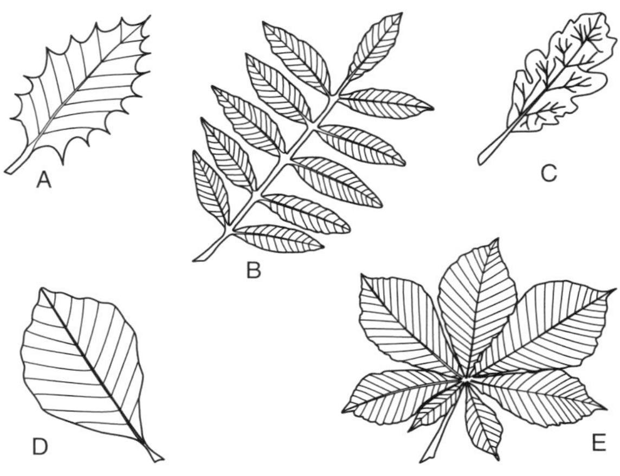

a) List in the correct order the letters which would complete the key if placed in the boxes.

1	Whole leaf made of leaflets	go to 2	
	Single leaf, no leaflets	go to 3	
2	Leaflets in pairs	Ash	B
	Leaflets not in pairs	Horse chestnut	☐
3	Spines present	Holly	☐
	No spines	go to 4	
4	Leaf edges wavy	Oak	☐
	Leaf edges smooth	Beech	☐

(4 marks)

b) Name **two** plant groups which have vascular tissue. *(2 marks)*

3 The diagram shows a fungus found on bread.

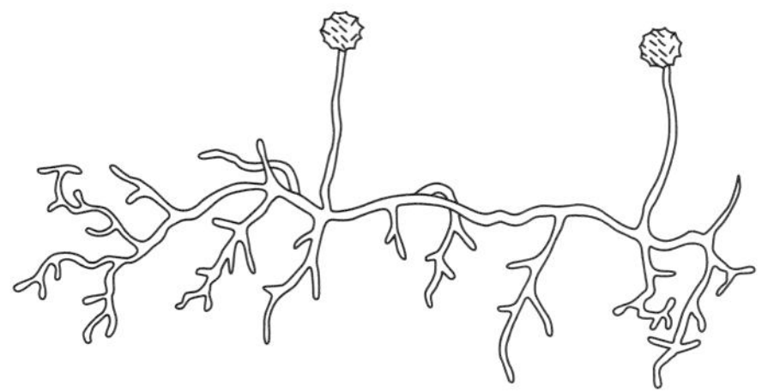

a) Name a fungus. *(1 mark)*

b) Describe how a fungus can spread from one loaf of bread to another. *(2 marks)*

Fungi are saprophytes.

c) What is meant by a saprophyte? *(1 mark)*

d) Explain why fungi cannot photosynthesise. *(1 mark)*

4 The scale drawing shows a blue whale.

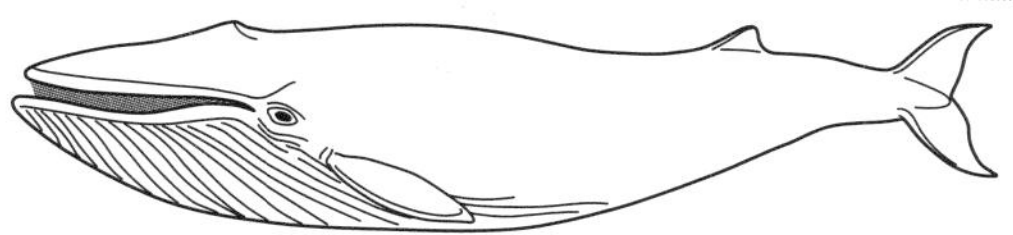

a) **Measure** the length of the drawing of the blue whale. *(1 mark)*

The drawing is 200 times smaller than the actual whale.

b) Calculate the actual length of the blue whale. Show your working. *(2 marks)*

Whales are mammals adapted for life in the sea.

c) Give **one** feature, shown in the drawing, which is an adaptation to movement in the sea. *(1 mark)*

d) Give **two** features of mammals. *(2 marks)*

e) Suggest how a thick layer of fat under the skin would adapt the blue whale for life in the sea. *(2 marks)*

Index

C

D

E

F

G

H

I

Q

R

S

T

U

V

W

X

Y

Z